# *HERBV*

# *NATURALLY*

## *Christina Stapley*

Author of Herbcraft Naturally
Herb Sufficient

## *HEARTSEASE BOOKS*

# *DEDICATION*

For my father who taught me respect for knowledge from the past and an abiding love of books, and for my mother who has passed on to me her practical talents.

## Photography

Cover, 'herb cushions' and 'Serenity garden'
Di Lewis, courtesy of Ebury press.
Others Christina Stapley.

ISBN: 0-9522336-4-9

Printed in England by St. Richard's Press Ltd.
Chichester. West Sussex. PO19 2TU

The author gratefully acknowledges the professional advice of Sabine Johnstone M.N.I.M.H., Elizabeth Gibbs. R.S.Hom, Pamela J. Smith R.G.N. Aromatherapist I.S.P.A. on references to herbal and homoeopathic remedies and essential oils and their properties, respectively. Also John Wakefield, M.V.B., M.R.C.V.S. for advice on the poisons section relating to animals.

Herbs can be powerful substances whether applied as oils or taken in other forms. This book is not intended as a medical reference source. The author cannot take responsibility for readers use of recipes or possible allergic reactions. Please note cautionary guidelines with recipes.

# CONTENTS

# FOREWORD

I wrote Herbwise Naturally to answer the many requests for information from those who attended my lectures and workshops. The response to publication of the first edition in 1993, was so favourable that I followed it in 1994 with Herbcraft Naturally, then, in 1998 with Herb Sufficient.

Herbwise has been out of print for some time and I am delighted to be responding again to requests for its return.

There is little change in the content of this second edition, with the exception of the addition of the pages on irritants and poisons. This has been prompted by numerous calls for information, from those involved in horticultural therapy and caring for animals.

Safety in herb use is also, as before, a priority. A warning on possible problems from making herb oils at home issued last year by the Ministry of Agriculture, Fisheries and Foods has replaced the recipe in the cookery section. In the first edition of Herbwise I warned against taking St. John's wort internally for depression without medical advice. Self-medication is always dangerous when applied to conditions other than the everyday problems we expect to treat at home. It is particularly so when a combination of herbal medicine and drugs is involved and there may be unforeseen consequences. I am happy to say that the valuable external application of St. John's wort oil, is still considered to be safe in this respect. The latest guidance is included in the medicinal section.

On a lighter note I have added 2 herbs to cultivation and cookery. In the past 10 years salad rocket has leapt from obscurity to being on sale on food counters alongside parsley, mints and basil. I suspect purslane also has the potential for a similar return to our salads and recommend it.

In the planning section I have given additional information on larval foodplants for butterflies and plants to offer the adults nectar. The drop in butterfly numbers continues and it is up to us all to offer the best habitats we can.

The most notable change to this second edition is the new binding which will enable readers to return again and again to favourite recipes, following them with ease. My partner in Heartsease Books, Sue Crook and I are delighted to offer this guide to growing and using herbs which is reader friendly in every way.

C.M.S.

# ILLUSTRATIONS

# Planning a Herb Garden

I cannot imagine a more enjoyable way of spending a wet and windy afternoon in winter or spring, than planning a herb garden. The very words immediately feed your imagination with scenes of sunlit summer days, filled with the fragrances of herbs, fluttering butterflies and buzz of bees at thyme or lavender.

When making a new herb garden it is a great pleasure to list the fragrances you wish to enjoy: fennel, angelica, marjoram, thymes, bergamot, honeysuckle, roses, chamomile, lavender, rosemary and so on. The lemon herbs could fill a corner of their own with lemon balm, lemon verbena, lemon mint, lemon basil and thyme and lemon-scented geraniums. Make a note of those herbs you will want to grow for harvesting to use in cookery, fragrant mixtures, remedies or flowercrafts.

Every herb garden can be a place of serenity and beauty in all seasons. To give it a sound beginning, think of it first as a winter garden. List the evergreen herbs you wish to grow and mark these on your plan to best effect. In a temperate climate you might choose rosemary, bay, germander, box, thyme, hyssop and sage. (The last three could lose their leaves in a severe winter, but will remain green in mild ones).

Now you will see a framework which can be enlivened with spring colour. Clumps of violets, lungwort and primroses add vivid interest, and each has its own uses after harvesting. Thinking on through the spring towards summer, forget-me-nots, lilies of the valley, cowslips, sweet cicely, and Solomon's seal will flower in April and May.

Once into the summer season, borage, marigolds, roses, pinks, thyme and many more offer endless combinations of variegated foliage and bright flowers. With the warm weather, too, will come the need for a seat to sit in the sun and take pleasure in the garden.

Late summer adds the delicate pink of marshmallow petals and exuberant yellow button tansy flowers. The tall sunflower with its massive head tilted as coyly as a shy maiden, towers above them as the seeds ripen. By now a new interest has come to the garden with a fascinating array of seedheads. The elegant umbels of dill and fennel appear, attracting first the slender willow warblers to cling amongst their swaying branches in my garden, and then the pretty goldfinches which feed on their seeds. The heavier "cauliflower" heads of angelica and slight skyscraper lovage umbels are already stripped bare, when spires of motherwort and evening primrose seedheads rise amongst the spiky teazles which bring more delighted finches. Elderberries have already ripened to hang down in regal clusters, while rosehips are swelling but need frosts yet to prepare them for harvest. So, to winter again.

Let your imagination wander in the garden as you would like it to be through a whole year and make notes of the delights you mustn't miss. Then, with your fanciful thoughts and inspirations already captured on paper, you can look at the tables and diagrams which follow, to help you convert dreams into a practical reality.

If a garden is carefully thought out from the beginning, it will be far less trouble to manage. The width of paths, size of beds, choice of herbs will all be crucial to giving you a garden which in time will virtually take care of itself. Even a small plot can grow its own fertilizer and pesticides, together with herbs that will attract useful insects and wildlife to help you maintain a healthy garden.

The 12 point summary which follows is a guide to the basic areas which need careful thought if you are to enjoy your herb garden to the full.

1.    Your first consideration should be the outer boundary of the herb garden and whether this provides the shelter necessary from high winds and frosts. A herb garden facing south will obviously need less protection than one facing east. Guard particularly against north-east winds.

2.    If you feel an extra fence or wall is needed, remember the form it takes can add shape and character to a herb garden. You may wish to build a pergola or other divisions within the garden before you start planting out. Fences, walls, pergolas and arches are all enhanced by climbing plants. Honeysuckle, old-fashioned roses, jasmine and hops will all give them a soft, romantic charm.

3.    All herbs must be accessible for harvesting. No bed should be more than 1.2m (4ft) wide if you can reach both sides, or, if there is a wall behind, 0.6m (2ft) wide.

4.    When planning paths to divide the beds, make sure at least one leads to a seat where you can enjoy the fragrance and serenity. Also be sure they are wide enough to take a wheelbarrow if necessary. Make your paths a minimum of 35.5cm (14in) wide. It is good to be able to walk side by side with a friend in the herb garden if you have sufficient space to provide a wider path.

5.    Weeding paths can be hard work and so lay a protective covering beneath gravel or bark paths which allows water to soak down through, but stops perennial root weeds from coming to the surface. Bark paths will need topping up with an extra layer at least once a year. If brick or stone paths have cracks or holes, fill them with herbs suitable for paving.

6.    Look at the suitability of your soil for growing herbs. Most herbs will tolerate all but strongly acid soils. If rhododendrons, azaleas and heathers do well in your garden, then many favourite kitchen herbs may be better set into a mix of soil and potting compost in tubs or pots. A few herbs require acidity and peat should be dug into alkaline soils for wintergreen, witch hazel or broom. In general, Mediterranean herbs prefer poorer soil. Lush growth from fertilizers does not necessarily mean better quality. If your garden is mostly clay and holds the water, dig it deeply, mixing in compost and gravel to aid drainage before planting lavenders, thymes, savory and like herbs. Fennel, on the other hand, will flourish there.

7.    Consider sunlight and shade in more than one season. The extent of sunlight in winter is very important when judging the likely effects of frost. Make sure you know also how tall each herb could grow. Some, such as lovage, angelica and fennel will cast considerable shade over surrounding plants.

8.    Plant only herbs which you will harvest for use, or wish to enjoy in the garden for fragrance. Herbs grown for sheer curiosity can make extra work you will regret. The best way to keep a herb from spreading or becoming straggly, is to harvest it regularly.

9.    Even harvested, most herbs will spread, if not in their first year, then in the second or third. Leave each plant plenty of space. Place rampant herbs, such as mints, in containers, or use their energy in corners where weeds are difficult to control.

10.    Place annual herbs amongst perennials, avoiding bare patches in winter, interplanting good companions where you can. Every bed should have herbs in flower in more than two seasons.

11.    If you have small children in your family, or to visit, or keep animals, consult the list of poisonous herbs and place these carefully for safety or omit (see pages 163-168).

12.    Grow yarrow, comfrey, and —if you have room—a clump of nettles to help you care for the health of your plants. Include herbs that will attract useful predators to feed on any pests.

# Herb Heights
## Tall
angelica
bay (up to 6m 20ft)
clary sage
dill
elder
elecampane
evening primrose
fennel
honeysuckle
hop

jasmine
lovage
motherwort (warm climate)
mugwort
myrtle (warm climate)
roses (climbers)
rosemary
sunflower
tansy

## Medium
agrimony
anise
avens
bergamot
betony
borage
caraway
comfrey
coriander
cotton lavender
curry plant
feverfew
geraniums (scented)
germander
horehound (white)
hyssop
*iris germanica*
lavender
lemon balm
lemon verbena

marigold (pot)
marshmallow
mints
nettle
oregano
parsley (French)
pennyroyal (upright)
roses
rosemary (cold site)
rue
sages
St. John's wort
salad burnet
southernwood
sweet cicely
tarragon
valerian (Greek)
vervain
wormwood
yarrow

## Low growing
basil
chamomile
chervil
chives
cowslip
forget-me-not
garlic
heartsease
lady's mantle
lavender (dwarf)
lungwort
marigold *(tagetes)*
marjoram

mint (creeping)
nasturtium
parsley (curled)
pennyroyal (creeping)
pinks
primrose
purslane
rosemary (prostrate)
salad rocket
savory
thymes
violas
wild strawberries

**Herbs to decorate pergolas, arbours and trellis.** Early and late honeysuckle, evergreen honeysuckle, wild honeysuckle, winter honeysuckle, golden and common hop, white or yellow jasmine, climbing roses, climbing nasturtium.

# Herbs for Hedges
## Tall
elder (many are ornamental)      *rosa rugosa*
hawthorn                         snowberry

## Small
box                              lavender (dwarf)
cotton lavender                  rosemary (short var.)
curry plant                      sages
germander (wall)                 thymes
hyssop *(aristatus)*             winter savory

**Note:** With sages and rosemary, regular trimming is particularly important. Lavenders can be left to flower around the edge of a knot. This was also done with thrift in past centuries. Hyssop can be clipped short, but the rock hyssop *(aristatus)* makes a better low hedge.

# Herbs for sun or shade

| In shade | Sunny position | |
|---|---|---|
| angelica | basil | hyssop |
| chervil | bay | jasmine |
| elder | borage | lavender |
| forget-me-not | caraway | lemon balm |
| lady's mantle | chamomile | lemon verbena |
| lungwort | comfrey | lovage |
| marshmallow | coriander | marigolds |
| mints | dill | marjoram |
| nettle | elecampane | marshmallow |
| sweet cicely | evening primrose | motherwort |
| violet | fennel | myrtle |
| wild strawberry | feverfew | nasturtium |
| | garlic | oregano |
| | geranium | pinks |
| | germander | purslane |
| | hop | rose |
| | horehound | salad rocket |

# Herbs for urns, wooden containers and window boxes
## In smaller tubs and window boxes

| | | |
|---|---|---|
| basil | germander | parsley |
| bay (young) | hyssop *(aristatus)* | pinks (low) |
| chervil | lavender (dwarf) | primroses |
| chives | lemon verbena | savory (winter) |
| cowslips | marigold *(tagetes)* | Spanish sage |
| garlic | marjorams | thymes |
| geranium (scented) | nasturtium | |

**In larger troughs**

| | | |
|---|---|---|
| bays (large) | geraniums (scented) | horehound |
| lavender | var. lemon balm | mints - |
| clove pinks | rosemary | sages |
| southernwood | wormwood | |

## Low growing herbs for paving

| | |
|---|---|
| chamomile *(Treneague)* | creeping mints - Corsican mint, (needs shade) |
| creeping pennyroyal (may discourage ants) | pinks-low growing |
| thymes, caraway, basil, or pine scented | violas |

## Bee herbs

| | | | **Pollen only** |
|---|---|---|---|
| angelica | anise hyssop | bergamot | agrimony |
| betony | blackberry | borage | bogbean |
| broom | burdock | catmint | castor oil plant |
| chamomile | clary sage | clovers | nasturtium |
| coltsfoot | comfrey | dandelion | roses |
| deadnettle | dill | elecampane | St. John's wort |
| evening primrose | fennel | foxglove | sweet rocket |
| golden rod | hollyhocks | honeysuckle | |
| horehound | hyssop | ivy | **Propolis** |
| knapweeds | lavender | lemon balm | balsam poplar |
| marigold | meadowsweet | motherwort | hollyhock |
| oregano | pennyroyal | poppies | sunflower |
| rosemary | sea holly | savory | |
| sunflower | teazle | thistles | |
| thymes | viper's bugloss | woodsage | |

**To bring predatory insects to eat aphids** - hoverflies, lacewings, ladybirds, or wasps.

| | | | |
|---|---|---|---|
| angelica | anise | *calendula* | chamomile |
| chervil | dandelion | dill | fennel |
| golden rod | hyssop | ivy | lemon balm |
| mints | nettle | sages | sunflower |
| tansy | *tagetes* | yarrow | |

**To deter wasps** — hemp agrimony

**mosquitoes, midges** — lavender, feverfew, sweet gale

**flies** — tansy, pennyroyal, basil, nettle, mint, lemon herbs

## HERBS TO BRING BUTTERFLIES

Trees and shrubs - balsam poplar, blackthorn, bramble, dogrose, dogwood, elder, hawthorn, holly, honeysuckle, ivy, lilac, sweetbriar.

**Food plants for larvae** - blackthorn, borage, cowslip, holly, ivy, *lonicera periclymenum*, nasturtiums, nettle, primrose, sweet rocket, sorrel, thistles, viola, wild strawberry.

## HERBS — FAVOURITES

brambles - white admiral, red admiral, gatekeeper

*calendula* - tortoiseshells

campions white butterflies,

dandelion - brimstone, orange tip, white butterflies

elecampane - tortoiseshell, painted lady
Greek valerian - painted lady, tortoiseshells, peacock
hyssop - small heath, tortoiseshells, small white, peacock. Also burnets
knapweed - whites
lavender - skippers, white and yellow butterflies, tortoiseshells
mints and water mint - comma, red admiral, gatekeeper
nettle - attracts greatest variety which lay eggs on the leaves, brimstone, comma, peacock, red admiral, tortoiseshells.
oregano - gatekeeper, tortoiseshell, peacock, common blue, holly blue and meadow brown
ragwort - ringlet, peacock, cinnamon moth
sorrel - copper
sweet rocket - orange tip
tansy - peacock, tortoiseshell, red admiral, holly blue
thistles - whites
thymes - burnets, tortoiseshell, gatekeeper
wild strawberry - grizzled skipper
yarrow - comma, tortoiseshell, gatekeeper

## Herb Flowers

| Spring | Early - mid summer | |
|---|---|---|
| cowslip | agrimony | lady's mantle |
| forget-me-not | avens | lavender |
| heartsease | basil | marigold |
| honeysuckle | bergamot | mints |
| lungwort | betony | motherwort |
| peony | borage | nasturtium |
| primrose | chamomile | oregano |
| rosemary | chervil | pinks |
| sweet cicely | clary sage | roses |
| violet | coriander | rue |
| wild strawberries | cotton lavender | salad burnet |
| | curry plant | St. John's wort |
| | elder | thymes |
| | feverfew | valerian |
| | heartsease | vervain |
| | honeysuckle | wild strawberries |
| | hyssop | yarrow |
| | jasmine | |

| Late into autumn | | | Mild winter |
|---|---|---|---|
| avens | germander | nasturtium | borage |
| bergamot | heartsease | pennyroyal | heartsease |
| borage | honeysuckle | pinks | honeysuckle (winter) |
| dill | hyssop | savory | jasmine |
| elecampane | lavender | sunflower | marigold |
| evening primrose | marigold | tansy | rosemary |
| fennel | marshmallow | thymes | |
| feverfew | mints | yarrow | |

# The Kitchen garden

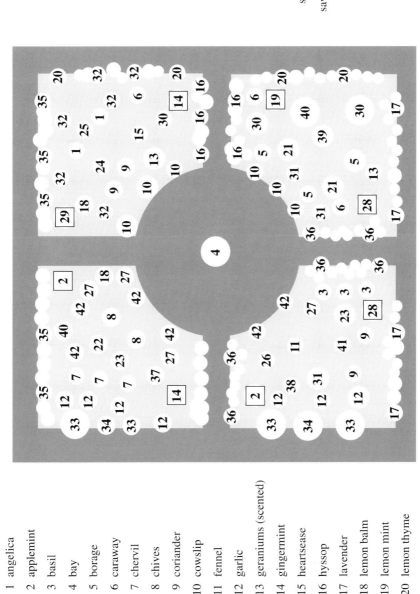

1 angelica
2 applemint
3 basil
4 bay
5 borage
6 caraway
7 chervil
8 chives
9 coriander
10 cowslip
11 fennel
12 garlic
13 geraniums (scented)
14 gingermint
15 heartsease
16 hyssop
17 lavender
18 lemon balm
19 lemon mint
20 lemon thyme
21 lemon verbena

22 lovage
23 marjoram
24 nasturtium
25 nettle
26 oregano
27 parsley
28 peppermint
29 pineapplemint
30 pinks
31 pot marigold
32 primrose
33 rose
34 rosemary
35 sage
36 savory (winter)
37 savory (summer)
38 salad burnet
39 sunflower
40 sweet cicely
41 tarragon
42 violets

☐ container

# Physic beds

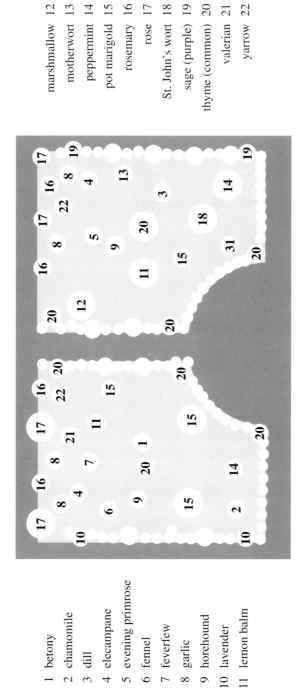

1 betony
2 chamomile
3 dill
4 elecampane
5 evening primrose
6 fennel
7 feverfew
8 garlic
9 horehound
10 lavender
11 lemon balm

marshmallow 12
motherwort 13
peppermint 14
pot marigold 15
rosemary 16
rose 17
St. John's wort 18
sage (purple) 19
thyme (common) 20
valerian 21
yarrow 22

12

# Serenity garden

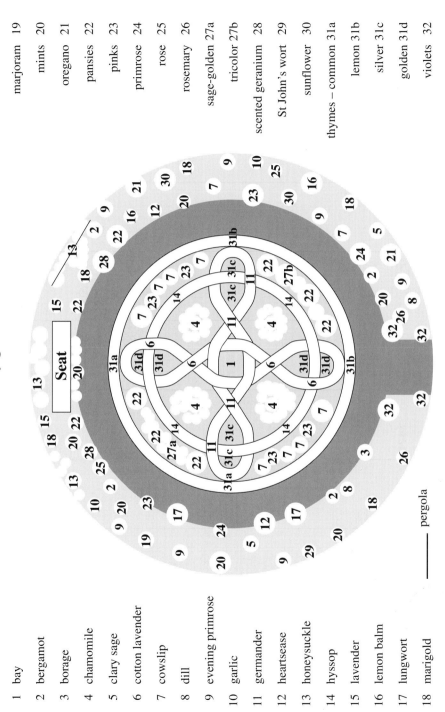

1 bay
2 bergamot
3 borage
4 chamomile
5 clary sage
6 cotton lavender
7 cowslip
8 dill
9 evening primrose
10 garlic
11 germander
12 heartsease
13 honeysuckle
14 hyssop
15 lavender
16 lemon balm
17 lungwort
18 marigold

marjoram 19
mints 20
oregano 21
pansies 22
pinks 23
primrose 24
rose 25
rosemary 26
sage-golden 27a
tricolor 27b
scented geranium 28
St John's wort 29
sunflower 30
thymes – common 31a
lemon 31b
silver 31c
golden 31d
violets 32

—— pergola

# 21st Century herb garden

| | |
|---|---|
| 1 applemint | 21 lemon geranium |
| 2 basil | 22 lovage |
| 3 bay | 23 marigold |
| 4 bergamot | 24 marjoram |
| 5 borage | 25 nasturtium |
| 6 chamomile | 26 parsley |
| 7 chervil | 27 pineapplemint |
| 8 chives | 28 pinks |
| 9 comfrey | 29 primroses |
| 10 coriander | 30 rose |
| 11 dill | 31 rose geranium |
| 12 eau-de-cologne mint | 32 rosemary |
| 13 fennel | 33 sage |
| 14 garlic | 34 St John's wort |
| 15 gingermint | 35 savory |
| 16 heartsease | 36 sweet cicely |
| 17 honeysuckle | 37 thymes |
| 18 jasmine | 38 violets |
| 19 lavender | 39 yarrow |
| 20 lemon balm | |

□ containers for mints

— pergola

# Making a knot garden

**K**NOT gardens were once a status symbol. Sometimes they included a family coat of arms, or geometric shapes copied from the door arches, windows, or other features of the house itself. They provided a focal point in small and large gardens alike, also serving as a fragrant place to lay washing out in the sun to dry. Best of all they gave a valuable harvest of herbs when the hedges were clipped, several times a year.

A closed knot consists of the interlaced ribbons of contrasting foliage, with either coloured sand or gravel, or flowers filling the geometric shapes between the low hedges. An open knot is made on a larger scale with paths dividing the shapes to enable you to walk between the beds, harvesting and enjoying their fragrances.

There are many patterns to offer inspiration. These can be found in old herbals, gardening books and in period needlework. Perhaps a motif in the architecture of your own house could provide the basis of a pattern. It is best not to be too ambitious at first, however. Complex patterns can set complex problems later on when you come to trim the hedges to maintain their shape.

To make a really effective knot you will need an area of at least 1.8m (6ft) square. A great many plants are needed, which means the only way to make a "poor person's knot garden", is to set out cuttings and have rather more patience in waiting to enjoy the finished result. Having decided on a plan for your garden, prepare the area by removing all weeds thoroughly and raking away any stones as you level the ground. You can then begin marking out the lines of your knot with string tied to sticks. For figures of eight, or repeated circles, it may help you to cut the shape from card and lay this on the ground as a template. Remember the width of fully grown plants will be 10-15cm (4-6in). It is easy to place your lines too close together.

When making the line of a hedge I like to set plants about 10cm (4in) apart. Germander, silver cotton lavender, hyssop and winter savory will all give quite speedy results at this distance. The taller hedge germander gives a better hedge than the lower wall germander in the first years. More care needs to be taken however to stop it from producing too much growth in wet seasons and becoming unwieldy. Wall germander is more difficult to obtain and slower growing, with a tendency to creep sideways. Do not feed the ground where savory is to be planted, as this weakens the herb's resistance to frost. Thyme can be set a little further apart at 15cm (6in) as with dwarf lavender. Full-size lavender, rosemary and sage, (green purple or golden) are all suitable for the outer edges of an open knot garden, and can be set at 20cm (8in) intervals. Lavender and sage will both benefit from feeding. It is worth the effort to dig a deeper trench than necessary, laying rich compost at the bottom, with a little soil beneath the plants. If the ground is not well drained, set some gravel beneath lavenders and thymes.

Once your hedges have been set, water them well and keep moist for the first one or two weeks if the weather is very hot and dry. Cuttings in particular need shading from strong sunlight. This can be achieved by attaching some net curtain or muslin to sticks and setting this over the plants. Trim the herbs immediately if necessary to establish the shape you wish to create. Clip the herbs with particular care where the "ribbons" of different foliage meet, to give the impression that one dips below the other. Dark green germander and silver cotton lavender contrast well together in this way.

It is a good idea to place lavender or thyme at the outside of a closed knot so that these can be allowed to flower for a short period, giving fragrance for passers by.

If you are using flowers rather than sand or gravel to fill the spaces between your hedges, you must be sure to allow yourself places to stand when clipping the central herbs. This is easily done by setting "stepping stones" of chamomile at strategic points. These are best made of the non-flowering cultivar, *Treneague*. Once established, chamomile may well spread invasively, in which case a strip of metal or wood set deeply into the ground will help to keep it under control.

The Elizabethans loved to plant cowslips, bulbs and pinks in their knot gardens. Primroses, heartsease, winter pansies, French marigolds (known charmingly as "velvet flowers" in the era of knot gardens), variegated sages, dwarf tulips and miniature daffodils are all suitable to add colour to your knot. A bay tree, myrtle or rosemary can be planted, or set in a pot if removal is necessary in frosty weather, at the centre of the knot. This might be trimmed to a fanciful shape for the most striking effect. If you have a sheltered herb garden, you might like to plant an orange or lemon tree. Again this could be lifted and taken indoors in winter.

However you plan and plant your knot garden, be sure it can be enjoyed either from the upstairs windows of your house, or from a seat, raised a little if necessary, in the garden itself. You will soon find lasting pleasure in watching your plan growing into shape and changing from season to season.

## Garden seats

It is important that the seats in your garden should reflect the general atmosphere you have worked to create. There are many stone, wooden, and ironwork seats available to meet every taste. A chamomile seat based on those in earlier gardens can be a wonderful pleasure in dry weather.

Site it in a sunny, sheltered spot if possible so that it will dry out quickly after rain. Having done this, do not neglect watering the chamomile in very dry weather. The base can be faced with wood, stone or bricks and should form a box to contain rubble or gravel for drainage, topped with a good thickness of compost mixed with fine, sandy soil. The chamomile, cultivar *Treneague* should be planted 7.5-10cm (3-4in) apart to cover the seat. A low growing thyme can be mixed in with the chamomile. Creeping pennyroyal can also be interplanted, but care needs to be taken not to allow this to become dominant over other herbs.

A trellis arch above the seat will help you to give shelter, offering support for a cover if you should decide to use one in persistently wet weather. Train honeysuckle or fragrant roses over the arch for an especially romantic setting. You will have made the perfect tranquil seat on which to meditate or just daydream.

## Paths

These can be expensive, or relatively cheap. They may be set to last for years or as temporary measures which can easily be moved. If you feel you may wish to change the design of your garden at a later date, then it is best either to sow grass paths with occasional stepping stones of treated wood or stone, or to put bark chippings down in a thick layer. The latter will need topping up once or twice a year.

Gravel is more expensive and the ground needs especially careful preparation. Remove perennial weeds thoroughly and lay protective material beneath the gravel which allows moisture down through, but stops any weeds growing upwards. Otherwise your path will need many hours of weeding as it is not advisable to use weedkiller so close to herbs which you intend to harvest.

Brick paths are wonderfully effective in cottage gardens, and around sundials and fountains. If you can treat yourself to a brick path then do so. Chamomile, creeping thymes and mints, salad burnet, and yarrow have all been set as mixed fragrant green paths in gardens over the centuries. If your garden tends to become waterlogged, however, or if the path has heavy use in winter, always set firm stepping-stones amongst the plants. Chamomile is particularly susceptible to damage when the ground is wet. Remember also you will have the task of preventing your fragrant path from spreading into the neighbouring beds.

## Chamomile lawns

Chamomile lawns on a large scale are a considerable risk if your garden is susceptible to frost. However, a small area of lawn around a seat, or as a scented path or green area in a sheltered garden can be charming and very effective. *Chamaemulum nobilis,* syn. *Anthemis nobilis,* has been used historically for lawns and should not be allowed to flower unless you wish the effect of a mead. It should be remembered that meads were dug up and replaced every few years. For a really super, modern lawn the non-flowering cultivar, *Treneague* is recommended.

To make a chamomile lawn, first prepare the ground carefully, which means removing all perennial weeds. Rake the soil level and free of stones. Roman chamomile can be sown on site in late spring. A little wood ash sprinkled in along with the seeds is helpful. Alternatively, grow the seedlings in a cold frame or greenhouse and plant out 10-15cm (4-6in) apart when they are about 2.5cm (1in) high in early summer. Larger plants could also be bought from nurseries. Keep well watered at first.

Once established, chamomile can withstand droughts far better than grass and will remain green. It is more likely to suffer if it becomes waterlogged. Therefore choose a sunny site. As the plants grow together, keep the spaces between them carefully weeded. The gaps should have closed by full summer and your new lawn will then be ready for a light trim with the shears.

Chamomile lawns are cut and rolled about three times a year. It will do your lawn good to walk on it in all but really bad weather. You can start doing this as soon as the plants have had their first cut. An older lawn can be cut with a lawnmower with the blades set high.

Small patches of chamomile lawn can be used effectively as stepping stones in a large bed of low-growing herbs or flowers.

## A period garden

The Elizabethan period is to me the most fascinating for herb gardens. Enthusiasm for both herbs and herb gardening was high and all manner of grand and rustic schemes were explored in designs.

The idea of a square crossed by paths or channels of water, with a fountain, sundial or ornamental tree at the centre, formed the basic plan. This concept was imported into Britain by the Crusaders and reflected the garden of Eden with four rivers flowing forth. I might never have understood the intense wonder of such an oasis amidst a dry, barren landscape, had I not visited Malta a few years ago. There, in the medieval city of Mdina, having walked the bare, narrow city streets with no sign of green, we opened a door in a wall to enter a miniature paradise.

I will never forget that small courtyard with its fountain and intersecting paths. Shaded by lemon trees laden with fruit, fragrant mints were interplanted with striking pure white lilies and red geraniums. Climbing roses covered the walls with brilliant red blooms. Such a "little piece of heaven" has been my aim ever since and so I can empathise with the Elizabethan dream of making a garden a true "paradise". The order of geometrically shaped beds within the square, contrasted with the Elizabethan delight in setting many entirely different herbs side by side for the effect of changing foliage and flowers.

The whole design was appreciated from a covered walk, usually on two or more sides of the elaborate garden, for at this time ladies were expected to keep a white complexion by avoiding the sun. The walk was shaded by trees trained to arch overhead, or by jasmine, roses, vines, honeysuckle, privet, or even scarlet runner beans which hid the wooden framework. This cascade of greenery might be so thick that windows were cut into it to give a view of the garden. The whole created a cloistered effect, so perfect for protecting and displaying herbs to their best advantage. Seats, chamomile or stone, were often placed in the shade of the walk or under an arbour for shade.

Most of the herbs that are widely available today were introduced before or during this period. Amongst the favourites of the time were pinks and carnations, the clove-scented gillyflower (which might also refer to wallflowers and stocks), being planted in abundance. With many old varieties still in existence, we can recapture some of the heady, spiced fragrances of an "Elizabethan" garden.

Other prized herbs were lavender, rosemary, thyme, hyssop, thrift, cotton lavender, rue, wormwood, fennel, sage, parsley, marjoram, tansy, mints, pennyroyal, cowslips, borage and marigolds - to name only a few.

Seats could be scented banks of thyme and chamomile beneath shady arbours of honeysuckle and roses. Fountains were much loved, particularly joke fountains which showered unsuspecting guests with water as they approached. To make them a greater attraction to the unwary, they were surrounded by such herbs as low-growing thymes and pennyroyal.

An Elizabethan garden was a mini-paradise with abundant fragrance and colour, spiced with a surprise or two if possible and containing either an "open" or "closed" knot of herbs. The "open" knot, which I have included in my own kitchen and physic garden, consisted of shaped beds of herbs, each enclosed by a low hedge, and paths which allowed you to walk between them. The "closed" knot which I have made as the centrepiece in my serenity garden, is one large bed of interlaced herb hedges, laid out as if the "ribbons" had been "knotted" into a graceful pattern on the ground. The low hedges can be left with coloured sands between them as contrast, in the fashion of a parterre; but I prefer the earlier version which places chamomile or herb flowers and contrasts of foliage to fill the shapes. There is scope to use plenty of imagination.

Even small Elizabethan gardens would have fruit trees, either trained against the walls or in an orchard at one end. This area gives the opportunity for a mead of wild flowers amongst low grasses, or the conventional chamomile lawn sometimes set for playing bowls. Scented "allies" - walks beneath rose-covered arches where burnet, watermints and thymes or chamomile grew underfoot were enjoyed.

### A scented bank

"I know a bank where the wild thyme blows, -
Quite over-canopied with luscious woodbine,
with sweet musk roses, and with eglantine."
*A Midsummer Night's Dream, Act ii, scene i.*

Such banks of low-growing fragrant herbs, beneath arches overgrown with roses and honeysuckle, were once favoured in gardens. A scented bank beneath an arbour can still prove a source of lasting pleasure. Or you may prefer to create a sunny, fragrant bank of earth to cover rubble removed when clearing a neglected garden, or to make an attractive division between the vegetable and flowerbeds.

Most of the low-growing thymes, pennyroyal and chamomile will thrive in a quite shallow soil which is relatively poor. The mints will need richer earth but will send their roots between stones and beneath obstacles if necessary to find it.

A scented bank of this nature needs careful planning and maintenance from the beginning if it is not to be taken over by one or two dominant plants. Large patches of thymes and chamomile will only be required if you want to use the bank as a seat. Eau-de-cologne mint is lovely around the edges of this area, but will have to be controlled. Heartsease makes beautiful splashes of colour on the bank and in a warm winter can flower all through the year. However, if they are to be left to seed, then they will soon become a nuisance, setting their seedlings amongst the chamomile. Low-growing pinks are one of the better edges for your chamomile area as they require less control. Pennyroyal gives a fresh, minty scent when trodden on and will survive being used as a seat. It is credited with keeping ants away which makes it an attractive choice, although this claim is not proven. Planting a few primroses and violets will give the bank a simple beauty in spring while the mints are absent or only just showing. Cowslips could also be added.

If you are cultivating ground which has been covered in perennial weeds, such as ground elder, it may be best to plant wild strawberries as an initial ground cover. These quickly spread and choke out the weeds, avoiding the need for chemicals. The following year they can be removed, to make room for chamomile and thymes. Wild strawberries are lovely in wild situations, but should be kept in a bed to themselves in gardens as they are so invasive. Another herb which will provide effective ground cover in the same way is sweet woodruff, *Asperula odorata* (see Herbcraft Naturally for cultivation).

As a general rule plant chamomile, thymes, creeping mints and pennyroyal about 10cm (4in) apart. Larger mints and pinks will need twice as much space. Always remember mint planted on a slope will keep spreading towards the bottom for wetter conditions. Weather permitting, your bank should be a mass of fragrant leaves and flowers by the second season. Clipping the chamomile twice a year and harvesting mints and thymes will then make future gardening a joy.

## Good Companions in the garden

**E**VERY garden is a living community. Certain plants set side by side will actively help each other to grow strong and healthy. Others will wage war with toxic root secretions or by emitting gases which affect the growth of surrounding plants. There are many relationships which have been observed and are now used by knowledgeable gardeners.

Companion planting can be used to:-
1. Guard against attacks by such pests as cabbage moths, beetles and aphids.
   This is achieved through offering fragrant cover or acting as decoy catch plants:
   e.g. Campions, sweet cicely and feverfew all attract blackfly away from other plants.
   Having attracted large numbers, these heads can be removed or left for a ladybirds'
   feast. In the case of sweet cicely the heads can be wiped clean to keep the seeds.
2. Draw nutrients from different levels of soil and provide shade where necessary.
3. Raise the content of essential oil in nearby herbs. Nettle, so often despised as a
   weed, may raise levels by up to 80% in some herbs.
4. Strengthen weak plants and nurse them back to health. Yarrow, chives and
   chamomile are well known as the "nurses" of the plant world.
5. Intensify flavours or fragrances. Several combinations in the vegetable garden will
   do this, while yarrow is helpful with herbs, flowers and vegetables alike.
6. Attract useful insects such as ladybirds and hoverflies to feed on aphids and other
   insect pests.

The true, complex inter-relationships of plants are still not entirely understood. We know that certain plants, such as *tagetes,* protect plants around them from pests by releasing powerful root secretions, which they use to defend themselves. Some of the aromatic herbs simply provide a camouflage of fragrance which keeps pests from finding the tender vegetables amongst them. The success rate of these will naturally be linked to weather conditions, for the herbs need sunlight to draw out their fragrance to the full.

Companion planting is not always successful, but it is most certainly worth trying. A healthy garden is a garden which is not entirely free of pests, for the predators which feed on them need food to remain. One of the unfortunate effects of chemical sprays is that they kill both pests and nature's own control mechanism in the form of predators which feed on them. This leaves the plants wide open to further attack. The more we encourage nature to take charge, the better our results will be and the less work involved in gardening.

A combination of companion planting with the additional resources of good natural compost, organic fertilizers and pesticide sprays which are made from plants grown in the garden and harmless to pets, children and bees is recommended. There is no necessity to poison the earth and we can take real pleasure and satisfaction from watching healthy plants growing in a healthy environment. On the whole, diseases attack weak plants, which are deficient in nutrients. If your plants are well fed on compost and liquid feed made from the herbs, they will be unlikely to have problems. Patience is needed at the beginning as nature establishes balances. During this time you will find the natural pesticides and fungicide which follow, of particular value.

Just as some combinations of plants can be helpful, there are several which should be avoided. The advice on this goes back thousands of years, the Roman writers on agriculture being the main sources. One generation after another has warned against planting wormwood close to delicate plants. Fennel should be set apart from caraway, dill, beans and tomatoes. It has long been thought unwise to plant sage, rosemary, or any other aromatic herb close to cucumber. Basil and rue are supposed to hate each other and when set together, one is likely to die, and so on.

You may find it helpful to keep a note in your diary of any combinations of plants you find unsuccessful and then try the same two together in different sites, to check for other factors, such as soil or climate protection.

**In the flower border**
A double insurance ground cover beneath roses in a flowerbed is chives and parsley. Chives, giant chives, or even better, garlic chives will help your roses to resist disease. I also plant a few cloves of garlic around my roses each autumn. Setting parsley so close to roses has the dual bonus of protection from aphids and giving you more resolve not to use poisonous sprays. It can be tempting as you see a mass of greenfly descend upon your choice blooms, but they should be gone within a week once your garden is established. A trellis support for roses gives small birds a place to perch as they feed on the pests, which they will do eagerly, given the opportunity. Marigolds are an additional benefit to your roses, and nasturtiums can be sown in rose-beds to discourage aphids and smother weeds.

*Tagetes* with the strong smell are necessary to guard your flowerbed against nematodes. These can be interplanted with roses, pinks and carnations to good effect. They may also leave a healthy patch of soil ready to take bulbs in the autumn.

Chamomile yarrow and chives will help if planted in a bed where the flowers are not doing well. A single plant of chamomile is more effective than a large patch. More yarrow can be planted, but remember this will spread.

**In the herb garden**

Rosemary and sage complement each other and can be particularly useful as a low hedge. Nettle used here and there as a companion plant increases the essential oil content in some herbs, such as angelica, peppermint and sage. Peppermint partnered with chamomile gives a better quality in the chamomile but does not appear to do the peppermint any good. Chamomile, yarrow, chives and salad burnet dotted about the herb beds will be helpful in a more general way. Chervil does well sown alongside fennel in summer, as the fennel provides shade and then dies down in autumn when chervil needs more light. Oregano and tarragon thrive well together and thyme and heartsease show a great affinity in my garden.

**In the greenhouse**

One or two plants of chamomile in the greenhouse amongst young seedlings can help them to resist damping off. If the seedlings already have a problem, water the plants with water in which you have steeped chamomile flowers for a day or so. Nasturtiums, *tagetes* and thyme are a good insurance grown amongst your other plants to control white fly. I have been told that mint grown in the greenhouse also deters pests. Essential oil of peppermint dripped in doorways can stop ants from entering, or send them out again when dripped into a nest. Mice also hate it.

Alternatively you may wish to use one of the biological controls now available.

**In the vegetable garden**

Here the possibilities of companion planting almost require a computer to work them out. The following herbs have been recommended by a number of experienced gardeners and have proved their worth to me. For more extensive reading on the subject, refer to the bibliography.

*Chervil* set amongst lettuce and radish helps to protect the young leaves from greenfly by attracting ladybirds and may give the radishes a hotter flavour. It also makes an attractive combination.

*Borage* brings the bonus of bees to the vegetable garden with its elegant flowers. Slugs do not like the prickly leaves of mature borage and may be turned away by rows of it between the brassicas. Borage is continually recommended as a partner for strawberries. This partnership can be taken further by garnishing dishes of strawberries with borage flowers.

*Dill* has been put forward both as a good companion for carrots and also as a bad one in various works. I have found it to be helpful sown with my carrots which then escaped carrot-fly and were healthy. It does not always germinate ahead of them however. Dill can be sown with beetroot or cabbage. It also deters spider mites.

*Hyssop* can be beneficial to protect from flea beetles, and is recommended to be grown with vines.

*Savory* interplanted with beans is a prime example of partnerships which work well. This is the herb most used in seasoning any bean dishes and it is also the herb to plant amongst broad beans to keep them safe from blackfly and bean beetle. You might also set sweet cicely, campions or feverfew nearby as blackfly catch plants. Pot marigolds, or *Calendula,* are useful planted amongst tomatoes to give a good crop of fruits, and a mulch of extra marigold plants from those parts of the garden where they have self-seeded with too much enthusiasm, is also good. Marigold petals make a very attractive and tasty garnish to tomato dishes.

*Garlic* and other members of the onion family can be useful in giving a protective odour around a variety of crops. The main rule to remember is not to plant too many of any particular vegetable together. Interplanting with a variety of herbs and vegetables, giving a mix of flowers amongst the green foliage is far more attractive and healthy.

*Rosemary and Sage* planted in a border can be the best way of containing a vegetable garden if you really object to setting cabbages in your flowerbeds. These aromatic herbs help to keep cabbage moth, carrot fly and other pests away. Others for this role are southernwood and thyme.

It is an interesting experiment to grow those herbs and vegetables together which you would naturally partner in the kitchen. For instance, plant basil and tomatoes together as both of these need some protection. Caraway and cabbage should be a helpful combination, with the caraway providing an aromatic cover for the brassicas.

### In the orchard
Small beds around fruit trees can look really attractive and at the same time be used to give rings of protection against pests. Climbing nasturtiums can be really impressive wrapped around a tree trunk and are reputed to deter woolly aphis. Garlic is a healthy deterrent for tree borers, and chives should be grown for treatments against fruit scab.

### Garden fertilizers
Stinging nettle makes an excellent fertilizer. Every garden of decent size should have a patch or a few patches of stinging nettles, in sunny situations or in a sheltered wild corner. These will bring butterflies, early ladybirds and easily earn their keep by giving nitrogen-rich goodness. Cut down the nettles in early June, late July and August to leave young growth for butterfly larvae, filling a bucket or larger container three-quarters full. A few to one third torn comfrey leaves can also be added. Top up to the brim with water, preferably rainwater, and cover. The brew is now left for two to three weeks, during which time it will begin to ferment.

Do not disturb this liquid until you have finished every other task in the garden as the smell will soon send you indoors. After the first week, if there have been some hot days, the liquid will already be useful to pour into the ground before planting out young seedlings. When it has darkened and thickened it should be diluted half and half before watering the ground before planting young plants. The evil brew will give you exceptional crops of tomatoes and is similar in composition to a tomato fertilizer. More nettles and comfrey leaves can be added as you are using the nettle fertilizer, to enrich it further; and leave the lid off during heavy rain to top up the level.

The strong nettle liquid is very effective also at removing blackfly from broad beans. For this, use it full strength if new, then diluted by half, and water the affected foliage until it drips.

Comfrey is perhaps the best fertilizer of all and gives abundant crops of leaves that can be used liberally. These can be added to compost, made into liquid fertilizer, with or without nettles, used as a green mulch, or wilted before laying in the bottom of potato trenches. Chop the leaves for a liquid feed and immerse in rainwater as with the nettles. The last cut of comfrey each year can be wilted before laying in the bottom of potato trenches where the following spring's early crop will be grown. The site of future onion beds is also a good idea.. In either case cover with straw.

Comfrey can also be applied as a compost between fruit bushes, cover with lawn mowings or cut sprays of wormwood to help against rust. Nettle, comfrey and yarrow can be mixed into a rich liquid feed. Dilute before using.

**Folia feeds**

For plants with evident mineral deficiencies, dressings of natural compost can be boosted by watering the roots and leaves with a folia feed made from certain herbs. The herbs should be picked in mid-morning, after the dew has dried. Borage stems contain a large amount of potassium, tansy is also potassium rich with other minerals in valuable quantities and dill offers potassium and sodium. Yarrow is especially mineral rich with copper, potash and lime. More potash could also be obtained from sunflower stalks, but these are best burnt and the ash sprinkled around weak plants.

To make a folia feed, tear the fresh herb into cold water. About 6 tablespoons of chopped herb will be sufficient to 1 litre (2 pints) of water. Avoid using an aluminium pan and bring the brew to the boil. Remove from the heat, leaving to cool before straining. Dilute to 5 litres (1 gallon) with cold water. Stir well and water the plants within a short time.

**Horsetail fungicide and Feed**

Put 4 tablespoons of dried horsetail into 2.4 litres (4 pints) of water. Avoid using an aluminium pan. Bring to the boil. Simmer for 20 minutes, then set aside and leave covered to steep for 24 hours. Strain before use. The recipe is diluted before watering the foliage, this quantity being sufficient for 10 litres (2 gallons). The spray will keep for one or two weeks in a screwtop jar in a cool place and can be used again for two subsequent applications, this time watering the roots of the plant.

**Chive fungicide**

A strong brew of chive or garlic can be effective against mildew or mould if applied at an early stage. This is useful on fruit, such as gooseberries, and some herbs. Th dried herb is more effective but I have had success with the fresh in mild cases. Pour 0.6 litres (1 pint) of boiling water over a handful of chives — including some bulbs with the green leaves. Leave to steep, covered, for about half an hour. Stir, strain and dilute half and half with water. With garlic four or five cloves will be sufficient to each 0.6 litre (1 pint) of water.

**Insecticides and pest repellents**

The best control of insects is brought about by attracting the predators which feed on them. These include other insects, birds and animals. If your plot offers safe homes for them with no chemicals used and a habitat provided, they will certainly come.

Toads, frogs and other wildlife which eagerly eat slugs are encouraged by a small pool. Toads enjoy the shade of spreading sage bushes and mints. Hedgehogs are also valuable friends for the gardener. A hedge will offer cover for small birds and if you are fortunate you may find thrushes nesting in your garden. Trees, small piles of logs and plant cover help to build useful habitats.

To discourage snails and slugs by other means, plant eau-de-cologne mint as a barrier or use layers of pine needles, horsetail, or other prickly leaves around tender plants. Essential oil of pine can be dripped onto bark laid around the foliage. Torn comfrey leaves will give slugs and snails an alternative and usually preferable, food, but these then have to be renewed each day. Gertrud Franck in her book on Companion Planting suggests another method for desperate gardeners. Collect large numbers of slugs and snails, dropping them into a bucket of boiling water. This is left to stand for 24 hours before being used to water the ground as a deterrent around tender plants.

Cats, rats, rabbits and deer can all be a problem to gardeners. Barriers of dried teazle heads can be a good deterrent, or a hedge of wormwood, or, in the case of rats, catmint. Many animals hate garlic, mustard, or pepper.

Remember seed and fruit-producing plants such as sunflowers, angelica, fennel, teazles, honeysuckle and a wild rose, or *Rosa rugosa* hedge will bring finches and other birds. In late summer slender willow warblers set the fennel stems swaying as they dart from one to another in my garden and the goldfinches gather eagerly amongst the sunflowers and teazles.

If birds should be a pest themselves in spring, nipping off buds or pecking at young peas, they can be discouraged by setting cuttings or sprays of curry plant around the affected plants.

Golden and orange flowers, such as marigolds, encourage the most voracious aphid eaters — hoverflies. You could plant a patch with buckwheat to give them a particular treat. A nettle patch not only draws many butterflies but also some very early aphids which should be left to attract the first ladybirds. These will then be established in your garden before the aphids are a problem to roses and other plants.

A sudden plague of the pests can be discouraged by coating the affected flowers and leaves with a brew of garlic and pepper. Crush two cloves of garlic to each cup of water and add half a teaspoon of pepper for good measure. Leave this to stand for a few hours and then add a little soap before spraying affected plants. Alternatively dried elderflower, lemon verbena, eucalyptus or wormwood can be sprinkled on plants. **Do not** use the last two on foodplants.

Needless to say, the best way to avoid pests is to have a healthy garden, and natural compost prepared on the spot is the best medicine. There are plenty of books giving detailed instructions on how to make a compost heap, compost bins being generally preferred in towns. These should be 2m (6ft) square to break down garden waste quickly, with herbal activators such as nettle, added at intervals. Any of the herbs suitable for folia feeds will add those same minerals to a compost heap and as many of these should be included as possible. Chamomile should be kept to a minimum however, as it works best in a small quantity.

## Herb Cultivation

Growing a large variety of herbs over many years has enabled me to view the plants as individuals. In the following pages details of the needs of the 60 herbs runs alongside accounts of their specific qualities which can work for the gardener's benefit.

There are good companions which are mutually helpful, for instance, rosemary and sage. Herb nurses, such as chamomile and yarrow, can be set by ailing plants, while unhelpful wormwood should be kept at a distance. The dominant energy of mints, tansy and wild strawberries can be channelled to keep invading weeds from awkward corners and boundaries.

Soil well fed with natural compost, additional liquid herb feeds, and, when necessary, fungicides or pest repellents are the keys to an easily run garden. With a healthy environment and thoughtfully placed herbs, regularly harvested at the times suggested, you can enjoy a garden where natural predators keep any pests under control.

Advice on propagating herbs and increasing their essential oil content is given together with observations on the common sites of herbs in the wild. Their geographical distribution has been taken from *The Encyclopedia of Herbs and Herbalism, edited by Malcolm Stuart, published by Black Cat, 1987. A Modern Herbal, Mrs. M. Grieve. F.R.H.S. published by Jonathan Cape, 1931 and Herbs, A Concise Guide in Colour, translated by Olga Kuthanova, published by Hamlyn, 1983.*

| Common Name | Latin name |
|---|---|
| angelica | Angelica archangelica |
| anise | Pimpinella anisum |
| avens | Geum urbanum, G. rivale |
| basils | Ocimum |
| bay | Laurus nobilis |
| bergamot | Monarda didyma |
| betony | Stachys officinalis |
| borage | Borago officinalis |
| caraway | Carum carvi |
| chamomile | Chamaemelum nobile |
| chervil | Anthriscus cerefolium |
| chives | Allium schoenoprasum |
| comfrey | Symphytum officinale |
| coriander | Coriandrum sativum |
| cotton lavender | Santolina chamaecyparissus |
| dill | Anethum graveolens |
| elder | Sambucus nigra |
| elecampane | Inula helenium |
| evening primrose | Oenothera biennis |
| fennel | Foeniculum vulgare |
| feverfew | Tanacetum parthenium |
| garlic | Allium sativum |
| geranium (scented) | Pelargonium |
| germander | Teucrium |
| honeysuckle | Lonicera |
| hyssop | Hyssopus officinalis |
| lavender | Lavandula |
| lemon balm | Melissa officinalis |
| lemon verbena | Aloysia triphylla |
| lovage | Levisticum officinale |
| marigold (pot) | Calendula officinalis |
| marjoram & oregano | Origanum |
| marshmallow | Althaea officinalis |
| mints | Mentha |
| motherwort | Leonorus cardiaca |
| nasturtium | Tropaeolium majus |
| parsley | Petroselinum crispum |
| pennyroyal | Mentha pulegium |
| pinks | Dianthus |
| primrose & cowslip | Primula |
| purslane | Portulaca oleracea |
| rose | Rosa |
| rosemary | Rosmarinus officinalis |
| rue | Ruta graveolens |
| sage | Salvia |
| salad burnet | Sanguisorba minor |
| salad rocket | Eruca vesicaria |
| savory | Satureja |

| Common Name | Latin name |
|---|---|
| St. John's wort | Hypericum perforatum |
| southernwood | Artemisia abrotanum |
| sunflower | Helianthus annuus |
| sweet cicely | Myrrhis odorata |
| tansy | Tanacetum vulgare |
| tarragon | Artemisia dracunculus |
| thymes | Thymus |
| valerian | Valeriana officinalis |
| viola | Viola |
| white horehound | Marrubium vulgare |
| wild strawberry | Fragraria vesca |
| yarrow | Achillea millefolium |

## Key to abbreviations

| A | annual | S | shrub |
|---|---|---|---|
| B | biennial | S-S | semi-shrub |
| P | perennial | T | tree |

## *Achillea Millefolium*      **P**      **YARROW**

THERE are a number of varieties of yarrow. All of them being perennial. They can be propagated from seed, or by dividing the root clumps. Yarrow spreads quite rapidly through its root system and if set amongst flowers or herbs is best divided every second year. Some varieties are more vigorous in their apparent desire to take over the garden than others.

Wild yarrow which has white flowers, sometimes intermingled with pink (depending on the type of soil), spreads faster than the cultivated forms. It is also the yarrow used medicinally and in cosmetics. It can still have a place in the garden as a companion plant (see page 20) as it increases the flavour and fragrance as well as the general health of the surrounding plants.

It has long been recognized that yarrow is beneficial on grazing land, increasing fibre content and giving up to 40% more protein as a mixture with other grasses. The herb can be used for paths in a vegetable garden as it is happy to be trodden on and will respond well to being mown. The edges could be left to flower, though not to seed. A metal strip to contain yarrow would be helpful if it is used as a path.

Most mature yarrows produce flowering stems up to 90cm (3ft) in height. Wild yarrow, which is a native plant in Europe, Asia and America, has soft green foliage with many segments, giving a feathery effect. I have seen it looking completely "at home" on the top of an exposed hill in Ontario, Canada. Red yarrow has similar leaves although they are slightly heavier in form and have striking red flowers. Other cultivated yarrows with yellow flowers have much larger grey leaves, very different from the wild yarrow. Only the flower has changed little in appearance.

Yarrow blooms for a long time during the summer, and for medicinal and cosmetic use is dried with the flowers as they first open. The distance needed between plants varies with the use for which they are being grown. Since it is such a valuable companion plant however, it is a pity not to take advantage of this by setting other plants between small clumps of yarrow. It will then protect them with its root secretions.

Yarrows will grow almost anywhere, and will flourish in stony, poor soils. However, they do like some sun. Cut down dead growth in autumn, dividing the plant in spring.


## *Allium sativum*      **B-P**      **GARLIC**

NOW cultivated world-wide, garlic originated in central Asia. Grown in Europe, around the Mediterranean, for centuries, it was also known by the Indians of North and South America. Chicago was named "Cigaga-Wung", Place of the Wild Garlic - when early explorers made it their campsite.

If the cloves are planted in late autumn in a temperate climate, rather than on the shortest day - the time recommended by some - then you can harvest garlic in the following summer.

The easiest way to grow the herb is to take a few cloves from a head of garlic bought for cookery and set these into good, rich soil, either in early autumn or in late spring. Garlic can be set in partial shade, although it likes the sun, but do not place it where sunlight will be excluded. It is one of the best companions for roses, helping to keep them healthy and in turn, enjoying the enriched ground you will almost certainly have prepared.

Push the cloves about 3cm (2in) into the soil with the pointed end upwards, around 15cm (6in) apart. Green shoots will soon appear and grow to resemble tall chives. It used to be believed that if garlic was planted in this way when the moon was full, then it would grow large and round, looking like an onion.

If you are setting your garlic in the vegetable patch rather than amongst herbs, then take care not to place it too close to peas or beans, or it may hold back their growth and development.

Harvest the bulbs when the green shoots droop and turn yellow.

## *Allium schoenoprasum*  P  CHIVES

CHIVES are native to northern Europe and a few grow wild in the U.K. Italy and Greece. The herb is also found in the wild in North America. It has become naturalised in parts of Canada and America, where it "escaped" after being introduced by the Pilgrim Fathers.

Chives make a lovely low edging to herb beds or even flowerbeds. The plant will grow to about 25cm (10in) high if left to do so. Chives for kitchen use should never be allowed to become so tall. Keep them cut down to less than 10cm (4in) for the best flavour.

It is tempting to leave them to flower and a few dotted here and there will make a good show of pretty pinkish purple blooms. Again, those for the kitchen should have any flowerbuds removed. Harvest regularly and unless they are planted in good, rich soil, feed chives every three or four weeks, or more often if they are in pots. Give them a good dressing of compost in the autumn.

For steady growth they like semi-shade which gives the herb moist soil. Large clumps should be lifted and divided in autumn. Set the small clumps of 6 to 10 bulbs about 20cm (8in) apart. If you drink ground coffee then save some of your used coffee grounds to spread around the chives.

Chives also like chalk and are found growing wild near limestone. They are hardy plants but cannot be expected to give harvests through cold winters. To continue gathering their green stems pot a few bulbs when you divide the clumps in autumn and take these indoors.

## *Aloysia triphylla*  S  LEMON VERBENA

WHEN growing lemon verbena it is best to remind ourselves, particularly when the weather is cool and approaching autumn, that this herb is a native of South America. Originally growing in Chile, Peru, Brazil and Argentina, it was introduced to North America and Europe in the late 18th century.

It remains one of the most tender plants in the herb garden. In very sheltered southern locations it has reached a height of 4.5m (15ft). However in a temperate climate lemon verbena is more usually a pot plant taken outdoors in summer and wintering on a south-facing windowsill, or in a greenhouse.

I trim the herb in spring to encourage new growth and take stem cuttings at this time. They need care to become established in sandy soil and should not be set alongside the parent plant where strong sunlight could scorch them.

The long, narrow, elegant leaves have a delicious lemon scent. Cutting the herb back, before moving the plant out into a garden bed or tub, helps to stop the herb becoming woody. Set in a sunny garden lemon verbena will reward you with luxuriant growth. Do not be tempted to give it rich soil in this situation, or it will be more likely to die if a light frost catches you unprepared in autumn.

Pot the herb up again ready for winter as soon as the nights become noticeably cooler, so that you can then take the plant indoors as necessary. At this point it may still be especially attractive with tiny, deep pink flowers. The extra thought and care required by lemon verbena is rewarded in so many ways, you will find it a pleasure.

## *Althaea officinalis*  P  MARSHMALLOW

ONE of the "older" plants in the herb garden, marshmallow has been cultivated since the eighth century, and possibly earlier. It has also been gathered widely as a wild plant from salt marshes and moist areas throughout Europe, parts of Asia, Australia and eastern North America.

The soft, velvety grey-green leaves make it an attractive addition to herbaceous borders as well as beds kept strictly for "herbs". Marshmallow has delicate pink or white flowers, borne in clusters on the upper parts of the stems in late summer, when many herbs are past their best. With their subtle grace, they look well against the taller elecampane, another "cottage garden" herb.

The seeds which follow appear to have been packed into the seedheads in the most efficient way possible. They are circular discs set tightly into a ring which used to be referred to as a cheese. These large seeds have a good germination rate, producing seedlings with almost circular serrated green leaves, reminiscent of lady's mantle. These will take into their second year before approaching the size of a mature plant, which can reach 1.8m (6ft) in height.

Marshmallow, as the name suggests, thrives in moist, sandy soil where it is open to the sun. The herb was once gathered in large amounts for medicinal uses and making real marshmallow sweets, from the marshes around the Thames estuary in London, England.

Root clumps can be divided in spring, or in autumn, when the root is harvested for confectionery. Cut the plant down ready for winter at the same time.

## *Anethum graveolens*  A  DILL

DILL is a hardy annual with soft, feathery, grey-green foliage. It grows to about 90cm (3ft) in height and will usually need some support or shelter from strong winds. Dill may have originated in India, Iran and Egypt or in southern Europe, and should be looked upon as a sun-loving plant. It was introduced to Britain by the Romans and taken to America by the settlers where it has been cultivated particularly in Ohio and Oregon for the essential oil. It is also grown widely in Michigan, Idaho and Indiana.

The seeds are tiny, giving about 25,000 to 28g (1oz). Do not bury them; simply press lightly into fine soil in a sunny place. Sow in succession, about once a fortnight from spring until midsummer and thin to about 20cm (8in) apart.

You can begin harvesting the leaves once the plant is established, but, always leave some! Once the seeds begin to ripen, cut down the whole herb. The seedhead can be dried, hung upside-down indoors, leaving the seeds to fall away as they are ready. If you wish dill to seed itself, simply leave one seedhead until all the seeds have dropped to the ground, then cut down. Do remember how light the seeds are. On a windy day they can be sown some distance away.

Dill should not be grown close to fennel if you wish to sow the seeds or allow the plants to seed themselves. These two herbs are very closely related and you may find they cross pollinate, leaving you with new plants which are neither truly one nor the other. (See page 21).

## *Angelica archangelica*      **B-P**      **ANGELICA**

ANGELICA has been grown in Scandinavia at least since the twelfth century. In France the herb has been cultivated for the liqueur industry near Clermont Ferrand. Large quantities of angelica are grown in southern France and Spain to be candied. Some authorities believe Mary Queen of Scots may have brought the first angelica plants to England from France since she was fond of angelica in confectionery. In this century there have been large centres of cultivation in France, Germany, Spain and The Netherlands, while the fields of angelica once harvested near London all vanished long ago.

A tiny first-year angelica seedling gives little idea of the true nature of the herb. A second-year plant yields handsome, deeply cut leaves which will begin to shade the surrounding area. In maturity it can be majestic, (my tallest angelica reached 3.5m (11½ft). More usually they grow to 2.7m (9ft) in height. Depending upon the climate, angelica will take two or three years to reach full growth, flower, shed numerous seeds, then die. The life of a plant can be extended for a further year or more, by cutting out the flowerheads as they appear. Wear gloves to clear away the stems if you have very sensitive skin as the juice can cause allergic reactions. Since angelicas grow in Siberia, Greenland and Iceland, as well as in the more temperate regions, you need have no fear of frost damage. They seem to thrive on cold winters. Young angelicas simply die down in late autumn to ground level, springing miraculously into energetic life in spring. Their rate of growth is astonishing as they reach full height in three to four months and their need of rich, moist soil is understandable. An old wall nearby helps to hold moisture and give protection from high winds, which easily damage the tall stems. Third-year plants often need staking. In full sun and an open position angelica will be considerably shorter. If the weather is hot and dry for any length of time, water the plants regularly, adding some nettle liquid feed (see page 22) every few days.

By midsummer mature angelicas will almost certainly be flowering. Allow one flowerhead to seed, as you will want more plants to follow on in successive years. The germination rate of seeds drops dramatically if they are gathered and kept any length of time before sowing. More seedheads attract beautiful finches which can leave the plant with rather tattered leaves as they eagerly eat the fallen seeds. The settlers took angelica with them to America and the herb can be found in the Old Salem Medicinal garden, where the planting is based on plant lists and plans of Bethabara Gardens at the first Moravian settlement in 1761. American angelica, *Angelica atropurpurea* is paler in colour than the European variety, with less heady fragrance and smaller, flatter flowerheads, more akin to those of lovage. It is a perennial, growing to 1.5-1.8m (5-6ft) in height in damp areas from Labrador in Canada to Delaware and westwards to Minnesota.

*The Chamomile seat overlooks an open knot of herbs.*

*Golden hop, jasmine, honeysuckle, climbing rose – make a fragrant "Covered Way".*

# Planning

*When planning a herb garden remember how tall herbs grow, add spring colour and herbs to attract bees and butterflies – see "Peacock" on hyssop below.*

*Ripening seed heads, (Angelica above), hips and berries attract birds: while sage and other herbs encourage toads and other gardener's "friends".*

# Planning

*In a cottage garden herbs may be appreciated in formal "knots" or simple abundance.*

## *Anthriscus cerefolium*      **A**      **CHERVIL**

ORIGINATING in the Middle East, the Caucasus and southern Russia, chervil was brought from the shores of the Mediterranean across Europe by the Romans. In France it has remained an important herb in kitchen gardens, known as *cerfeuil*; while in Germany and Britain chervil is widely cultivated. The English so valued it that they took it with them to America.

Chervil is a pretty herb, with a fairy-tale quality in its lace-like leaves, light as a butterfly's wing. The tiny white flowers seem insubstantial, as if a puff of wind would blow them away. The herb has more strength in flavour than its appearance would suggest and a stronger will for survival. As long as there is sufficient drainage, chervil will thrive in quite poor soil.

Once you have chervil in your garden and leave it to seed, then more will rapidly appear. Seedlings can mature to give you a tasty harvest in five or six weeks. The lifespan of the plant is considerably shortened by dry, hot weather, when it will soon go to seed. Sowing seeds yourself, every three or four weeks, will ensure a constant supply of the herb through the summer. Once the heat of the sun dries the earth, it is wise to sow chervil in the shade offered by a taller plant, such as fennel, which will naturally die down and be cut back later in the year. Chervil can remain in the garden as a green harvest through mild winters, when it will appreciate the sun.

The herb does not like to be handled. It can be transplanted with great care but should be considered shy of interference. When gathering the leaves pull them gently rather than cutting them and always harvest from the outer edges of the plant first.

In hot weather and as the plant begins to form seeds, the leaves may begin to turn a reddish mauve which only adds to its attraction. The seeds as they ripen point upwards as long, black spikes.

Chervil can be grown indoors for winter harvests, or to bring plants on early in spring. A plant or two overwintered in a cold frame or greenhouse can also help you to begin the season early. Mature plants can grow to 35 or 45cm (15 or 18in) in height so do give them 'headroom' if you want them to go to seed.

## *Artemisia abrotanum*      **P**      **SOUTHERNWOOD**

SOUTHERNWOOD is both an attractive and useful herb. The soft, feathery pale green-grey leaves invite you to handle them, releasing their pungent odour as you pass by. The herb can be planted in large tubs on either side of a doorway or seat for the summer to good decorative effect, keeping insects away as a bonus. I recommend large tubs as this semi-shrub may not thrive in waterlogged soil and likes to be well fed.

It comes from southern Europe and the Middle East and has also been introduced in North America where it has become naturalised. It is not surprising therefore to find full sun given as a good position for the plants. I have, however, grown it with equal success in partial shade.

It is a bush which easily becomes untidy and straggly if it is not tended regularly, which often means its possibilities as a decorative herb are not appreciated. Trim the growth back by at least a third, or even half in late spring or early summer. At this time the best of the cut stems can be set as 10-12cm (4-5in) lengths in potting compost to grow as cuttings.

At the end of summer clip the herb back again less severely. The harvest of foliage is perfect at this time for drying to repel moths. Southernwood may flower at the end of summer, the flowers being so tiny and pale, they may not even be noticed when surrounded by other herbs.

Southernwood will grow to around 0.75m (2½ft) in height if left untended, but may then produce only scanty foliage at the tops of rather bare stems. It can be clipped to form a 30-45cm (12-18in) hedge which has the advantage of acting as a barrier to insects for low-growing plants nearby. A southernwood hedge is also useful in a small front garden near traffic, where it copes admirably with polluted air.

## *Artemisia dracunculus*       P-with care.       TARRAGON

MANY people are convinced that French tarragon with its fine, narrow leaves and valued flavour is far superior to Russian tarragon, which is heavier in form, hardier and only similar in flavouring.

When living in the north-east of England, I lost my French tarragon so regularly to frosts, which came well into June at times, that I gave up trying to grow it. Having experienced frost in June in the south for the past two years with the same result; I am inclined only to grow French tarragon, which originated in southern Europe, in a pot which can be taken indoors as necessary at night. Indoors it will be happy on a light windowsill. Remove it from the pot, enriching the soil each year, and do not allow it to become waterlogged.

Russian tarragon, *Artemisia dracunculoides,* is certainly not a suitable herb for a pot on the windowsill. In the garden if left alone, it will take over a herb bed with ease, apparently regarding this as its territory, and if not divided regularly each autumn, will extend this boundary rapidly. This tarragon, as the name suggests, comes from Siberia and Asia.

A mulch of compost will give good results and the herb will need staking if it is not vigorously harvested, as it grows to 90cm (3ft) tall and more. It is a good idea to cut down the flowering stems before they seed, rather than waiting for the season to end.

## *Borago officinalis*       A       BORAGE

BORAGE adds the beauty of its star-like flowers to barren places in the wild. It may have originated in the western Mediterranean, but is now naturalised over a much wider area. Introduced to America by the early settlers, borage appears in John Winthrop's seed order in 1631. It is listed in U.S. seedsmen's catalogues in 1806. In France Louis XIV admired the flowers and had the herb grown in the gardens at Versailles.

It grows from 30-75cm (1-2½ft) tall. The care of borage in regular harvesting of flowers and leaves is essential to keep it from becoming straggly and unruly.

Sow the large, black seeds in a sunny position. Borage is most effective grown in clumps on a bank or in a raised bed, as the flowers tend to droop a little. The plants also support one another through windy weather. After the first year, unless you harvest all of the flowers before they can go to seed, borage can usually be relied upon to seed itself, which it does prolifically.

Borage can be grown in tubs and may be taken indoors as young plants in the late autumn to give flowers for winter use. Often, if the summer starts early, borage can flower, go to seed and having sown itself, will provide a second generation of plants for the autumn. In a sheltered spot it is quite hardy. I have known borage to be in flower in midwinter if the season is mild.

Borage likes chalky, sandy soil, but will grow in almost any soil conditions. Its favourite place for obvious reasons, is along the edges of the compost heap. The roots are very good for breaking up clay soil. They also make good companion plants, (see page 21).

## *Calendula officinalis* A POT MARIGOLD

MARIGOLDS are a joy to grow. So easy that once you have some in the garden they will almost always decide to stay on, setting their own seed. If you are not a real fan of marigolds creating bright splashes of orange colour amongst your other flowers or vegetables however, the simple remedy is to remove the flower heads before they form mature seeds.

Originating in southern Europe, pot marigolds have been grown in England over many centuries. The seeds of *Calendula* were taken to America by early settlers; John Josselyn, writing in 1672, mentions them.

I have seen marigolds flowering in a sheltered corner in January in southern Britain, grown from seeds dropped by the parent plant in autumn and germinated before the cold weather arrived. Equally, I have seen marigolds flowering on late in the year. A few marigolds can of course be deliberately sown in autumn in cold frames or a greenhouse for winter flowers.

Marigolds can grow to 45-60cm (18in to 2ft) in rich soil; or they may come to maturity as dwarf plants in poor conditions. They make wonderful companion plants for tomatoes, ensuring a good harvest of fruit. In fact, pot marigolds are friendly, helpful companions to all other plants.

There are four distinct types of marigold. "French marigolds", *Tagetes,* were brought to England from France by Huguenot refugees in the 16th century and the herbalist Gerard grew them in his garden. They can be very effective as a bedding plant, giving small, pretty flowers to edge a herb bed and provide a dye. The rather evil-smelling *tagetes* are the ones to grow to protect pinks from nematodes which might otherwise destroy their roots. They are also good to make a bed safe before planting bulbs in the autumn. Low growing, they add colour to the herb garden over the summer period and the seeds can be gathered in autumn and sown in the following spring. As they are frost shy, it is best to bring the young seedlings on in a cold frame or under cloches until well into early summer when they can be planted out as they are coming into flower.

The "Mexican marigold", *Tagetes minuta* is becoming more readily available and is grown from seed. Although its name suggests a tiny plant, it is much taller than other marigolds. This plant can be used to overcome couch grass roots. Bear in mind when using it that it can also attack other starchy roots of nearby herbs. Woody roots will not be affected. Care should be taken in handling this plant which can give unpleasant side-effects if the stem pierces your skin.

Both French and African marigolds come originally from Mexico, which explains why they vanish from gardens at the first frost.

## *Carum carvi*       **B**       **CARAWAY**

CARAWAY is a useful herb which can be brought to maturity and produce seed in less than two years, by sowing the seeds in autumn rather than spring. A little protection should be given to the young seedlings over the winter to ensure success.

If you wish to grow sufficient plants to supply your culinary needs, caraway is best grown in long rows in the vegetable patch and covered with cloches. This method also helps to avoid the plants becoming waterlogged in a wet winter, especially if you are using a raised bed system to grow your vegetables. A wet winter can be lethal to caraway, whether it is a few months old or still tiny seedlings.

Do not sow caraway near fennel as they dislike each other and neither will thrive.

Caraway leaves resemble carrot tops, so they will appear quite at home with the vegetables. In fact you can also eat their long, yellow taproots. Caraway will produce tiny, white flowers in umbels during its first spring, which later become the distinctive, spicy seeds. Cut the seedheads as soon as the seeds turn brown and finish drying them indoors in a paper bag. The plant will be over 60cm (2ft) in height by this time.

The herb grows wild in Europe and is cultivated over a wide area from Russia, through Scandinavia, to India as well as in North America. It was taken across the Atlantic by the Pilgrim Fathers and is naturalised in some parts of America and Canada.

Caraway is grown commercially in Germany and Holland, Dutch caraway seeds being darker than the English variety and of a high quality.


## *Chamaemelum nobile*       **P**       **CHAMOMILE**

THERE is probably more confusion about which chamomile is which and which similar herbs are not chamomile, than there is with any other herb. The true chamomile is quite distinctive, if you know exactly what to look for. The yellow centres of the flowers are conical in shape and hollow. Other plants, such as "stinking mayweed", which are similar from a distance, have a different scent, or, in some cases, smell. It is best to buy chamomile from a reputable source and grow this in your garden until you are familiar with it, before trying to identify plants in the wild.

German chamomile, *Matricaria chamomilla,* or *Matricaria recutita,* is gathered for medicinal purposes. It grows at field edges and roadsides over much of Europe and Asia. Chamomile is mainly cultivated commercially in France.

The double-flowered chamomile *Chamaemelum nobile "flore pleno",* was introduced to Germany from Spain in the late Middle Ages. This form or matricaria are considered best for teas as they are not bitter. Chamomile was taken by early settlers to America but, to my knowledge, is not found growing wild there.

Seeds are readily available and can be sown in early spring to flower from early summer to autumn. The height of the plant varies according to soil conditions from 20cm (8in) to over 30cm (1ft) tall. Since chamomile has a lolling habit - making it appear untidy - and seeds freely, it is best contained by other plants, rather than used as an edging to a border. Pansies or wild heartsease make pretty and functional partners to chamomile, helping it to remain upright, especially in a raised bed.

Unless using chamomile as a companion plant (see page 21), sow the seeds thickly in a sunny position, ideally in sandy soil. Harvest flowerheads for more flowers and cut back in autumn.

## *Coriandrum sativum*  A  CORIANDER

**M**ENTIONED in the Egyptian *Ebers papyrus,* early scriptures and by the ancient Greeks, coriander has been cultivated for over 3,000 years. The early settlers took the herb to America in the 17th century, and at this time the seeds were being added to the famous eau-de-carmes liqueur, made in Paris. In Britain cultivation of the herb is enjoying a revival.

To use the seeds in cookery, you will need numerous plants and so do decide at the outset how much room you seriously want to give the herb. One or two plants grown for their leaves are a pleasant and useful addition to the kitchen garden.

Sow the seeds after the worst frosts are over. They can be sown in rows or clumped together in a more natural arrangement. Coriander does not transplant well, meaning careful thought should be given to the site.

Traditionally, coriander is said to be healthiest when grown near chervil, dill, marshmallow or hollyhocks. Sow coriander away from fennel, or it may hinder the formation of the fennel seed, although it may also help anise. If coriander seeds are sown in single pots under glass they can be brought on at the beginning of the season. Being a herb used to a hotter climate, coriander likes a sunny, sheltered position. A wet, cool summer may bring you a poor harvest of seeds, but do not despair. For a long time it was thought a viable commercial proposition to grow coriander on a field scale in southern England for gin distilleries, therefore your enterprise can be successful.

It is unlikely you will enjoy the strong fragrance of the plant if you grow it indoors. Coriander flowers are white, or pink, and borne on delicate umbels. In a flowerbed they are inconspicuous, compared to the seeds. Coriander grows to 60cm (2ft) in height.


## *Dianthus*  P  PINKS

**T**HE seeds of *Dianthus caryophyllus* are readily available and it is a great joy to see the bright red flowers opening in July of the second year. Harvest the flowers as they open for cookery or fragrance. Other forms of old-fashioned, clove-scented pinks which were known as clove-gillyflowers and sops-in-wine may be found in specialist nurseries. They enrich the herb garden with their heavy, spicy perfume and beautiful flowers, some of which seem to have been individually painted with a fairy paintbrush.

*Dianthus caryophyllus,* is a native of southern Europe. Pliny wrote of it in the first century A.D. saying it came from Spain where the flowers were used to spice wines. We too can use clove-scented pinks in wines, punch bowls, syrups and cookery, while other brightly patterned varieties contribute their own fragrances in the garden and pot-pourri.

Choose a sunny, sheltered, well-drained position for your plants. A wet, stormy summer can do more damage than frost at times. Although perennial, they are not very long-lived. It is wise to take cuttings after flowering and keep younger plants in moist, fine soil and compost. Pinks also respond to layering, or the roots can be divided in early autumn.

In areas where frost attacks the plants well into the year, they will grow happily in a sunroom indoors. Make sure the pot has good drainage. Wild pinks tend to grow on ruined walls and amongst rocks.

I once read a stern warning not to plant pinks where hyacinths had grown but have been too fond of my pinks to test the combination. Experiments of a very different kind were recorded by Hill in his Herbal of 1568. The practice of burying spices beneath the roots of pinks to enhance their clove-like odour was then in fashion. No cottage garden could be complete without these charming, fragrant herbs. Certainly they were sufficiently regarded to be taken to America by settlers. Anyone who grows roses, especially old-fashioned roses, will find the perfect partner for them in pinks.

## *Eruca vesicaria*        A        SALAD ROCKET

IT is interesting that when I prepared the first edition of this book, ten years ago, I felt that this herb was not sufficiently known and eaten to include it. Now it is commonly on sale alongside other salad herbs. Native to the Mediterranean area, salad rocket was brought by the Romans and was a regular part of summer diet from then until the 19th century.

Salad rocket, as the name suggests, grows quickly, providing spicy leaves with little difficulty. Harvest regularly as the older leaves can take on a bitter quality. It can be grown as readily in a window box as in the garden and may be safer there from slugs which also relish the plants. Sow in rich soil in succession from spring on to midsummer to continue to enjoy the fresh flavour, harvesting after 6-8 weeks. If you do not allow the plants to flower they will flourish a little longer.

The flowers on those you leave to grow on and provide you with seed have 4 whitish pink petals with dark veins. They always remind me of tiny windmill sails. These can very quickly run to seeds which are carried in long cases. A careful watch needs to be kept in order to gather them exactly as they ripen. It is a good idea to sow salad rocket and lettuces together.

## *Foeniculum vulgare*        P        FENNEL

GARDEN fennel is a close relative of dill and has a similar area of origin. The main difference at first sight is the texture of the feathery leaves, which tend to be finer and more delicate, as well as a slightly lighter green.

The cultivation of fennel was encouraged in central Europe by the Emperor Charlemagne in the eighth century. The plant may have been brought to Britain by the Romans. The Anglo Saxons were certainly familiar with it. The herb was introduced into America by the Pilgrim Fathers.

Fennel grown for commercial use varies slightly in seed quality, shape and size, according to the country. German or Saxon fennel is chosen for medicinal use and tends to produce smaller, flatter seeds. Roman, Galician, Russian, Roumanian, Indian, Persian and Japanese are all slightly different. It has largely been grown for pharmaceutical use in France, Germany, Hungary, Bulgaria and the U.S.S.R.

Fennel grown in the right conditions can grow up to 1.8m (6ft) tall and be quite a sturdy plant. More often however it will need a site sheltered from strong winds, or some support as it grows taller. The herb likes moist soil and will thrive on clay, so long as there is not a prolonged spell without rain.

Wild fennel is a familiar roadside plant in parts of Britain and appears on chalky cliffs and along river estuaries.

Sow the seed in early spring and then successively for more young plants. Thin them to about 30cm (12in) apart. Cut the plants right down after harvesting or when the plant has seeded. The seeds are quite different from those of dill, being much larger. As with the dill, little attention beyond harvesting is needed once the plants are established. Fennel is useful in companion planting (see page 30); however, as explained under dill, the two plants should not be placed close together.

## *Fragaria vesca*     P     **WILD STRAWBERRY**

SURELY nothing could be easier to grow - as long as you are not concerned with growing anything delicate nearby! Wild strawberries grow naturally in hedgerows and woodlands. They will thrive beneath trees or bushes and can make a total ground cover amongst shrubs, working quickly to eradicate even such stifling weeds as ground elder and bindweed.

Kept partially in check by a raised bed, or growing in a container, wild strawberries can be a joy even to those who quickly tire of removing the many runners which they seem to produce endlessly.

I have found them of tremendous use in helping to tame long-established perennial weeds. Their cheery white flowers are most welcome in late spring when they appear beside bluebells and cowslips. They continue to lighten dark corners beneath the trees well into the summer.

The long season of wild strawberries means that while the rich fruits are ripening in early summer, flowers are still opening to provide more tasty delicacies later in the year. In good conditions, with sufficient moisture they may continue fruiting until an early frost. We have enjoyed fruits from wild strawberries with more flavour than cultivated varieties, which certainly grow as large as the smaller cultivated "cousins".

They are both hardy against frosts and resistant to pests and diseases, which makes them a good choice to provide fruit if you have the space for a large patch of the herb.

Just three or four young plants taken as runners and set 20cm (8in) apart can cover an area 90cm (3ft) square in a single year, given rich, moist soil. Care of the plants consists simply in giving them a mulch of leafy compost each autumn, harvesting the fruits and cutting back runners as soon as they approach the boundary you have set for them.


## *Geum urbanum, Geum rivale*    P        **AVENS**

HERB Bennet, or Herb Benedict, *Geum urbanum,* can be seen wild in hedgerows in Europe, central Asia and Russia. The small yellow flowers, resembling buttercups, give way to round seedheads of soft but 'spiky' balls. The leaves are narrower and smaller when higher up the stem. The brownish yellow root contains a large amount of pith and when dug in early spring if the weather is dry, (25 March is the traditional day in Europe,) has been credited with a spicy fragrance for pot-pourri.

In the eastern states of America, water avens, better known as "Indian Chocolate", has been harvested as a medicinal herb. Water avens, *Geum rivale,* is a close relative of herb bennet with similar medicinal uses. The root is also gathered in spring for drying. It is known as drooping avens because the flowers, which are mostly a pretty, deep purplish pink, hang down in a bell-like fashion. An occasional cream flower appears. The leaves grow in large rosettes from the base of the plant, reaching some 15cm (6in) in length with the flower stems high above at 30-40cm (12-15in). When the flower petals have dropped they leave an umbrella like arrangement of spokes to the seedhead which resembles that of herb bennet expanded in all directions.

Both herb bennet and water avens like some shade with moist, fairly rich soil. Water avens plants can be divided in spring and autumn, and seedlings will grow readily from either. Cut flower stems back after the petals have dropped to avoid self-seeding and, with water avens, to encourage more flowers later in the year.

More cultivated plants have been hybridized from these. Two other wild varieties, Alpine Avens, *Geum montanum* and Creeping Avens, *Geum reptans,* each have yellow flowers and grow in mountainous areas in eastern France and Germany.

## *Helianthus annuus*      A      SUNFLOWER

GERARD, in the 16th century, likened the centre of the sunflower to unshorn velvet and the placing of the seeds in this great flowerhead to a honeycomb in a beehive. At that time the sunflower, then known as the marigold of Peru, was newly introduced to Britain from America. The marvellous uses of the herb were barely explored. Although the North American Indians grew sunflowers as a crop, the first settlers did not do so and it was much later that the mammoth Russian sunflowers came to be grown on a large scale in America.

Growing in the U.K. the traditional view of the sunflower, against an old cottage garden wall, is one of nostalgic charm. In a practical sense they serve usefully to dry out a damp cottage wall, since they take up large quantities of water to produce such amazing growth in a single season. Sunflowers over 3m (10ft) high are not unusual and they can, if well fed and watered, grow much taller.

Seeds of numerous varieties are now on sale and a personal choice can be made to grow giant or smaller sunflowers. In either case if you wish to be sure the seeds will mature before autumn draws in and there is any risk that an early frost might take your crop, it is wisest to sow the seeds early, under glass. Young plants can be set outdoors in early summer with protection from slugs given by spiky herbs or essential oil. (see page 23).

Sunflowers will grow just as well when sown in the open garden and with a good season may mature in early autumn. Plant out in rich ground, and keep well watered while the plants are establishing themselves. Several sunflowers in a block will help to support each other in strong winds. It is a good idea to stake a single plant quite early on as the large leaves are heavy, even without the weight of a flower, which may be several pounds as the seeds are ripening. There may be one thousand in a single head. I have grown sunflowers with equal success in full sun and partial shade. Whether or not they really turn their faces to the sun is an interesting point; Gerard didn't seem convinced and neither am I.

To harvest the seeds, wait until the head hangs down and the back of the seedhead begins to turn yellow. Then cut the head with some stem and stand it in a warm place to dry completely when the seeds can be removed more easily. The Russians invented a spiked object like a round comb to ease the seeds out quickly. The remainder of the stem can be harvested for the fibres at the same time, or burned to release its valuable content of potash which should then be dug in to feed the soil in your vegetable garden.

Once you have grown sunflowers you will probably want to keep on producing an annual harvest. Do remember however, unless there really is only one suitable place for them in your garden, to move them to a different site each year. Sunflowers take a lot out of the soil which must be replaced if they are to grow well again in that corner of the garden. (see also companion planting, page 23).


## *Hypericum perforatum*      P      ST. JOHN'S WORT

THIS is a herb I simply would not be without. On the other hand, its prolific seeding habits ensure I am never likely to be so. The difficulty of controlling the spread of St. John's Wort comes partly because the flowers, and therefore, the seeds, are not all ready at once on a single plant.

The golden, star-like flowers are so pretty that they tempt all but the stoutest of heart not to cut the herb down before seeds are already formed. The brown seedheads are decorative and useful in dried flower arrangements and posies.

Mature plants will also spread gradually, taking over a bed with steady persistence. The fresh, green toothed leaves, with their distinctive tiny red dots at the edges, identifying the oil glands of the plant, grow on reddish stems. The whole plant adds a decorative note to any flowerbed, and grows to about 90cm (3ft) in height. In mild winters some green leaves remain at ground level.

In early summer check the upper leaves for insect infestation. If the affected leaves, which will be found closed around each other as a protection for the eggs inside, are removed at this point and burned, this will solve the problem. A regular spray of garlic infusion (see page 24) about this time will help to deter pests.

Growing wild throughout Europe and naturalised in America in woodland clearings, at the edges of woods, and on open scrubland, St. John's wort seems to prefer chalky, lime-rich soil. I have seen it equally at home on the quay by the lakeside at Stresa in Italy and growing amongst prehistoric ruins in Malta. There, it was a tiny shadow of the plant which grows in more temperate climates. Surviving in a pocket of dusty sand on the rocks, it showed the tenacious nature of the herb. Hardy in the extreme, St. John's wort may be a survivor in Britain from pre-glacial times. Long may it remain.

*Hyssopus officinalis*  **P**  **HYSSOP**

**H**YSSOP seeds readily, coming to maturity by the second year. All varieties of hyssop produce quite a pungent scent when their leaves are bruised and give a pleasing display of pink-purple or white flowers. These resemble those of rosemary, colouring several inches of the stems with their beauty. They will bring bees to your garden, being as attractive to them as thyme, borage or lavender.

In Europe it is sometimes seen near ruined abbeys where it was once grown as a medicinal plant. The medicinal use of hyssop ensured its introduction to America by early settlers.

The narrow, pointed leaves of hyssop make neat, compact hedges when well trimmed. Larger or smaller varieties suit either a knot garden, border edging or boundary at 30cm-1.2m (1-4ft) high. It is a useful edging to a vegetable patch, giving protection for brassicas from cabbage-white butterflies. Hyssop partners well with grapevines, giving a better harvest of fruit. Originating in the Mediterranean, it likes similar warm, sunny conditions, but the soil should not be rich.

*Hyssopus aristatus,* the rock hyssop, has smaller, more compact leaves and flowers of a deeper hue which appear a little later than those of the taller varieties. It tends to be less hardy as a semi-evergreen in temperate climates. Rock hyssop can be planted in a sunny wall, or rock garden, or makes a central herb of elegance for a small bed filled with thymes and low growing herbs. In this situation it can be trimmed to a pyramid or ball, acting as a focal point.

Take cuttings in the spring which will root quickly in fine soil mixed with potting compost. Young plants should be set 15-20cm (6-8in) apart for a continuous hedge. The largest hyssop will need 30-45cm (12-18in) between plants. Trim the herbs again to harvest the flowering stems. Divide plants in autumn.

## Inula helenium         P         ELECAMPANE

IF you have the space for this herb, which grows up to 1.5m (5ft) tall or more, and has large, velvety leaves, it will certainly be worth the little attention required. Elecampane is perfect for creating the atmosphere of an old cottage garden. It looks completely at home against hollyhocks, or an old stone wall. The flowers are rather like small sunflowers, bright yellow and opening as flat upturned discs providing a landing area for butterflies.

As its size suggests, elecampane sends deep roots in search of goodness and moisture. Along with lovage, angelica and comfrey, it likes a rich, moist soil. It also needs sunshine. The roots can be divided in autumn or spring, when they are also harvested for use.

Like most perennials, elecampane remains relatively small in the first year and only flowers in the second and following years, when the thick stems grow steadily upwards. Then the hairy leaves begin to spread a soft canopy above surrounding low-growing herbs.

The flowers open from distinctive buds in high summer, to be followed by fluffy, pretty seedheads. The many seeds should be gathered and some sown in spring. To keep this hungry herb under control, it is best to remove most of the seedheads before they are ready to scatter their progeny to the four corners of your garden. The seeds germinate freely and young plants will benefit from partial shade. These can later be set some 90-120cm (3 to 4ft) apart.

Elecampane is sturdy against strong winds. It probably originated in central Asia and has since been brought to Europe where it is cultivated in Belgium, France and Germany. Introduced to New England by settlers, it grows wild from Nova Scotia to Ontario in Canada, and in North Carolina and Missouri in the United States. In Europe, it can sometimes be seen growing close to the sites of ruined abbeys, a relic of past physic plots.


## Laurus nobilis         T         BAY

GROWING bay is one of the great joys of tending a herb garden. In ancient times the fate of a bay tree was very closely linked with that of its owner. This ensured bays received very special care. I have always felt a particular bond with my bay trees and nurtured the oldest through long, cold winters in a centrally heated atmosphere it really did not like. On spring and autumn days I carried the tub in and out of the protection of the house to give it as much sunshine as possible.

Young bay trees must be protected from frost if they are to thrive. As with most Mediterranean herbs, bitter winds can do even more damage than frosts. Older trees will lose new growth, but usually the main part of the tree survives.

If your tree remains in a pot, remember to remove it carefully at least every second year, gently uncurling any potbound roots and re-potting in fresh compost and a larger pot as necessary. With a tree indoors in winter, spray the leaves with water when you water the soil and in spring add an iron tonic. These can be bought or home nettle liquid fertilizer used (see page 22). I have known this restore bays to health from very poor condition.

Stem cuttings can be taken in early summer or autumn and will need careful protection for a full year while they are establishing roots. Clipping bays to shape can give dramatic results, although I prefer to see them growing naturally.

In the 17th century, John Evelyn praised the case standards which were then imported from Flanders, writing, "..with stems so even and upright, heads so round, full and flourishing... that one tree of them has been sold for more than twenty pounds...".

In milder climates and in sheltered situations bays can reach 4.5-6m (15 to 20ft) tall, decorated in early summer by clusters of tiny creamy male and female flowers. In the right weather these are followed by dark berries.

Willow leaf Bay, *Laurus nobilis angustifolia,* is a bay with very narrow, pointed leaves. It was originally hoped this tree would resist the damage of cold winds better than the sweet bay, but this is not the case. I have found them even less hardy in cold conditions. In a very sheltered position however, they make a charming centrepiece in a formal bed. Golden Bay, *Laurus nobilis aurea,* has mainly golden leaves with touches of pale green. This is hardier than willow leaf bay and can be alternated with sweet bay in the garden plan to great effect.

## *Lavendula officinalis*       P       LAVENDER

NO herb garden could be complete without lavender, which is closely identified with the "English" garden, even though it did not originate in the U.K. Lavender does, however, have an affinity with the British climate. This Mediterranean herb of the southern Alps gives the best oil when grown in the damp English "summer" weather. It is mostly the percentages of linalyl acetate and cineol which vary. The former being four to five times as great in English lavender compared to French. It will thrive in a shady place but is more aromatic in full sun.

The Pilgrim Fathers took the herb to America, writing later - they had not found it suited to the North American climate. Nowadays, a number of specially hardy varieties are available which are grown in the United States, blooming in June and again in September in some areas. These include, "Two Seasons", "Dark Supreme", and "Short 'n' Sweet", all from *Lavandula angustifolia* advertised along with "Fat Spike", *Lavandula angustifolia* X Intermedia, "Grosso".

To grow lavender from seed means waiting until the second year for flowers and in colder climates providing protection for young lavender plants at least under cloches. It is otherwise satisfying if beginning a new garden. Once you have plants established, cuttings are a better propagation method as these will be true to the parent form while seedlings can vary.

About 12.5cm (5in) of new growth can readily be taken from mature bushes in early summer and set in pots of sandy soil with the protection of a plastic bag over the pot to maintain them in a moist atmosphere. Leave them beneath this protection for about four weeks, then give them a further two weeks in the pot by which time they should be rooted and ready to plant out. Cuttings should be well established by early autumn. Being perennial, they make a good, evergreen hedge in a temperate climate. This will be helpful to edge herb, flower, or vegetable plots. Plant young lavenders 15cm (6in) apart, thinning them in the following year. A close beginning will give you the hedge effect much faster, but mature plants kept too close together may be liable to disease in damp weather.

To give lavender a really good start, dig a deep hole and lay a little old manure or good compost in the bottom. Cover this with soil and then set the plant into the hole above this extra nourishment.

The secret of keeping lavender from becoming woody and needing replacing every few years is to trim right back to the previous year's growth when harvesting the flower stems. At Norfolk Lavender farm, in England, where this is done by their harvester, bushes twenty years old are still healthy in growth and giving a good annual harvest. Trimming must take place early enough to give the plants time to make a little new growth before there is a danger of frost. Continue to feed the herb with compost or liquid feeds in spring and autumn.

Numerous varieties of lavender are available. "Munstead" remains popular, while "Hidcote" does not appear to be seen as often as it once was. The dwarf white, *nana alba,* growing 15-20 cm (6-8in) high is a pretty edging for knot gardens. White lavender was once very popular and it is a joy to see it returning. White *Lavendula stoechas* offers a complete contrast with the bulbous flowerheads and a succession of flowers beginning before the other lavenders and continuing for several weeks. The dark-flowered "Grappenhall", growing to 60-90cm (2 to 3ft) is beautifully scented. Many charming curiosities make wonderful diversions amongst the lavender beds, but they do need indoor protection from frost. *Lavandula dentata,* with finely serrated leaves and *Lavandula canariensis* from the Canary Islands, which grows to a tall, 90cm-1m (3 to 3½ft) need special attention to survive cold winters. The latter giving the welcome benefit of pretty purplish flowers in the depth of winter.


## *Leonorus cardiaca*        P        MOTHERWORT

THIS herb never fails to draw the attention of gardeners as well as those interested in herbal medicine. Introduced into Britain as a herb from Siberia in 1658, motherwort appears to have been popular in gardens. Many plants escaped into the wild and the herb was once not an unusual sight in hedgerows. Today a wild plant of the herb is a rare find. Motherwort has, however, grown as a native plant in much of Europe. Settlers took it to America for medicinal use and it is now naturalised over a wide area of the United States.

In good, loamy soil, motherwort may grow as tall as 1.2-1.5m (4 or 5ft) but is more usually around 90cm (3ft) tall. The strong, square stems withstand wind and weather well, although if planted on a bank, by midsummer the tall spires of pinkish mauve flowers lean over, giving an even more realistic impression of a lions tail - hence the latin name, *leonorus.*

In the wild, motherwort has grown well on limestone. In the garden these perennial plants with attractive, palmate leaves at the lower part of the stem and longer, almost pointed leaves growing out in pairs between the whorls of flowers on the upper stem, grow well in chalky soil.

Later in the autumn when the bees no longer hang in drunken ecstasy from the open flowers in the evening peace, the seedcases form. These cup the seeds in a spiky, protective grip, making gloves a necessity when gathering them. At this stage the herb can be cut down to a few inches high, ready for winter. Left standing tall, they will readily seed themselves, rapidly colonising your garden. The plants can be divided in autumn.


## *Levisticum officinale*        P        LOVAGE

THE herb is a native plant of the Mediterranean, its home being in the mountainous districts of northern Greece, the Balkans and southern France. I have seen a magnificent specimen growing in a small garden high in the Italian Alps, a wonderful surprise as I rounded a corner of the track.

In this century lovage has been grown commercially in Provence, the Dauphins, Thuringia and Belgium. Essential oil for perfumery is distilled from the whole plant. The Pilgrim Fathers took lovage to America, where it has become naturalised in the eastern states.

By the second or third year of growth, a single lovage plant will give even a large family sufficient herb for their needs. Lovage grows best in a rich, moist soil, fed in spring and autumn with compost to produce a striking and attractive plant.

Left to itself, this perennial herb will steadily increase in girth until it occupies the circumference of a good-sized tree. However, once your friends and relatives have tasted lovage soup, or experienced the herb in fresh salads, they will be asking you for a plant and you will find no shortage of new homes for excess lovage. Simply divide the root clumps in spring or autumn, taking root from the outer perimeter of the plant until it is the size you require. Each piece of root should have a bud for growth. These new plants must be kept well watered until they are established. With this care, the success rate is high.

Whether you dry all the harvested herb or not, lovage will benefit from being cut down to a height of about 15cm (6in) in late spring and again in summer. Leave the "heart" of the plant untouched. If left to flower the leaves will deteriorate and be subject to insect damage. A regular spray with nettle fertilizer (see page 22) can help to avoid this problem, removing any poor foliage at the same time.

Lovage will grow in an open sunny position, or less vigorously in partial shade. For anyone not wanting too large a plant, it is better set in some shade. A healthy, mature lovage can reach about 2.7m (9ft) in height, bearing tiny, inconspicuous flowers high above your head. If you wish to gather these seeds for cookery, or to steep them in brandy to make lovage cordial, be careful to examine them regularly. Out of sight can be out of mind and it is easy to miss the best time for harvesting them. Lovage seedlings are not usually a problem in the garden, for the plant is not likely to self-sow readily. They are so light, they probably blow far away. Seed saved for sowing in the following spring will germinate well in good conditions.

## *Lonicera periclymenum*      S      HONEYSUCKLE

HONEYSUCKLE is such a beautiful shrub when in flower that I grow several varieties in order to have flowers in early summer, in autumn and from Christmas through into the spring. *Lonicera periclymenum* is the honeysuckle which should be used in cookery. For anyone wishing to enjoy honeysuckle syrups, tea or wine, this is the honeysuckle to grow.

Plant it next to an archway, against your house wall, or to cover an unsightly shed and it will reward you with deliciously fragrant flowers from late spring into summer. Cuttings are best taken when flowering is finished. These can be set in a tub of sandy soil and kept in the shade until the following spring when they will be growing vigorously and ready to plant out. Too much shade will reduce the number of flowers, but honeysuckle will grow almost anywhere. It simply needs a support to grow against and will be better for a trim after flowering. At this time I cut mine back quite hard, which gives me long stems for basketry.

The cultivar *serotina* is a late Dutch honeysuckle and this will flower during the weeks following the early *periclymenum*. I have planted the two to cover my honeysuckle arch into the knot garden, one on either side.

The name *Lonicera* was given to honeysuckle in honour of Adam Lonicer or Lonitzer (1528-86), a German physician in Frankfurt, who wrote on natural history. Early Dutch or Belgian var. *Belgica* had been imported to Britain by the late 17th century. The North American Trumpet honeysuckle was introduced by John Tradescant the younger before 1656. *Lonicera semperivens,* has wonderful scarlet and yellow tubular flowers. In Provence the flowers of *Lonicera caprifolium L. Lonicera etrusca,* and *Santi L. gigantea* are treated for their perfume.

For winter I grow an evergreen honeysuckle and to enjoy honeysuckle flowers in midwinter, *Lonicera fragrantissima*, a hardy honeysuckle with leaves of a pale green against other deep blue-green honeysuckle foliage. This herb comes from China, grows at a slightly slower pace than other varieties and opens glorious white flowers soon after Christmas in mild winters, or even earlier in December. More and more flowers follow on, occasionally well into March. My winter honeysuckle grows against a south-facing wall next to the front door so that we may enjoy it to the full on dark winter days.

Stem cuttings can be taken when the herb is cut back in early summer and rooted in a tub in the shade before planting out. It will flower the following year on the new growth.

Both *Lonicera periclymenum* and *Lonicera caprifolium* are found growing wild in hedgerows. The complex tubular flowers will keep their creamy colouring with pink, folded edges, when dried in silica gel. The berries which follow honeysuckle flowers may be poisonous and should be removed if small children play close to them. Otherwise their orange colour can be attractive against the leaves in autumn and bright finches and other small birds will come to eat them.

## *Marrubium vulgare*      P      HOREHOUND

THE herb probably originated in the Mediterranean and is native to southern and central Europe, Asia and North Africa. It appears to suffer, if at all, from cool, wet weather in summer and autumn, rather than from actual frosts. Although rarely seen growing wild, I have found it growing high on an exposed cliff-face in North Wales. An ability to withstand frost must have been of great importance to its survival when the herb was taken to North America by settlers. Adapting well, it is recorded as a much-used medicinal remedy amongst the pioneers as they travelled westwards.

One of the most distinctive of the medicinal herbs, horehound never fails to catch the eye. The soft, pale grey leaves of the plant in spring have edges that almost seem to have been gathered with thread - as if the herb is dressed up for a special occasion. In winter and early spring these leaves can be very tiny, clustered together in tight whorls. As the white stem grows upwards to reach about 45cm (18in) or more, the woolly down of the leaves is less obvious and they become greener. In summer the tiny crowns of flowers open around the leaf joints. The many minute white flowers are unremarkable, however, they leave seedheads which are exceptional in dried flower arrangements. These should never be gathered, or handled when wearing a woollen garment as they cling tenaciously.

Horehound likes a sunny position with shelter from cold east winds. Since its main use is in providing fresh leaves to treat colds - unless you stock your herb cupboard efficiently in summer with horehound candy or syrup - it may be to your advantage to bring a plant or two indoors for the winter. In this way your potential harvest may be safeguarded, for although some leaves are generally available whatever the weather, the herb rarely produces new growth in the garden in the colder months. Plants can be divided in spring and set about 25cm (10in) apart. Stem cuttings are taken in autumn and overwintered with protection from frosts and cold winds. The seeds are best saved until spring, as horehound produces few self-sown plants.

## *Melissa officinalis*      **P**      **LEMON BALM**

LEMON balm originally grew in the Mediterranean, through to Iran and Siberia. Taken by the Turks when they captured Jericho, lemon balm was so valued in these ancient times that it was guarded constantly and the harvest stored in the Royal Treasury. In the Middle Ages the herb was introduced to areas north of the Alps and generally cultivated in monastery physic gardens. The Pilgrim Fathers took it to America where it is cultivated in herb gardens today.

Lemon balm is a familiar plant, but perhaps unknown to many people as a herb. Familiarity has, in many cases, bred a contempt which this delightful plant does not merit. With a strong reputation for being invasive, it is a plant too often removed, rather than harvested. Regular harvesting of the young tops will ensure the energy which it might otherwise have put into spreading a mat-like clump of roots is used up to your satisfaction.

I always think of it as the "nun" of the herb garden. Whatever the quality of the soil, lemon balm will thrive as long as it receives sufficient sunlight. Never crowd lemon balm with taller herbs as then it is likely to develop mildew and the foliage will be useless.

Since it is the leaves you are wishing to harvest, lemon balm should not be allowed to flower. Always harvest the plant for drying just as the flowers are opening. At this time it will have the greatest quantity of essential oil.

The herb will stand partial shade, although it enjoys the sun, and if you have a bank to clothe with plants, its spreading roots can help to hold the soil of the bank in place. Lemon balm can reach a height of 60cm (2ft). It will be a healthier plant, offering more useful leaves however if it is harvested twice or three times a year for drying or freezing. Make your last cut at the end of the warm summer weather as nights are becoming cooler, leaving the plant neatly cut down for winter. Apply a light covering of mulch to protect it against the frost. When spring comes and brings new growth then the herb can be lifted and the roots divided to give more plants.

A very attractive variegated lemon balm is slightly less hardy than the green herb. Plant in full sun as shade can cause the leaves to revert to green. Give protection from fierce summer heat, however, or the leaves may be scorched in brown patches. Cut down in the same manner to obtain a harvest of exceptionally attractive leaves which can be used in the kitchen as garnishes and in fruit salads, or summer drinks.

## *Mentha*      **P**      **MINTS**

THERE are in all, about 40 different kinds of mint, although most people are only familiar with two or three. The diversity of appearance and fragrance amongst them is their greatest source of wonder to me. Exploring the mint "kingdom" can fill a garden in itself.

Those I find most useful and attractive are applemint, gingermint, the variegated pineapplemint, eau-de-cologne mint and peppermint. All like a rich, moist soil and are invasive to varying degrees. In a large garden mints left to spread in chosen areas can be a marvellous help in combating persistent weeds. This is particularly appreciated in dark corners, where other plants would simply die.

They can, alternatively, be grown in containers, but will do their best to escape. Burying mints in tubs and buckets in a bed too often results in a barren patch of soil inside the container with triumphant fresh shoots of the herb appearing on the outside. If you use an old sink or stone trough on a patio, be sure to change the soil every second year when you cut the plants down in autumn, refilling the base container with fresh compost. Peppermint, in particular needs this change of soil and can even benefit from a change of scene at intervals. If this is neglected, it is likely to suffer from rust. If rust does attack your plants, cut the stems at ground level and burn the affected tops. Straw should also be burned on the soil over the roots in the following winter to eradicate the spores.

Mints are readily propagated by root division, or by picking stems about 12cm (5in) long in spring or early summer to set in a clear jar of water on the windowsill. These will grow roots within a fortnight or three weeks at the outside and can be planted out in shade.

Gingermint, *Mentha gracilis variegata,* is my personal favourite. Not quite as invasive as some mints, it appears relatively late in spring and enjoys a little more sun than most. The tiny, purplish crowns of flowers around the stems are exquisite, although allowing this mint, as any of the others, to flower, is a mistake if you are truly interested in the health of the leaves. A wonderful cookery herb for desserts and summer drinks.

*Mentha suaveolens variegata,* variegated applemint, sometimes also known as pineapplemint, is another delicately shaded, pretty mint. Subtle in its charm, this herb makes a lovely edging for a flowerbed. Harvest taller stems to keep the herb no more than more than 20cm (8in), high for constant young growth.

*Mentha suaveolens,* applemint, has soft velvety leaves of Adam green with rounded edges. As hardy as any of the mints, it can cope with deep shade, stony ground and perennial weeds with ease. It will grow to about 60cm (2ft) in height although the foliage will be better if it is regularly harvested before it reaches full growth. Do not allow it to flower unless you can't resist the flowering tops for posies.

*Mentha X piperita citrata,* eau-de-cologne mint, is a glorious herb to grow beneath seats where its fragrance can be appreciated to the full. It also deters slugs. It is the best mint to set alongside dustbins and compost heaps to perfume the air. At path edges (as long as your path is not grass,) and under the windows of the house, eau-de-cologne mint will live up to its name with the sweetest scent. The leaves are rounded and purplish green. It will grow to about 45cm (18in) tall, if you have not already picked it for flower arrangements. The flowering tops are also attractive in posies.

*Mentha X aquatica citrata,* lemon mint, has green, lemon scented leaves, broader than spearmint, but not as rounded as applemint. It has a soft appearance, which fits the subtle nature of the plant. This herb could readily be placed in a fragrance, kitchen or tea garden. It is one of the shorter mints, generally no taller than gingermint.

*Mentha piperita,* peppermint, again is both a fragrant plant, which has particularly attractive tiny purplish flowers, and an important flavouring in cookery. Of the two peppermints, the black has a dark stem and produces more oil, although this is inferior in quality to that from the white peppermint which has lighter stems. Either will grow to about 60cm (2ft) in height, with pointed leaves.

*Mentha requienii,* Corsican mint, is a creeping mint ideal for covering banks of damp earth in the shade, or setting between paving stones, which must also be in the shade. Given continually moist conditions it will do well, but do not be tempted to set this herb on a sun-baked rockery as it will shrivel and die in dry heat. The herb has minute peppermint scented leaves, growing to only 3-5cm (1-2in). The purple flowers are equally minute.

The familiar garden mint is a native of the Mediterranean. It was introduced to Britain by the Romans and taken to America by the Pilgrim Fathers. The mints now grow throughout Europe and the United States.

There are many more varieties, but those I have included here have been the herbs I have found good uses for and really enjoyed growing. The pennyroyals also belong to the mint family but are listed separately. All mints take a lot from the ground and require feeding with a good mulch of compost in spring and autumn. An old method of bringing mint on early was to make a hot bed with a layer of manure beneath the roots. A little strong for my taste, but effective!

## *Mentha pulegium*          P          PENNYROYAL

CREEPING pennyroyal, also known as run-by-the-ground, does just that. The plants, almost flat to the surface of the soil, spread out in all directions to a distance of 30-60cm (1 to 2ft). The tiny, oval leaves, with their pungent aroma, form a mat covering banks or areas beneath shrubs. Although its growth is so vigorous, creeping pennyroyal is vulnerable to periods of drought, when the circular green mat may suddenly turn brown in the centre and the whole herb eventually dies, unless it is well watered.

In good conditions the flowering stems can be 15cm (6in) tall and give "body" to the appearance of the herb with fluffy crowns of pinkish mauve flowers. Being a member of the mint family, pennyroyal will appreciate enriched soil to support such enthusiastic growth.

Creeping pennyroyal is useful amongst chamomile on seats and banks. It can also be set into cracks in paving, around sundials and fountains and in scented walks where the rich peppermint aroma fills the air as the herb is bruised or disturbed. It has a reputation for keeping ants away, but it doesn't seem to be too effective with the ants in my garden.

When propagating creeping pennyroyal you will find that most runners already have roots if you trace them back towards the centre of the plant. These can easily be parted from the parent herb and potted up or transplanted. A little extra attention in keeping them moist for the first week will reward you with success.

Upright pennyroyal grows to 30-45cm (12-18in) tall and is quite simply a larger version of the same plant with similar flowers and leaves. Both enjoy some shade, although they can survive all but brilliant summers in the sun. Stem cuttings from upright pennyroyal will grow new roots if set in water.

## *Monarda Didyma*          P          BERGAMOT

THIS beautiful herb has shaggy, flaming- red flowers with numerous trumpet-shaped florets throughout full summer. Plant your clump where the flowers can be seen to advantage. They are really spectacular.

Having grown in North America from Ontario to Georgia around lake shores, bergamot is happiest in a sunny or semi-shade position. It also likes to have moist roots. The plant was named after Nicholas Monardes (1493-1588), a botanist and physician from Seville, Spain, who wrote a herbal flora of America. John Tradescant the younger, introduced the wild bergamot to England from Virginia in 1637. It is also naturalised in South America. *Monarda didyma* was raised from seed over a century later in 1744 by Peter Collinson.

Red bergamot is the best variety to grow for bergamot tea. Its leaves have a fruity, orange scent and the plant grows to about 90cm (3ft) in height. There is a wide range of hybrids with different coloured flowers, from purple to white, some of which grow as tall as 1.5m (5ft).

Wild bergamot, *Monarda fistulosa,* has leaves with a lemon fragrance and purple flowers amongst a softer foliage. Occasionally a red bergamot will revert to bear purple flowers, if moved to different soil and climatic conditions. Bergamot will take a year to establish from seed and is normally propagated by root division. Dig up the clump at least every second spring to divide. The inner core of the root is older and should be discarded. Re-plant the outer roots just over 30cm (12in) apart. If you do not do this then you will have a clump of tall bergamot around the outside with a shorter, poor centre. Keep well composted and cut back in autumn.

## *Myrrhis odorata*      P      SWEET CICELY

SWEET cicely is a joy to grow, reaching about 90cm (3ft) in height in the second year, with a good spread of attractive pale green, fern-like leaves.

Sow the seeds in autumn if there is likely to be a frost, since they require the freezing and thawing process to germinate. Alternatively, you can leave them in the fridge for a time before sowing, making sure the pot is carefully labelled. Allowing sweet cicely to seed itself is really the most satisfactory way of gaining young plants, and in northern areas you may find its prolific seeding habits need to be controlled. In this case when the young plants appear very early in spring, they can make useful ground cover for an area which you may use later for planting out seedlings grown indoors or under glass. You can usually depend upon a small harvest of the young leaves for drying, before digging them out.

Sweet cicely stems are crowned by tiny white flowers in early summer, which gives a pretty effect against the lacy foliage. These are followed by long green seeds pointing skywards, slowly turning shiny black as they ripen. Sweet cicely grows wild in northern Britain, along hedgerows and in woods.

It likes at least partial shade and moisture to produce the luxurious crop of leaves which can be harvested on past flowering through to the first hard frosts. Sweet cicely is an exception in that flowering has little effect on the quality of the leaves. Bearing in mind their later growth, the plants should be thinned to 60cm (2ft) apart, or, in good conditions they will grow together to form a "jungle". The taproots can become very large and are harvested as a pot-pourri fixative, or to candy, in autumn. The plant is not usually attacked by insects although the stems of the seedheads may attract blackfly which are easily wiped away or eaten by ladybirds.

## *Ocimum basilicum*      A-P      BASIL

Anumber of varieties of basil have been cultivated in Spain, France and Germany since the twelfth century. They are also grown across Europe, North Africa, southern, central and eastern Asia, and the tropical and subtropical regions of America. Basil is regarded as an annual or perennial herb according to the climate. In colder areas, subject to late frosts it will need special protection or it can be grown in pots as an indoor plant. Basil was introduced to North America by the early settlers and the dark opal, gingery variety used in salads was developed in Connecticut in the 1960's.

The pungent aroma of basil makes it a herb to grow at the front of the bed where you can appreciate it as you pass by. Or, if your garden has no sheltered corner for this tender herb, it will be happy in a pot on the kitchen window-sill.

Often basil is first sown in pots in the greenhouse or indoors to give the seedlings a chance against uncertain weather. Originating in India, basil is very susceptible to cold winds or frost. I have lost the herb in a sheltered garden in June to the lightest of frosts and in desperation have grown it under cloches.

With sun and shelter from the wind, basil can grow into a luxuriant plant, worth the attention of pricking out the main stem as it grows taller, and watering in the heat of the day. This last instruction, contrary to the needs of all other herbs, except, perhaps, chervil, has been followed for hundreds of years.

There are a number of varieties of basil. Bush basil, *Ocimum minimum,* may, in really protected conditions, become the perennial it is in the hotter climate of India. Try growing it indoors in a pot. It will grow to 15-20cm (6-8ins). Sweet basil, *Ocimum basilicum,* is sown in spring, then in succession each fortnight in a sheltered position. The leaves are four or five times larger than those of a bush basil. It grows to be about 45cm (18in), and has small, creamy white flowers late in the summer, if left to bloom.

Dark opal basil, *Ocimum basilicum purpurascens,* is a beautiful purple basil, a little shorter than sweet basil. It needs careful siting and is extremely effective in an ornamental garden amongst green herbs. Lemon basil, *Ocimum basilicum citriodorum* grows to about 30cm (12in), and makes an interesting addition to a group of lemon herbs. As more basil varieties become readily available, this has become a herb to collect as well as enjoy.

Whichever of the basil family you decide to grow, make sure they are protected from slugs with a barrier of spiky herbs and give a "Chamomile infusion" (see page 21) at the seedling stage to guard against damping off. Basil is a good companion to cucumbers and tomatoes but reputedly hates rue. Put them together at their peril!


## *Oenothera Biennis*      B      EVENING PRIMROSE

THIS is a herb most at home in a good-sized cottage garden. A clump of evening primroses set in a quiet corner behind an edging of lower-growing flowering herbs, such as thyme or hyssop, will delight you on warm summer evenings.

Evening primrose likes a sunny, open location with good drainage. It will be happy in clay or poor soil. I have seen it growing wild along wide roadside verges, and filling a sparse strip of dusty central reservation along a busy main road. It seemed sad that the beauty of the herb could hardly be appreciated in such a site.

Since the flowers are the true attraction of the herb, begin growing them with a second-year plant and seeds sown alongside it. In this way you will continue to have flowering plants in successive years. First-year plants have little interest to offer, with pale green leaves clustered together in prolific rosettes. In the second year the thick, hairy stem grows upwards to between 1 - 2m (3-6ft) revealing the leaves as long oval shapes.

The flowers have a soft, gentle quality which draws you out into the garden on early summer evenings, as they open at dusk, releasing a delicious perfume. A true plant of the moon, the evening primrose gives of its best when most other herbs have less to offer. In a silver, moonlit garden, evening primrose adds a touch of evocative reality to the dream-like atmosphere.

Sometimes, with a very hot, dry summer the plants will flower in a single year and then live on flowering through a second season. Harvesting the leaves, stem and roots should take place in the second year.

## *Origanum*          A-P     MARJORAMS & OREGANO

The number of marjorams available can easily cause confusion. Especially as some have more than one common name. *Origanum onites,* "Pot" or "French marjoram" is a perennial with green leaves and white-mauve flowers. It grows to about 30cm (12in) high and will be fairly hardy as long as the soil isn't too heavy. It may have originated in Sicily and has been grown in Britain for several hundred years.

*Origanum majorana*...is the familiar, "sweet", or "knotted marjoram", a half hardy annual, growing from 30-60cm (1 to 2ft) tall. It bears pretty globes of tiny white or purplish flowers which later turn grey against the grey-green leaves. Native to North Africa, it is less hardy than "Pot marjoram".

*Origanum vulgare*...is the popular oregano which is perennial. One form has pink flowers while another has more compact, purple flowers. Both are attractive, flowering all summer and reaching a height of about 60cm (2ft). *Origanum vulgare* is native to Europe and has been cultivated in gardens since the 13th century. It also grows in the United States.

*Origanum heracleoticum* is a half-hardy winter marjoram about 22cm (9in) high. Altogether a smaller version of the other marjorams, with strongly scented leaves resembling thyme.

There are two golden marjorams, the true golden marjoram, *Origanum vulgare aureum,* which needs to be protected from hot sun and the golden *variegata* which has green and gold leaves and pale pink or white flowers. Under certain conditions, the variegated marjoram may revert to a green-leaved plant.

In general marjorams and oregano like a dry, chalky or lime-rich soil. They need to be well drained and if the soil is regularly fed with compost they may reward your efforts with an increase in flavour. Cut the perennial herbs back in autumn.

## *Pelargonium*          P     SCENTED GERANIUM

MOST of the large genus of scented geraniums came originally from the Cape Province of South Africa. They were introduced to Britain in the 17th century. The potentials of rose geranium oil, however, were not recognised until 200 years later in France. Large quantities of rose geraniums are still cultivated for their essential oil, the best coming from Reunion Island.

When buying scented geraniums always check to make sure the perfume is the one you expect. Sometimes the scents can be interpreted differently by different people. Once you have your plants, whether they are rose, lemon, peppermint, orange or apple-scented, or another variation, with protection from cold winds and frosts they should thrive to give you endless pleasure. They can be grown as indoor plants in pots, in conservatories, or, in summer, out in the garden.

I like to bury the pot of the larger, lemon-scented geranium, *Pelargonium limonium* in the partial shade of my lilacs where it flourishes each summer, growing to a height of 90-180cm (3 to 6ft). Before the first frosts I dig it up to bring indoors for the winter, trimming it back to about a third of the size at the same time, for a harvest of dried leaves.

The smaller, rose-scented, *pelargonium graveolens,* gives a plentiful supply of leaves and flowers for cookery, fruit punches, cocktails and pot-pourri. This can be planted out in a sunny position, or kept in pots. A variety of potted scented geraniums can enhance the garden in summer, on steps, beside gateways and doorways and close to paths. In this way, you, and your visitors will release heady clouds of sweet fragrance as you brush past them. You will soon be asked for cuttings!

These can be taken in spring, while the plants remain on a sunny windowsill. Midsummer is another good time to take more. The cuttings will grow roots when set in pots of water, or can be rooted in sandy soil. Pinch them out at a few inches growth, for well-balanced plants.

No cottage windowsill seems complete without a selection of geraniums offering fragrance to the room. Their flowers are not as brilliant as those of bedding geraniums; theirs is a subtle charm, which invites you to linger, savouring it slowly.

Sunlight, a fresh, airy atmosphere and good drainage are simple requirements, easily met. Feed or re-pot with fresh compost each year and do not over-water, particularly in the winter period. If growing them in a dry, centrally heated atmosphere, spray the leaves occasionally, preferably with rainwater.

## *Petroselinum crispum*  B  PARSLEY

THE familiar garden parsley may have originated in Sardinia. Since introduction to Britain it has become naturalised. Popular now, Miller writes in the 18th century that it was cultivated in Holland long before the English would accept it. I have also been told that Bartram, in his American herbal, mentioned Virginia parsley reaching that State in the 17th century.

Today parsley is a herb which almost everyone with a vegetable patch, flower garden, or just pots on the window-sill, has continued to grow when other herbs went out of fashion. Indispensable in the kitchen, it is sufficiently attractive as a herb to be grown as ground cover under roses, which it helps to keep in good health. The combination of parsley and garlic chives, or garlic beneath roses will not only ensure you are not tempted to use chemical sprays against pests - not a good idea when you are eating the parsley - but the garlic will deter slugs and snails which might otherwise eat your herb. Parsley will grow well in sun or shade, making a pretty edging with its bright green, lacy leaves. Beside a gravel path parsley has an advantage in self seeding. Gravel holds the moisture and in a dry spring and early summer, parsley seedlings may well appear amongst the gravel, rather than in the herb bed. These can easily be transplanted to a suitable place, or potted up, despite all the superstitions about the disastrous results.

Growing the herb from seed without the aid of a gravel path can prove more troublesome. Many rituals and superstitions have grown up around the slow germination rate. The seeds can be soaked in warm water overnight before sowing, or sown in a seed tray and placed in the airing cupboard until shoots appear. Pouring boiling water over the newly sown seed area is another popular method. My own observations on sowing have been that sowing the seeds just before or at full moon means they are more likely to receive rain and grow quickly.

Plant about 20cm (8in) apart. The parsley will remain only a few inches high in the first year and then grow to over 30cm (12in) in the second season, as it prepares to flower and seed.

French parsley, *Petroselinum crispum neapolitana* is my personal favourite. The leaves are without the delicate coral appearance of the more common parsley, being flat with toothed edges and a darker green. French parsley, also sometimes labelled Italian parsley, grows taller, to about 60cm (2ft) and is better placed further from the edge of a flower bed. It sets seed more easily and is certainly a herb to substitute in those gardens where parsley has always been difficult to grow.

## *Pimpinella anisum*      A      ANISE

ANISE is an eastern herb, grown for thousands of years in Asia, Egypt and Greece. The Romans brought it to Britain at a period when the climate was, perhaps, warmer than it has been for some time. However, the recent hot summers have made the ripening of aniseed more of a certainty than it was. If the trend continues, this annual herb may be grown far more than formerly. The herb is also found in Belgium, Germany, Central America and Chile. In North America, the herb was so valued by settlers, that the First Assembly of Virginia declared in 1619, "each man unto whom a division (of land) is granted must plant thereon six anise seeds".

Growing sufficient aniseed to supply the needs of a household through the year is something which would require a large bed of the plants at least. It is however, satisfying to grow some aniseed for use and to keep a stock of plants. Anise likes lime in the soil and must be given shelter from late spring. A sunny position is vital.

Anise can be sown together with coriander seed which will help both herbs to germinate and develop as healthy plants. Since it is sown where it is to grow, a covering - which can later be removed - is the best answer for growing large amounts of the herb. It must be sown reasonably early to give time for the formation of seeds which is also helped by the combination of anise and coriander. As the umbels of creamy white flowers turn to seeds, wait until they are a greyish colour before cutting the stems and hang-drying in paper bags.

The herb grows to about 30-45cm (1-1½ ft) tall with rounded leaves having serrated edges, rather like coriander. The seeds of the two herbs are, however, entirely different in appearance, with anise long and thin, while coriander seeds resemble round balls.

## *Portulaca oleracea*      A      PURSLANE

THERE are several varieties of purslane, the summer is sometimes referred to as *oleracea, var. sativa.* It is more readily available than the winter variety *Montia perfoliata,* which also belongs to *Portulaceae* and is known as miner's lettuce. There is also a golden leaved, *P. oleracea var. aureum.* Purslane was probably brought to Britain by the Romans, having been grown for thousands of years in India and China. We find the herb enjoying great popularity in the 16th and 17th centuries.

The instructions for cultivation in the first gardening book, The Gardener's Labyrinth, by Thomas Hill, to sow the seeds each month from March to June, still hold. Having tasted purslane you will soon be eager to sow it in succession for a steady supply. The plants do best in rich soil and full sun. Set them about 15-20cm (6-8in) apart. The herb will grow happily in a pot or window box, reaching a height of about 15-30cm (6-12in). A row of purslane can also form quite a dense ground cover. The flowers are yellow and small, being followed by neat, sealed seed-pouches in the centre of the top rosettes of succulent leaves. These finally ripen and burst to reveal many tiny seeds. Only allow a few plants to flower to provide future seeds. All others can be cropped for a longer period if they are prevented from flowering.

Have a care when buying seeds as some purslane ha ve been developed to provide a dense ground cover with masses of flowers, rather than edible leaves. Clearly the flowers of these have come a long way from the originals. *Portulaca grandiflora* and other hybrids are grown for the carpet of colour they can provide.

## *Primula*  P  PRIMROSES AND COWSLIPS

THE primrose is an ever-welcome spring flower, which for many recalls fond memories of youthful walks in sunlit woods. Essentially a woodland European plant, although it can still be found on open banks at roadsides, it will thrive in moist soil, enriched with leaf mould or compost. If you have trees in your garden, then beneath them is the perfect site for one or two clumps of primroses, which will, in years to come, spread to form a flowering mass. Primroses are especially pretty in an orchard, mixed with bluebells, wood avens and other wild flowers and herbs. If you have no trees to shade the plants, they will appreciate an autumn mulch of leaf mould from deciduous trees.

By their second or third year, primrose clumps can be divided. A few flowers left on the plant to go to seed may also bring the bonus of a young seedling or two in the autumn or following spring. Although the leaf is similar to the polyanthus, the pale yellow flower is quite distinctive with its darker centre. Keep the two plants separate in the garden as they are very closely related. Primroses rarely grow much above 10cm (4in) in height, but can reach 15cm (6in).

The other member of the *Primula* family, which is greeted with even more enthusiasm by most people is the cowslip. Comparatively rare and with a beauty all of its own, the flowers of the cowslip might come from another plant family entirely. The clusters of golden "frilled bells" are a joy in my garden and generally follow those of the primrose.

Growing naturally in meadows and on sunny banks, cowslips can be planted in an open, sunny location. My favourite placing for them is between the low hedges of my "closed knot" where their stems seem to be on tiptoe to give the nodding heads a view over the other herbs. In open spaces between trees in an orchard, or close to path edges in flowerbeds are the places where the cowslip can be appreciated and healthy. On a sunny bank, particularly if the soil is chalky, is another alternative.

As with primroses, allowing them to seed themselves is still the easiest method of propagation. Both seeds need frost conditions to induce them to germinate. Larger plants can be divided in autumn.

If you have sufficient yourself, it is easy to find someone else who would love to be given some.

# *Rosaceae*                    **P**                    **ROSE**

THE rose family is so extensive, with old-fashioned bush roses, climbers, and modern, heavily scented varieties, all being useful inclusions in the herb garden. All I have space to give here is an idea of those roses I grow and love, with a few practical hints on caring for them. Whole books have been written on the subject and references to these will be found in the bibliography.

My garden contains mainly the very old varieties, best suited to give flowers for pot-pourri and cookery. *Rosa gallica,* damask roses and some *Centifolia.*

My first rose to be planted was *Rosa maxima alba,* a wonderfully vigorous rose which loves the heavy clay at the back of the cottage and is fast growing to reach its full height of 2.4m (8ft). I have given it the support of a trellis, which it certainly needs. Trellis against a rose also gives a perch for the small birds which, in the absence of pesticide sprays will eat many aphids, usually bringing such a problem under control within a few days. The second *alba* spreads its huge white flowers behind and above the trellis hood of the chamomile seat. To stop its enthusiasm covering all and to give more flowers in the following year, I cut these well back after flowering. Since the flowers appear on shoots grown in the previous year, it is not a good idea to prune this rose in late autumn as you might a modern rose.

It is a romantic idea to set a gallica rose in the centre of a flowerbed, but they have such vigorous growth habits, that it can lead to a tangled disaster. *Rosa gallica officinalis,* otherwise known as the apothecary's rose, grows in my liqueur garden. I have set it amongst other herbs, but need to be constantly watchful that they do not overcrowd the lower leaves which would then develop mildew.

The best preservatives against mildew are to give roses plenty of space, rich healthy soil, garlic planted around them and an annual treatment with horsetail infusion. (see page 23). All roses will, of course, benefit from both garlic and parsley as companion plants, parsley providing a useful and attractive ground cover in a rose bed. Giant chives could be planted instead of garlic with almost as much effectiveness. Garlic and onion waste should be included in compost made for the rose bed and the presence of garlic chives can help to avoid black spot. Another preventative for this condition is horsetail fungicide. Perennial lupins will give extra nitrogen. Mustard could also be used in this role in a rose bed as an early ground cover which is then hoed in, or cut and laid as a mulch.

*Rosa mundi* is another personal favourite of mine. A young bush, cared for as above, can give over 50 beautiful cerise, pink and cream striped flowers, as soon as it is established. It is a rose which can be set in a large herb bed with rather more confidence than the more "enthusiastic" *Rosa gallica officinalis.*

Another early damask rose is "maidens blush" with pink, wonderfully fragrant flowers, fading to cream with hints of "blush pink". It grows alongside the covered way. It is a moss rose, originally a sport of *Rosa centifolia,* over two centuries ago, giving its own, unique fragrance to the air. At the far end of the covered way grows *Damascena versicolor,* with heavy pink flowers. Over 1.8m (6ft) high, it was once known as the York and Lancaster rose.

The tiny white-pink-flowered banksian rose climbs over the side of the covered way towards the "modern" garden. Named after Lady Banks, wife of the explorer and naturalist Joseph Banks, this rose was introduced to Europe in 1796. The prolific abundance of pretty flowers and their sweet fragrance recommends it for any wall, arbour or fence around a herb garden. A climber from the past for the Elizabethan garden is the sweet-smelling musk rose, *Rosa moschata.* It needs protection from severe weather and careful tending, but rewards the gardener with a prize unusual in old-fashioned roses – it blooms more than once a year. *Rosa arvensis* and *Rosa eglanteria,* the sweetbriar, or eglantine, so closely associated with Queen Elizabeth 1 also grows over the chamomile seat and the dividing fence. Careful thought is needed when placing these roses however, as their thorns can be vicious.

As a hedge to the "modern" lawn I have set *Rosa rugosa,* with both red and white flowered, intermixed. These have come together to form a handsome hedge, 90cm (3ft) high in 3 years. The flowers in their case are simply an enjoyable prelude to the huge hips for wine, syrups or jellies. If they are gathered before the eager greenfinches come to eat them!

There are many rewards to growing roses, and many, many old roses well worth including in herb gardens. It is a good idea to look at specialist catalogues and to visit nurseries and gardens, such as Mottisfont Abbey, before choosing your own favourites.

## *Rosmarinus officinalis*  P  ROSEMARY

ROSEMARY is a lovely evergreen in temperate climates which grows at its very best close to the sea. It is a sun-loving herb which originated on the shores of the Mediterranean and is harvested in the wild in France, Italy, Spain, along the coast of North Africa and in Yugoslavia. It was introduced to Britain by the Romans and was known by the Anglo-Saxons. There follows a period with no mention of the herb until Queen Phillipa of Hainault received rosemary from her home-country during the Black Death. Taken to America by the Pilgrim Fathers, rosemary must be regarded as an indoor winter plant in colder areas. In the U.S. a gold and green variegated rosemary, *Rosmarinus officinalis,* "Joyce DeBaggio" is available.

In perfect conditions rosemary can grow to 1.8m (6ft) or more, but rarely reaches more than 90cm (3ft) in inland Britain. In warmer climates the beautiful blue flowers appear almost year-round. In cooler areas, with a north-facing site, they may only be open for a week or so. Planted against a south-facing wall, which offers sun, shelter from frost and moisture for growth, rosemary may flower from October to the following June.

Harvest rosemary when the flowers are open if possible for fragrant mixtures. This is when the herb is at its best. Always trim back further after flowering, preventing the bush from becoming woody.

To propagate, set some of the trimmings, about 15cm (6in) in length into a jug of water with 2 drops of Bach rescue remedy added. Remove the leaves from the lower 2.5-3cm (1-1½in) and on the following day add a little comfrey tea to the water, which should be changed every few days. In this way you can enjoy a table decoration which subsequently grows roots. In about four weeks the cuttings should be ready to plant out. Alternatively set cuttings, dipped in hormone rooting-powder into sandy soil, or a flowerbed in a shady spot.

Young rosemary is susceptible to frost. Unless you can offer a sheltered position, overwinter your new plants in a cold frame or indoors. In severe climates all rosemary will need to be taken indoors for the winter. Put some lime in the bottom of the pot, or add crushed eggshell to the soil and see the plants have plenty of light in the darkest period of winter.

The lower branches of rosemary can also be layered by pegging them into the ground at intervals, where they will produce roots. Rosemary makes a pretty and fragrant hedging which can usefully border a vegetable garden, deterring pests by covering the scent of attractive vegetables. As a hedge, plant 60cm (2ft) apart. Rosemary and sage are good companion plants, being mutually helpful to each other.

There are many varieties of rosemary, from the prostrate form which needs careful protection, to taller plants with white, pink or blue flowers. Miss Jessop is one which has an upright, compact growth, yet is not particularly hardy and needs a sheltered corner. Severn Seas is another favourite. Ornamental rosemary plants with gold or silver stripes on the leaves are not as hardy as the *officinalis*. The gold edged is referred to as gilded rosemary, and only the mature plants bear the markings.

Bitter spring winds can do more damage to a rosemary than a long frost, so always give them shelter from north and north-east winds in particular. It is well worth the extra effort to enjoy the herb. Rosemary is especially attractive set beside the house door as all who enter will release the fragrance as they pass.

## *Ruta graveolens*        P        RUE

RUE is a most attractive herb, the common rue having delicate blue-green leaves marked by the sites of the oil glands. The scent of rue however, can be less agreeable to many people, although this pungency gives it a useful role as an insect repellent. The small, yellow flowers, opening in full summer, can be included with a little foliage in posies to keep flies away.

Care should be taken when handling rue as those with sensitive skin may experience allergic reactions. Rubber gloves can be a wise precaution if you are likely to suffer from skin rashes. The herb grows to about 60cm (2ft) in height and likes a dry, lime-rich soil and full sun. The common rue was taken to America by settlers.

Jackman's Blue is a popular form with gardeners as the foliage is a striking blue on a bush of compact form. It is a particularly useful herb in decorative gardens as it is evergreen - or should that be, everblue? The variegated rue is, I feel, not as attractive as Jackman's Blue or *Ruta graveolens,* since the splashes of cream can revert to green-blue when conditions are not favourable for the plant.

Stem cuttings can be taken early in autumn when the rather insignificant yellow flowers are over. The bushes can be cut back again after spring frosts are ended to produce more cuttings and regulate the growth of the bush.

Seeds may be hesitant when it comes to germination. Rue was often planted near sage bushes in early gardens, to protect them from toads. The two herbs will grow happily side by side, Jackman's Blue complementing the creamy colour of the golden sage.

## *Salvia*        Semi-Shrub        SAGE

MOST herb gardens contain sage. It probably is not appreciated, however, that there are more than 500 different species, growing as far apart as America, North Africa, Southern Europe and the Himalayas. America claims 40 different wild sages.

In Britain sage is classed as a shrubby evergreen, which means it can be planted as an attractive hedge to outline vegetable beds, giving fragrant protection for brassicas against pests. It should be kept clipped to 45cm (18in) high, or it will become woody and need replacing.

The narrow leaved green sage is best for fresh use in the kitchen; while the broad leaved dries even better. Spanish sage is a delicate, finer plant in comparison, pretty in a herb garden. All three require a sunny position, giving slower, less aromatic growth in shade. Shelter from cold winds and frost are as important as good drainage.

Sage from seed is slow to mature and stem cuttings 10-12cm (4-5in) long, lower leaves removed, will root readily when set in a jug of water. As before, change the water frequently, adding a little comfrey tea. Roots should form in 2-3 weeks. Alternatively, a mature bush can be earthed up in autumn or spring, leaving just the tops showing. The clump can then be divided in early summer to plant out.

A mulch of good compost or old manure and soot is helpful in autumn. Variegated golden sage and the attractive tricolor sage will need extra protection from frost. Purple sage is quite hardy by comparison and very effective as hedging.

Bi-ennial clary sage, *Salvia sclarea* is the most magnificent member of the *Salvia* family in its second year of growth. At first insignificant with grey/green rounded leaves hairy and soft, it shoots up to 1.2m. (4ft) The spikes of heavily scented flowers appear, resembling large, lilac hops. These gradually open to allow the concertina-like contents to unfold into towering flower spikes with lilac bracts. Grow in shade or sun in rich soil. Seeds germinate readily.

## *Sambucus nigra*       T       ELDER

THE hardy common elder grows well in garden soil without the aid of fertilizers. It grows wild throughout most of Europe and in North Africa. Elders can be grown as decorative trees if they are given sufficient attention.

Elder cuttings can be started in spring or autumn, simply by taking new growth about 20cm (8in) long. In spring dip these cuttings in hormone rooting powder and plant in a tub of ordinary soil. Stand the tub in the shade and keep well watered until they are established. They will be ready for planting out in the autumn. Cuttings taken later in the year will need the protection of a cold frame through the frosts of winter before planting out in the spring.

The young trees grow well in the shade but will also stand sunny semi-shade. Remove unwanted side shoots as they appear and pinch out the top when the tree has reached the height you prefer. Pruning established elders in late autumn will encourage bushy growth. If you already have an elder tree which has been left to grow out of control, it can be cut back vigorously to a new shape.

The dwarf elder, *Sambucus ebulus* is also used for medicine. However, note that in America "dwarf elder" can refer to *Aralia hispida,* an entirely different plant.

You may like to have an ornamental elder in your garden. Numerous varieties are available from specialist nurseries. Ornamental forms are not all modern. Green-berried elders and some with gold and silver striped leaves had already been developed before the end of the 18th century.

*Sambucus plumosa aurea* has golden foliage with plumed flowers. *Sambucus variegata* has slender, pale leaves with golden edges. *Sambucus purpureum* has purple foliage. Perhaps the daintiest is *Sambucus laciniata,* with finely divided mid-green leaves, grown by Gerard, along with the white-berried alba. *Sambucus aureum* is golden leaved but must be grown in full sun or it reverts to green. *Sambucus canadensis* was introduced into Britain from North America in 1761. The variety *maxima* has 45cm (18in) leaves and flowerheads of a similar size. The blue elderberry grows naturally throughout much of the United States. The North American Indians harvested the *Sambucus caerulea* which has juicier fruits than European varieties.

## *Sanguisorba minor*      **P**      **SALAD BURNET**

SALAD burnet is one of the prettiest salad herbs and looks more at home in a flowerbed than the vegetable patch. The finely toothed, serrated green leaves on tall, central stems are attractive in themselves, without the added bonus of tiny clustered flowers which have red tops, making them resemble raspberries with a lower edging of "tassels".

In a mild winter the green leaves remain and the herb will aid nearby plants. As it matures the plant will spread to occupy 45cm (18in) and can grow to 60cm (2ft). Set them between 45cm and 60cm (1½ and 2ft) apart to allow for future growth. The roots can be divided in spring. A few seedlings may appear in the surrounding area, but the seeds are tiny and blown by the wind which also pollinates the plant. The extraordinary flowerheads have female flowers at the top of the "thimble" shape and male flowers at the base. Salad burnet is sufficiently decorative to grow in containers on a patio. The flowers continue for several weeks through the summer. It is a hardy plant, unlikely to be killed by frost. A wild burnet grows on chalky soils at roadsides and field edges in Europe and Asia.

In the 17th century, burnet was one of the herbs recommended to be planted, along with wild thyme and watermint, as a scented pathway. It is hardly surprising that such a well-loved herb was taken to America with the settlers. The "walks" or "allies" of those days need to be made again in modern gardens for us to appreciate their soothing effect on mind and body. If you wish to plant a path in this way, place stepping-stones amongst the herbs to take the heavy wear in bad weather and winter.


## *Santolina chamaecyparissus*    **P**    **COTTON LAVENDER**

ALSO known as French lavender, the herb is native to southern Europe, being introduced to northern areas, such as Britain, in the 16th century. Here it was received with enthusiasm for the silvery hedges it provides in knot gardens.

The delight of the silvery, feathered foliage of this herb is only exceeded by the pretty yellow,"button-like" flowers. An excellent hedging herb, it is often planted 15-20cm (6-8in) apart and clipped to give a fragrant edging to a path or flowerbed.

Stem cuttings taken from cotton lavender, in early summer, take readily in a sandy soil. Mature plants are at their best in a sunny position, but will grow in partial shade. They withstand frost well, although in temperatures lower than - 8°C (17.6°F) or with north-east, biting winds, plants are best covered with a layer of straw as a precaution.

Trimming must be carried out regularly during the first year, in spring and autumn, to ensure the plant is kept in shape as it can make woody growth, leaving bare patches if it is neglected. Do not leave this trim later than the first growth if you wish the herb to flower. Trim the whole plant when harvesting the flowers for posies and dried floral arrangements. This will give it time to recover before the frosts begin.

Left to grow to its full height cotton lavender will be 30-60cm (1 to 2ft) tall. It can form a neat hedge from 15-30cm (5-12in) high. When planning such a hedge, particularly as part of a knot garden, remember mature plants will be several inches wide.

*Santolina viridis* is a hybrid with green foliage and smaller, yellow flowers; consequently it is an altogether more delicate plant in appearance. It grows to 30cm (12in) tall. Give this herb a little extra care and shelter from high winds. *Santolina rosmarifolia,* as the name suggests, bears leaves with longer "spines" resembling rosemary and has yellow flowers. The sweet scent is not as pungent as the other *Santolinas*. *Santolina neapolitana* has altogether larger leaves which makes it better suited to a larger hedge, rather than a knot garden for instance. I have saved perhaps the best for last. It is the variety "lemon Queen", which has even prettier flowers, a creamy colour rather than yellow, with the petals set further apart.

Whichever *"Santolina"* suits your garden best you cannot fail to enjoy the delicacy of this unusual herb. In moonlight, or silver gardens, it really comes into its own.


## *Satureja*  A-P  SAVORY

SUMMER, winter and creeping savory are delightful herbs to grow, fulfilling three different roles in the herb garden. Winter savory, *Satureja montana,* is a Mediterranean herb, possibly first cultivated in Italy. It is remarkably hardy against frosts, considering its natural home. In very cold, frosty weather it will lose its leaves, but do not despair; on most occasions they will sprout green again in the warmer weather of spring. Tiny, young cuttings and seedlings are more susceptible to frost and will need protection. Straw can be laid over young plants as a precaution when the temperature drops suddenly. Poor soil can also be a help to savory in resisting bad weather conditions. In parts of America, where the herb has been grown since the days of the early settlers, it will be necessary to give savory the protection of cold frames or a layer or two of straw before winter.

Savory should be clipped back in early summer and again in autumn to give a neat hedging. Otherwise it will reach a height of about 33cm (14in). The white flowers, which resemble those of rosemary in form, are so pretty I leave my hedges to flower briefly before harvesting the flowering stems for posies. Stem cuttings take readily, needing shade at first. Once they have established roots they will be better in the sun.

Summer savory, *Satureja hortensis,* is a taller herb with paler green, delicate leaves and pretty, pink-lilac flowers, formed in late summer. If you are wanting to use the plants as a companion to broad beans against blackfly, bring the seedlings on under glass, before setting them out between the beans. You can alternatively set young winter savory plants between the rows of beans. A graceful addition to the garden through the summer, at the first frost of autumn, summer savory will be gone. In some years it has only a short season, but the garden would be a poorer place without it.

Creeping Savory, *Satureja repandra,* is a much lower- growing herb, suitable for scented banks, rock gardens or around paving. It enjoys the sun and dislikes frost, so needs to be sited with care. The tiny leaves release the savory fragrance and miniature white flowers will attract bees through the summer in the same way as those of the taller relatives. It may grow to a height of 7.5cm (3in) but prefers to spread outwards in a way reminiscent of pennyroyal.


## *Stachys officinalis*  P  BETONY

BETONY is a herb which can be included with equal justification in either a herb garden or a wild meadow patch. It has such attractive and distinctive foliage and flowers, I am surprised it is not also a commonly accepted plant in the flower garden. Betony grows in northern Europe and is naturalised in Norway and Finland.

The many pink-mauve flower trumpets which seem to proclaim the presence of the herb stand out from the tall flowerhead, facing in all directions and summoning the bees in great numbers. These will later mature into pretty, compact, brown seedheads, waving in the autumn breeze at about 60cm (2ft) in height.

Betony seedlings are unlikely to take over the surrounding area, in dry years few will grow and seeds kept for the following year seem to be equally hesitant. If the conditions are not right for betony, which in the wild would be surrounded by tall grasses, then you may increase a stock of the herb more easily by dividing the existing clump in spring or autumn.

While the rosettes of deeply toothed, dark leaves grow readily amongst other herbs, betony has a dignified quality which sets it apart, even before the flowers open in midsummer. It is happy with the shade from taller plants, but unlikely to thrive immediately beneath trees, although it can be found in the wild in open woodland.

## *Symphytum officinale*  P  COMFREY

THERE are several varieties of comfrey which are all hardy perennials. They vary in height from 75-90cm (2½ to 3ft) to the Russian, *Symphytum Peregrinum* which is much taller, with pale blue flowers. Comfrey is a valuable crop in America, the form with white flowers having been taken there by settlers to New England in the 17th century. The herb soon "escaped" and established itself in the wild.

*Symphytum officinale* has the greatest concentration of allantoin in the stems and leaves. Allantoin gives comfrey the important cell-proliferating action to heal wounds quickly.

Bocking 14, developed by the Henry Doubleday Research Association, is the most popular variety as it resists the rust disease which attacks *Symphytum officinale*. Signs of this disease may be seen in early summer as an orange powder on the undersides of the leaves. If this should happen the best course is to dig up the plant and put it in the bin. Various cures have been tried unsuccessfully. It is best therefore to grow Bocking 14 if you live in an area where wild comfrey grows at the roadsides and is likely to pass on the disease.

Comfrey likes full sun and a clay soil which will hold moisture. In the wild it can often be seen growing in great abundance along the edges of ditches or ponds. It is extremely partial to a dressing with mushroom compost, pigeon or chicken manure and will even tolerate fresh pig manure. It needs feeding as it grows vigorously, giving four to five cuts each year. Do not allow comfrey to flower if you wish to keep the leafy growth in full health and vigour.

Be very careful to think before planting your comfrey as it is unlikely you will ever succeed in digging up the entire root of an established plant. Every sliver of root left in will produce more leafy growth. Of course the value of comfrey to the gardener for compost and fertilizer alone, means you will never want to be without it.

The very large, hairy leaves of the mature plant will take up a fair space. Allow for a 30-45cm (12-18in) radius of the plant to be covered. Harvesting will keep it from needing more ground.

Divide the roots in spring for more plants. Comfrey seeds are not generally used as it takes too long to produce a plant large enough to harvest. Also most flowers are not fertilized as only the bumblebee can bite its way into the false bottom of the flower.

## *Tanacetum parthenium*      **P**      **FEVERFEW**

WHEN approached to sell this herb, I invariably respond by showing the interested party just what it looks like and pointing out that they have probably been weeding it out of their own garden for years. It is often the case that feverfew can be found growing in a garden, wild verge or even cracks in the pavement. This last location reveals the preference of the herb for dry soil and its powers of endurance in poor conditions.

Feverfew bears a distinct resemblance to chamomile, with its daisy-like flowers, and the two are often mistaken for one another. The bitter scent of the rounded, serrated leaves, is, however, distinctive. Feverfew seeds freely, making it a familiar herb, often otherwise regarded as a weed. It grows to about 30cm (12in) high, or more.

With its seeding habits controlled by simply removing the seedheads before they ripen, feverfew can become a welcome addition to sunny corners of the herb garden, where the white flowers will brighten surrounding greenery over long periods.

A native of south-east Europe, feverfew appears to have been introduced from the Balkans and grows prolifically in the wild. It was taken to America by settlers.

A double form of feverfew is also available with whiter flowers, rather like small chrysanthemums. The golden feverfew has lighter green leaves with gold patches, giving a pretty, variegated effect.

I cannot imagine anyone needing to take cuttings from such a prolific herb, but stem cuttings are successful. The plants can also be divided in the autumn. They are perennial and once planted will certainly remain in your garden, as they did in many cottage gardens in the past, nicknamed the "headache plant", often turned to in times of need.

Feverfew seems only to suffer from infestations of black fly, which can either be controlled with nettle liquid, (see page 22) or simply removed by cutting the herb back when they first appear. Alternatively use as a decoy catch plant.


## *Tanacetum vulgare*      **P**      **TANSY**

GROWING tansy can be a joy that turns into a battle unless it is adequately controlled. Always among the first herbs to sprout that fresh, vital green which heralds the spring, the young, feathery growth is a delight to see. Later in the year, however, as the roots creep out colonising your flowerbed it may appear in a different light.

In the wild, tansy grows along riverbanks and on waste ground across Europe. It has naturalised well in the eastern states of America, having been taken by settlers as a medicinal plant as it will tolerate most soils. In the garden the rampant habits of tansy are best harnessed to control awkward corners and areas at the back of flowerbeds which might otherwise be over-run by ground elder or other perennial weeds. I have used it very successfully to keep ground elder, ivy and nettles under control as they try to invade the boundaries of my garden. At the same time, at least part of the vibrant energy of the herb is used up in this battle for supremacy. As ever with herbs which spread by runners, effective control can be maintained by harvesting regularly, dividing your plant, or by setting it in a raised bed with a brick surround.

Growing to 1.5m (5ft) tall, tansy is not suitable as a container herb and is best set close to a fence or windbreak of some kind. It will almost certainly need staking in the early autumn as the tiny yellow "button" flowers are opening.

*Tanacetum crispum,* is a curly-leaved, lower-growing variety well suited to flower arrangements. The flowers are similar and the tiny seeds which follow can be sown in spring. Cut the herb down in autumn.

*Tanacetum hardjanii* is much lower-growing, and purely decorative with whitish grey leaves, and small clusters of yellow flowers. It is ideal for a silver garden


## *Teucrium*  P  GERMANDER

**M**OST of the large genus of *teucrium* are native to the Mediterranean region. Wall germander is a native of Europe, found on the Greek Islands and in Syria.

Despite the warmth of their area of origin, germanders are remarkably hardy, although needing protection from severe frosts. The herb likes sun and partners well with cotton lavender in a knot garden as the foliage of each provides a sharp contrast to the other. Hedge germander is easily trimmed and maintained in shape. The foliage has a rich, glossy appearance. Wall germander, *Teucrium chamaedrys* is lower growing and tends to spread which makes it less suitable for knot hedges. Hedge germander, *Teucrium divaricatum* growing to 90cm (3ft) tall in good conditions, can often be found mislabelled as the *chamaedrys* which causes great confusion. Since the true wall germander is rare, this mistake can be unnoticed for some time. Unfortunately I did not find out that I had made it before the first edition of Herbwise was printed and welcome the opportunity to set matters straight here.

It is easiest to propagate from 15cm (6in) stem cuttings taken in spring or autumn. Remove the lower leaves before dipping the stems into hormone rooting compound. These root well set into fine, rich soil in the shade. When taken in spring, plant out as small, bushy plants in autumn. Cuttings taken at the end of summer will need to be overwintered before planting out.

Set these 10-15cm (4-6in) apart to make a low hedge, trimming as necessary, possibly three times in the first year. Trim subsequently in spring and again during or after flowering.

I allow one bush in a sheltered position to grow freely, supplying me with around 100 cuttings every year, together with flowering sprays for posies. The deep pink flowers are small but very pretty against the dark, evergreen leaves.

Germander does not like to be waterlogged. Lighten heavy clay soils with compost before planting. My largest bush grows beneath the thatch however, where water pours around it each time there is heavy rain. The drainage is good and this periodic soaking does no harm.

Water germander, *Teucrium scordium,* is comparatively rare. The leaves are broader and soft to touch, with a pungent smell, unlike its relative. The herb grows in marshes.


## *Thymus*  S-S  THYME

**C**OMMON and wild thymes have the widest distribution, being most "at home" in southern Europe, although common thyme has been known north of the Alps since the eleventh century. Taken later by settlers to America, it is now found especially in the mid-west. There is significant commercial cultivation of thyme in France, Germany and Hungary.

In the herb garden there are many varieties, from the tiny, creeping thymes to the common thyme, which will grow to 30cm (12in) by its third year. It takes two years to grow from seed into a bush which will give you a harvest of leaves and flowers. Thyme also has a reputation for being of better flavour if it is grown from rooted cuttings rather than from seed.

If you have patience, sow the seeds in a sunny spot after the frosts are over. Alternatively, take stem cuttings or divide the roots of an established plant in early summer. The stem cuttings should be about 12cm (5in) long and are best picked as you harvest the plant. Remove leaves from the lower stem and dip in hormone-rooting powder, setting them in a pot of sandy soil with a polythene bag over the top to keep a moist atmosphere. Thyme sprigs will also grow roots when set in a jug of water as a pretty table decoration. Change the water regularly, adding a little comfrey tea to encourage rooting. They may take three weeks before they are ready to plant out. Shade for the first ten days, with regular watering, will help the plants to become established. After this a sunny position is best.

If common thyme, *Thymus vulgaris,* has not been harvested regularly, it will become woody and poor. Simply divide the roots and plant out the healthiest part which has new growth, or take cuttings. Give the plants a winter mulch before the ground freezes in winter. A small plant of common or lemon thyme can be potted and taken indoors in autumn for winter use. When the spring comes, outdoor plants should be cut back by a third to half the previous year's growth to encourage fresh shoots.

Lemon thyme, *Thymus citriodorus,* is a little less hardy and should be protected with straw in harsh winters. Thymes make lovely edgings for flowerbeds or vegetable gardens. Plant them 22.5cm (9in) apart for a low hedge to a herb bed. Either thyme will give you two harvests for drying, as the flowers first appear and later in summer. Lemon thyme can be earthed up leaving just the tops showing in spring and left until late summer when the buried shoots will have rooted and be ready to plant out. Thymes like fine, gritty soil.

*Thymus serpyllum,* wild English thyme, and *Thymus coccineus* can be planted as scented ground cover which will form a lawn. Use stepping stones for heavy use in wet weather.

## *Tropaeolum majus*  A  NASTURTIUM

ORIGINALLY from the forests of South America, the forerunner of this large-flowered nasturtium was introduced to the Indies and Spain, and eventually to northern Europe and Britain, almost 400 years ago.

I love to grow my nasturtiums sprawling over a bank facing onto the vegetable garden. There, they can attract butterflies which would otherwise lay their eggs on the cabbages. Unfortunately, nasturtiums can also be subject to aphid attack to a devastating degree. Add lime to the soil to give them extra resistance against pests. They will produce more flowers in poor soil. The brilliant yellow, orange and red flowers, showy and loud against the gentle shades of the herb garden, can be seen to advantage with a bank to themselves. The energetic stems will take the almost circular leaves, with their decorative markings, on up and around tree trunks, along fences and over walls. A distance of around 3.5m (12ft) can be covered by a single plant.

In the orchard their vigour can be used to advantage on tree trunks to protect fruit trees from woolly aphis. Nasturtiums do like plenty of sunshine. When sowing the seeds after the danger of frosts has passed, remember the "devil may care" attitude of growth of the plant, which ignores boundaries. The fruits can be harvested in late summer and autumn, or left to drop, sowing seeds for the following year. A number of varieties of nasturtium are available, including dwarf which are more controlled in their growth patterns.

*Tropaeolum minus,* known in Elizabethan times as Yellow Larke's Heels, had smaller, yellow flowers. Gerard, in his herbal of 1597, tells of the seeds he received from his friend, John Robin of Paris. This earlier form was replaced by *Tropaeolum majus* because of the enthusiasm for large flowers.

## *Valeriana officinalis*     P     VALERIAN

THERE is much confusion about the herb valerian. The red valerian grows in the wild and is also commonly cultivated in gardens; this is the familiar variety. The medicinal Greek valerian is quite different, with delicate white to pink flowers in June and a taller growth, reaching 1.5m (5ft) in height with good conditions.

Valerian will sow its own seed successfully if set in rich soil in a sunny position. It is a gregarious herb which will later thrive, with herbs of lower growth shading part of the stems and root system. Transplanting, to thin out a stock of valerian, is best carried out in the first year before the roots acquire the penetrating smell which gave the herb the well-earned name of the "phew" plant.

Later root divisions in succeeding autumns will make this distinctive odour familiar. Both cats and rats find it attractive. The leaves of *Valeriana officinalis* resemble lovage in being deeply serrated, but are clustered around much shorter leaf stems. They have an elegant appeal although they are sparsely placed on opposite sides of the deeply grooved stem. It is almost as if the plant suddenly remembers, as it grows taller, that it has not produced any leaves for some time and does so.

Once flowering, or seeding, is over, cut the plant down to concentrate the strength in the roots for harvesting. Valerian has been grown a great deal in Derbyshire, England, in the past for commercial use. Nettle as a companion increases the essential oil, while valerian brings earthworms.

There are several wild valerians, the shorter marsh valerian, *Valeriana dioica,* which interestingly has male flowers larger than the female ones, grows in wet, acid soils. *Valeriana officinalis* and the red valerian, *Valeriana ruber* with the much larger leaves, also grows wild in Britain, being native to Europe and Asia. It is naturalised in America and is occasionally used in medicine.

## *Violacaea*     P     VIOLET

THIS herb belongs to a huge family with 600 species, wild and cultivated. The home of the violet is probably North America, where over 70 different species are known. Yellow violets are found in Canada and North America. In Britain they are usually lilac through to mauve, with white violets as a welcome hedgerow plant.

As the violets open, I begin one of the earliest harvests of the year. After many years of gathering them, it never fails to give me a thrill and a kinship with the long past as I carry them into the cottage.

In 300 B.C. in Greece there was such a demand for violets that they were grown by the ton. Then different varieties followed on from each other to give flowers throughout the year. With careful planting we can still have violets from Christmas to midsummer, when other members of the *Viola* family, heartsease and pansies, can be gathered for similar purposes.

The flowers of violets can be white, purple, mauve or pink. My pink violets are the last to open their flowers in early summer, following the darker-leaved varieties. By then the white violets which grow wild along the hedgebanks of the lanes near my home are long gone.

*A central "closed knot" of hedges is enhanced by the outer bed of taller herbs.*

**(Below)** *Silver Thyme.*
**(Right)** *Golden sage.*

# Herb cultivation

(Top left) *Bush basil*                    *Angelica*

(Left) *Borage*

(Below left) *Chervil*                    *Southernwood*

*Coriander*     (Top right) *Clove Pinks*

(Right) *Wild strawberry*

*Herb bennet*     (Below right) *Caraway*

# Herb cultivation

*White lavender*

(Top left) *Hyssop*

(Left) *Honeysuckle*

(Below left) *Lovage*

*Bay*

Sweet violets, *Viola odorata,* will give the best yield of flowers if they are taken up each autumn when they will have sent out new growth. Remove the runners and set these 15cm (6in) apart. Keep them watered as they re-establish themselves and then cover with a mulch of leaf mould, protecting them against severe frosts and enriching the soil. Violets like shade from the afternoon sun, being really a woodland plant and will do best in rich soil. When you divide the herb in autumn, take some runners and set these under a cold frame. Given fresh air on sunny days, these may produce flowers as early as Christmas for a special posy.

Dog violets are not scented but can flower in spring and autumn in good soil. Double violets are mainly grown for their heavy scent. The ionine in violets does affect the nerves which control our sense of smell however, so that violet fragrance is enjoyed briefly and then seems to disappear. Violets were once grown in vast quantities at Grasse in France for violet perfume. The Parma and Victoria violets are still cultivated for perfumery.

Heartsease, *Viola tricolor,* can be annual or perennial according to the climate and is much taller than the violet, growing to about 45cm (18in). The shape of both leaves, which are long with green "spurs" below the main leaf, and the flowers, are quite different from those of the violet. Heartsease flowers throughout the summer, in delicate blends of yellow, cream and lilac-mauve, mixed and matched across the petals. I will never forget the joy of seeing a meadow sprinkled liberally with these pretty, delicate flowers on a tiny island in the River Tees in northern England. Heartsease partners well with chamomile in the garden as they help to support each other and both like sunny conditions. The herb is a European native, which has become naturalised in America. Cultivated pansies set amongst heartsease will result in many new variations of colour in a low-growing plant which otherwise resembles the cultivated, rather than the wild form. Occasionally a taller darker-flowered heartsease will appear, or one with blue in the flowers as a lovely surprise.

# Herbs in cookery

FOR anyone who has previously imagined parsley, sage, rosemary, mint and thyme were the only useful flavourings, this section will be a revelation. While meat recipes have been omitted due to the author's vegetarian preference, the accent is on healthy eating with plenty of variety, colour and exploration of delicious flavours. Vitamin and mineral-rich garnishes, sweeteners to save sugar, and herb salt substitutes are added to imaginative starters, soups, savoury main courses and desserts.

Luxury is not forgotten, with sumptuous elderberry cheesecake and honey rich with the goodness of roses. Fragrant lavender sugar and crystallised flowers may be used to decorate cakes flavoured with peppermint, rosemary, lemon herbs or rosewater.

A herb guide lists those herbs suited to egg, cheese or fish dishes, salads, cakes, desserts, individual fruits and vegetables. This, together with a table of herb strengths and notes on individual herbs and their uses, will tell all you need to know to be able to experiment confidently with your own recipes.

Details on drying and blending herbs to be preserved in soup mixes, mustard, pepper, vinegar, jellies, syrups, sugars and cheeses can be found in the preserves section. A guide to making herb teas and summer fruit punches and cordials offers the final touch for the perfect meal.

# In The Past

HERBS have been part of the diet of mankind since the very beginning, even before we made fire and experimented with cooking meat. Dividing "herbs" from "vegetables" is a comparatively recent idea in our history. For many centuries a number of plants from both categories enjoyed the common title of "potherbs".

In early times, the Iron Age for instance, fat hen - which we now remove from the vegetable patch as a weed - was commonly eaten. Ground elder, another "perennial weed" began its forays into our gardens as a deliberately introduced vegetable. Garlic, currently thought of as a medicinal herb with considerable respect, was classified as a vegetable until recently.

Some herbs such as Good King Henry, alexanders, avens, mallows, evening primroses and comfrey have been dropped from the menu for a variety of reasons. The flowers of clove pinks, borage, roses, marshmallow and heartsease were once highly popular in salads, fruit desserts and summer drinks. These vanished from the tables for a century or so and are now, happily, becoming fashionable again. Whether as an optional garnish or a flavouring, I am pleased to encourage their return.

Tastes change, but the basic roles of herbs in cookery have remained the same. From the earliest times herbs gave flowers and fragrances to enhance food which may well also have been much in need of their antibacterial properties. With occasional outbreaks of salmonella and other forms of food poisoning, we are reminded that they may still have such a role to play, even with the advantages of fridges and efficient ovens.

In the main, however, herbs are no longer covering the flavours of tainted food, nor is sage usually needed to combat the toxin, cadaverine. We use herbs much more with the aim of aiding digestion, particularly digestion of fatty or rich foods, and of enhancing flavours, fragrances and the appearance of tempting dishes.

With a range of convenience foods available and a lack of time found by so many working wives and mothers, freshly cut herbs have an important role in adding vitamins and minerals. Side salads or fruit desserts prepared at the last moment are the best ways of appreciating the goodness herbs have to offer. Healthy eating is a common aim and herbs are invaluable as aids to such a diet.

Garlic is as vital to our well-being in this century as it was long ago, when it guarded against the plague. Heart disease and cancer are both said to be prevented more effectively by including garlic as a regular ingredient in our main meal of the day. It also helps our bodies to cope with the toxins produced by pollution, and raises our resistance to infections.

The valuable minerals in herbs - calcium, magnesium, iron and sulphur - are all helpful to health. For those on restricted diets, herbs high in potassium or sodium can be substituted for common salt. Herbs can be aids to both slimmers and diabetics, as sweeteners. Sweet cicely is a safe herb for diabetics, giving an aniseed sweetness without raising the blood sugar level. Angelica, also used to sweeten fruit, can be included in jams and preserves, but will raise sugar levels in the blood. Florence fennel has been known for many centuries as a herb which gives strength and nutritional value, without weight gain. The seeds were once eaten to relieve hunger. They contain the bacteria-fighting sulphur.

Flavourings, seasonings, preservatives and colourings were once all obtained from herbs. Saffron, parsley, elderberries, pot marigold, rose and clove pink petals, all contain effective colourings, either released in their juices, when infused, or, in the case of rose and clove pink petals, when crushed with sugar.

Experiment is the key to success. I hope the following pages will inspire you to create more recipes and enjoy cooking with herbs.

# Herb flavouring guide

CHEESE DISHES. - Chives, marjoram, oregano, lovage, sage, thyme, garlic, basil, mint, nettle, caraway.

**Fish**. - Fennel, dill, rosemary, sage, parsley, lemon balm, bay, lemon thyme, oregano, tarragon, savory, nettle, angelica, chervil.

**Egg Dishes**. - Chervil, parsley, thyme, pot marigold, marjoram, chives, savory, tarragon, nettle, hyssop.

**Cakes and Pastries**. - Lovage seeds, rosemary, coriander, caraway, lemon balm, lemon thyme, scented geraniums, mint, pot marigold, clove pink, peppermint, rose, angelica, limeflower, sweet cicely, lemon verbena.

**Salads**. - Parsley, lovage, chervil, lemon balm, applemint, chives, Florence fennel, garlic, savory, basil, salad rocket, purslane and salad burnet. The flowers of pot marigold, borage, clove pinks, violas and nasturtium and sunflower seeds.

**Pickles**. - Coriander, dill, elderberry, sunflower seeds, lovage, bay, garlic, caraway, sweet cicely seeds.

**Jams and Jellies**. - Mint, savory, thyme, marjoram, oregano, sage, rosemary, basil, elderflower, elderberry, rose, lavender, lemon verbena, clove pinks, scented geraniums.

**Garnishes**. - Gingermint, pineapplemint, English cowslips, violets, clove pinks, roses, borage flowers, heartsease, nasturtium, primroses, pot marigolds, chive flowers, variegated lemon balm.

## Vegetables

*Peas* - mint, basil, fennel, salad burnet.
*Potatoes* - applemint, dill, fennel, chives, parsley, rosemary.
*Carrots* - dill, thyme, lovage, parsley, fennel, mint.
*Cabbage* - caraway, dill, sage.
*Beans* - savory, parsley, fennel, lovage.
*Onion* - sage, thyme, garlic, lovage.
*Mushrooms* - hyssop, salad burnet, thyme, garlic.
*Tomatoes* - chives, basil, pot marigold, oregano, bay, coriander.

## Fruits

*Apricot* - hyssop, sweet cicely, dill, caraway and sunflower seeds.
*Apple* - sweet cicely, rosemary, gingermint, scented geraniums, hyssop, lemon verbena, elderberry, caraway and coriander seeds.
*Banana* - gingermint, clove pinks, sweet cicely, lemon geranium.
*Gooseberries* - elderflower, sweet cicely.
*Melon* - rosemary, gingermint, rose, rose geranium.
*Oranges* - lavender, lemon geranium, lemon balm, gingermint.
*Peaches* - rose geranium, clove pinks, lemon thyme, rose.
*Pears* - rosemary, peppermint, gingermint, elderberry, clove pinks.
*Pineapple* - elderflower, lemon geranium, gingermint, pineapplemint.
*Plums* - gingermint, hyssop, sweet cicely.
*Rhubarb* - sweet cicely, rosemary, angelica.

## Herb strengths

| With caution | To taste | Generously |
|---|---|---|
| basil | caraway | chervil |
| bay | coriander | chives |
| garlic | dill | lemon balm |
| Greek oregano | elderflower | limeflower |
| hyssop | fennel | pot marigold |
| lemon verbena | lavender flowers | nettle |
| lovage | marjoram | parsley |
| peppermint | mint | sweet cicely |
| rosemary | nasturtium | sunflower seeds |
| scented geraniums | clove pinks | |
| sage | rose | |
| thyme | salad burnet | |
| | salad rocket | |
| | savory | |

# Traditional digestive seasonings

*Basil*   A favourite with tomatoes, pasta, pizza and rice. Included in curries, it spices sausages and flavours white meat, fish, omelettes and bland vegetables. Add fresh, dried, defrosted, as basil oil or basil vinegar.

*Bay*   An essential ingredient in bouquet garni, bechamel and tomato sauces. Flavours soups, stews, fish, rice and pasta. Antibacterial properties protect in preserves, pickles and marinades. Fresh or dried.

*Caraway Seeds*   Increasingly added to cabbage, coleslaws, dumplings and pickles. Cooked with baked apples, in gingerbread and other cakes. Young leaves chopped over salads or soups make a digestive garnish. Roots can be cooked as a vegetable.

*Coriander*   Fresh leaves in salads, garnishes, tomato sauces and spiced dishes. Whole seeds in pickles, chutney and sauces. Add ground to cakes, dessert toppings, gingerbread and biscuits. In curry powder. Roots can be cooked as a vegetable.

*Fennel*   An excellent fish herb. Add chopped leaves in sauces, or laid over fish to be grilled or baked. Chopped leaf can garnish fish or cheese salads. Pound seeds for winter flavouring, use fennel vinegar or fennel oil.

*Garlic*   A dramatic seasoning, both digestive and antibacterial. In stews, soups, sauces, pate and cheese dishes. Best known in garlic bread. For subtle effect rub round salad bowl. Flavours mushrooms, onions, fish, oil, vinegar and butter.

*Hyssop*   Added with savory to help digest beans and pulses. Tangy herb in stuffings, stews, with mushrooms and fish dishes. Antibacterial and digestive action on meat fats similar to sage. Green herb partners well with apricots, peaches, and apples.

*Lovage*   The most important herb for vegetarians. Adds yeasty body to soups and casseroles. Fresh leaves and short stems give peppery, celery taste to salads and cheese dishes. Seeds spice bread, cakes and savoury biscuits. Hollow stems can be candied. Fresh, dried, as lovage oil or lovage vinegar.

*Marjoram*   Both cultivated and the wild marjoram, oregano, are perfect in cheese dishes. Milder marjoram is included in mixed herbs, blends of "sweet" herbs, and used to flavour egg dishes or preserves. The stronger, white flowered Greek oregano is best on pizza, with tomato sauces and fish dishes. Also in sausages, meat and pulse recipes. Fresh, dried or in herb vinegar.

*Mint*   Familiar digestive. Mint sauce and mint jelly are old favourites. Mint flavours peas, potatoes, carrots and dried fruits. Peppermint in desserts counteracts rich food. Gingermint partners melon, grapefruit, pears, and bland fruits, aiding digestion. Fresh, frozen or in preserves.

*Rosemary*   Again antibacterial and traditionally added to rich foods for special occasions. Well known with fish and poultry or white meats. Add also to cream, bland desserts, cakes and shortbread. Use fresh, dried and ground, as rosemary oil or rosemary vinegar.

*Sage*   Gained its place in stuffings and sausages as an antibacterial protector and preservative. Sage aids the digestion of fatty foods, both meats and fish. Also partnered with cheese and pasta. Fresh, dried or in vinegar blends.

*Savory* In mixed herbs. Winter savory may be preferred in stuffings, bean casseroles and stews. The best seasoning and digestive for all bean recipes. Either savory may be used in fish dishes, especially with trout. Summer savory seasons sausages and bean or fish salads. Savory can be added to pickles and preserves. Fresh, dried, in oil, or vinegar.

*Tarragon (French)* In fines herbes, bearnease sauce, sauce tartare, hollandaise sauce and some mustards. Flavouring for white meats, fish and eggs. Most popular herb vinegar. Add to omelettes, seafoods and pickles.

*Thyme* Antibacterial. It is often mixed with other Mediterranean herbs, as in bouquet garni, mixed herbs and fines herbes. Thyme is best in stuffings, with beans, pizza, cheese and nuts. Fresh, dried or as vinegar.

## Seasonings - a closer look

*B*ASIL Bush and sweet basil are usually regarded as the varieties to use in cookery. The tiny Greek basil which grows in compact, round bushes, is my own favourite. I add the fresh, pungent leaves at the last minute to sauces, and sprinkle them over cucumber and mushrooms in salads. The best seasoning for tomatoes, whether they are cooked or raw, and for courgettes - basil is invaluable in ratatouille.

If adding dried basil, a longer cooking time will bring out a more pungent flavour. The essential qualities of fresh basil, are however, not improved in this way. Choose young growth and tear it into the dish shortly before serving. In many recipes basil is best appreciated as a single seasoning, rather than added with other herbs.

*Bay* Many cookery books recommend using dried bay leaves rather than fresh. I prefer to pick each leaf from the tree as I use it, tearing the edges to release the powerful flavour. For those who wish to dry the leaves as neat, flat shapes, please note the partially dried leaves are placed under heavy weights to gain this effect. Bay is indispensable in gourmet cookery for bouquet garni and flavouring sauces. Marinade recipes also frequently include a bay leaf.

We can extend our experience with bay by adding the herbs distinctive flavour to rice dishes. This can either be achieved by placing a bay leaf in the rice while it is stored, or setting a torn leaf or two in the stock or water to be taken up by the rice as it cooks. This method can be equally effective when poaching fish, or rehydrating pulses.

*Caraway* Although associated with Victorian seedcakes and much promoted by Prince Albert's taste for the seeds, caraway has been an ingredient in British cookery for much longer. Hardly a meal was served in some Tudor households without a dish of these digestive seeds, or their inclusion in sauces, cakes or gingerbread. Whether seedcake appeals to you or not, you may wish to try caraway seeds sprinkled over cabbage as it is cooking - as an anti-dote to the smell, as well as a flavouring. It is tasty in coleslaws and pickles, or added to apple desserts.

If the feel of the seeds between your teeth is a problem, try grinding them in the same way as coriander and adding the powder cautiously to cakes and desserts. Young caraway leaves can be chopped over salads or soups and for the adventurous, old recipes reveal the root as a vegetable.

*Coriander* Coriander used to be one of those herbs bought annually when making pickles, which might easily remain at the back of the cupboard until the next year. It seems its historical associations with gingerbread and other cakes vanished for a time in dust covered cookery books. With the present revival of interest in herbs and the history of cookery, coriander is returning to the common use it deserves.

Many savoury dishes are enhanced by the addition of a few coriander seeds during cooking. With tomato or vegetable sauces, they can be placed in a twist of muslin with other herbs, for easy removal before serving, or pushed into the flesh of a chunk of vegetable to be lifted out later. Coriander spices marrow, cucumber, beetroot and cauliflower.

Ground coriander can be bought for curry mixtures, or to add interest to desserts such as apple crumble. Try a spoon or two in ginger and fruit cakes, or sprinkled over almond biscuits.

*Fennel* This is one of the oldest-known culinary herbs. The broth was an early slimmer's dish, which eased hunger without putting on weight. Roman bakers placed sprays of fennel leaves beneath loaves of bread to bake in the extra flavour. Fennel can be included in herb breads to good effect.

As a seasoning, fennel has always been associated with sauces to cover fish, and fish cookery. This can be extended to salmon or tuna salads. It partners peas, potatoes and carrots well.

Fennel seeds used to be coated with sugar and eaten as comfits to ease indigestion in the same way as caraway. They were also chewed during long sermons in church to quiet pangs of hunger. In a mild winter the leaves may still be used fresh, but on frosty days pounded seeds can be added instead.

*Garlic* Amongst seasonings, garlic is well known. In many countries where fevers and plagues were endemic, garlic became a regular part of the diet for its powerful protection against disease.

The pungent flavour and odour seem to attract either love or hatred. The English have always tended to be cautious about it, but the health-giving qualities are winning more and more converts. Numerous recipes include garlic with many ingredients and the preparation masks the flavour. The juice can be extracted with a garlic press and added to sauces or salad dressings. It compliments mushrooms, spinach, and aubergines and often accompanies onion. Garlic oil and vinegar are much used in meat and fish cookery.

Chewing parsley leaves or cumin seeds at the end of a meal can help with "garlic breath", but the best solution is to share the meal with your friends.

*Hyssop* A little-known flavouring today, hyssop shares many of the protective properties and actions of sage. The taste is pungent, but in quite a different way. Bitter and tangy, it is a herb to be used sparingly.

The herb partners fruits and vegetables equally well. Traditionally a seasoning in Continental sausages and an ingredient in stuffings for rich poultry, hyssop can be used in many dishes. Most cooks prefer to soften its dominant bitterness with a blend of milder herbs such as summer savory, marjoram or chervil, when adding it to bean casseroles, savoury pancakes or egg dishes. A little chopped hyssop can be sprinkled over mushrooms in salads.

In desserts hyssop and sweet cicely may be added together to apples or apricots as they are pre-cooked for puddings. If adding fresh hyssop alone to an apple pie, just five or six leaves will be sufficient, torn into fragments and laid under the pie crust.

*Lovage* Without doubt my favourite herb for seasoning soups, lovage has a powerful flavour rather like a spicy, pungent celery. Leaves can be chopped into salads or stews before the stronger stems are tried. Lovage is refreshing added raw to salads in which fruit and vegetables are mixed. It is at its very best however, with onion and parsley in soup. The rich, yeasty flavour which this herb adds to the stock makes it a gourmet experience. The taste is reminiscent of celery, chicken and mushroom combined.

In vegetable and bean casseroles lovage continues in this important role of adding body with flavour. For those on salt-restricted diets, the herb can make a very acceptable alternative seasoning, either when used alone or mixed with savory and dill or nettle.

Lovage can be added to soft cheeses, or pounded with butter to act as a flavouring as it melts over cooked vegetables. Lovage also adds "zing" to stir-fried dishes.

The stems can be crystallised in the same way as angelica, but tend to be rather strong for modern taste. The seeds can also be harvested as a spice to sprinkle over cakes, bread and biscuits.

*Marjoram* This "sweet" herb is included in many dried mixes. Still acting to preserve the food against bacteria, it has a much milder nature than sage or rosemary. Marjoram combines particularly well with thyme, parsley and lemon herbs. It lightly flavours vinegar or butter. Also cooking oil during frying.

*Oregano* This pungent seasoning features in Italian cookery and is best known partnered with pasta and pizzas. As a fresh herb I much prefer the stronger flavour of Greek oregano and often substitute it for marjoram in cheesy recipes. The herb is not as familiar in fish dishes as it might be. To appreciate the possibilities, try cooking tomatoes and onion seasoned with oregano and a hint of rosemary and spoon this over baking fish.

*Mint* The **Mentha** family contains many varieties, some better suited to cookery than others. The common garden mint is the accepted companion to new potatoes and peas as they are boiled. Applemint is my own favourite with peas, potato salads, or chopped into cream cheese sandwiches. Spearmint has a stronger flavour, and can be added to desserts such as blackcurrant puddings, or chopped sparingly amongst dried fruit in small tarts. All mints can be frozen or preserved in vinegar or savoury jellies.

Gingermint is equally effective in savoury melon starters, or pear desserts. The variegated leaves make it an attractive garnish for fruit salads and drinks alike. Peppermint is more often used in the form of a strong tea to flavour cakes or desserts. Pineapplemint leaves are also variegated and make a delightful centrepiece for any buffet, set with flowers and gingermint leaves into a sweet jelly.

*Rosemary* The herb has a versatile and powerful flavour which can be used with equal confidence in both sweet and savoury dishes. The early, rich bridal cakes were spiced with rosemary, which also acted as a digestive. In modern fruit cakes it can still be valued for bringing out the flavour of the fruit with a spicy richness. It is too good to restrict to fruit cakes, so try the exotic touch of rosemary in plain buns with a little candied peel. Or add ground rosemary to shortbread or biscuits. The spiky leaves can be ground at home along with the sugar for a recipe, or fresh rosemary pounded and added to boiled fruit cakes while they are on the stove, and removed before baking.

Rosemary and cream are good partners in rich fruit desserts, especially with apples, pears or rhubarb. In savoury dishes rosemary combines well with peas, onions, potatoes, tomatoes and cauliflower, resulting in a variety of recipes with that special flavour. Although I have only anecdotal evidence, there may be a connection between eating dishes very heavily flavoured with rosemary and miscarriage. This was after a cooking time of several hours. The same might apply with sage. This was, however, with unusually strong seasoning.

*Sage* As early as Roman times, sage was added to dishes following veal and venison, for its digestive qualities. It actually assists the body in coping with fats and so has accompanied such fish as eel and rich meats in goose or pork recipes.

Sage can be just as useful to counteract the indigestion which may result from eating pulses or pasta. Try sage in macaroni cheese to add interest.

Broad leaved sage is the best plant to grow for drying. Whole or crumbled dried sage leaves are both useful in different recipes. Fresh sage is however, available for most of the year and adds a finer flavour than the dried which, if not carefully prepared and stored, may become musty.

Sage was once popularly eaten between bread and butter and became an important ingredient in some regional cheeses. The modern housewife no longer labours to make hard cheeses, but sage cottage cheese offers a quick and simple method.

**Savory** A valuable herb to grow if you like slightly tangy seasonings. Winter savory is not as bitter as tarragon, but can add a distinctive flavour to sauces. It has the particular digestive properties needed to counteract the unfortunate effects of eating large amounts of beans and other pulses. Savory and beans are long established partners. In fish cookery, the herb is associated with trout. Both winter and summer savory can be dried and mixed with other herbs to season stews and casseroles. Summer savory, with its milder flavour may be preferable for egg dishes.

Winter savory, slower growing and consequently stronger in taste, can be picked as a fresh herb for much of the year. During periods of frost the leaves fall and a stock of preserves in the cupboard will be welcomed. The Romans made a sauce with savory which they served in much the same way as we serve mint sauce. Savory vinegar will add flavour in cooking, while savory jelly is a delicious accompaniment to many dishes.

**Tarragon** This exceptional seasoning is regarded as essential by many cooks. Classic sauce recipes require it and tarragon also finds a place in some mustards.

French tarragon is definitely a more delicate herb with a finer flavour. Young growth of Russian tarragon can however be used when French is not available. Try tarragon with seafoods, in fish dishes and with white meat. Tarragon vinegar is without doubt the most popular of all the herb vinegars, and is stocked by most foodstores.

**Thyme** A traditional ingredient of stuffings, thyme has anti-microbial and digestive properties. Common thyme generally offers the strongest flavour and medicinal qualities. The actual strength of thyme as a protector in sausages and with game, for instance, varies according to the growing conditions. Vegetarians can be as enthusiastic in their use of the herb to season cheese, nut and pulse dishes. Thyme is delicious in recipes with hazelnuts.

Thyme cheese and thyme honey were enjoyed by early Greeks and Romans. If available, the fresh herb is best. The dried herb can be improved by including newly opened flowers. When drying thyme, remember a full bowl of fresh herb will dry down to a number of twiggy stalks and the leaves from these give a very small amount indeed.

The lemon variety enables us to extend our experience with thyme into sweet desserts and cakes. A strong infusion of the herb in boiling water or milk is made and added to the recipe. Lemon thyme can be mixed with lemon balm for sweet recipes.

# Salt and pepper alternatives

THE common salt we add to our food contains sodium and chloride in equal amounts. The level of sodium in our blood is controlled by the kidneys which retain or excrete fluid to keep a healthy balance. If the sodium level becomes too high, then the kidneys will retain sufficient fluid to dilute it. A persistently high level means a greater volume of blood passing through the blood vessels and more fluid in the cell tissues. High blood pressure can be the result.

Potassium works together with sodium in the body. A natural balance between the two is necessary to health. Nettle and certain other herbs contain sodium and potassium, a mineral which modern diets tend to lack. These herbs can be used to "salt" foods without added burden to the kidneys.

### Basil
The intensity of the spicy flavour of basil is increased in some varieties. Dried basil tends to lose this quality and I prefer to sprinkle torn, fresh leaves of basil over salads as a pepper substitute.

### Borage
This is a herb very high in potassium which you may find in older cookery recipes. Modern research has led to warnings that eating borage leaves may be harmful because of the alkaloids they contain. Borage flowers are perfectly safe as a garnish, but unfortunately the potassium is in the stems and leaves.

### Dill
With a slightly "peppery" flavour to both seeds and leaves, this herb might be described as a "complete condiment". It is a natural choice when seasoning fish dishes containing cod, or halibut which are low in salt. Smoked or tinned fish are generally high in salt to begin with.

Some recipes add dill seeds which have quite a powerful flavour. The leaves are not as strong, but use cautiously until you are accustomed to them.

### Lovage
This herb mixes well with nettle and adds a strength of flavour which will be appreciated by those who once enjoyed heavily salted foods. This is not to say the taste will be the same, but it is an enjoyable alternative. Lovage should always be included when seasoning soups or vegetable casseroles.

### Nasturtium
The leaves are easily dried on a rack in a warm, dry atmosphere at less than 40°C (104° F) to retain their rich, green colour. Once rubbed down to a fine green powder, they can be sprinkled on food as an alternative to pepper. Use very cautiously as the flavour is strong and large amounts can be harmful.

### Nettle
Clearly, chopped fresh nettle is not suitable as an additive to a salad! However, dried nettle is the most versatile of the herb seasonings. This can be bought, or the nettles cut on a dry day (with rubber gloves protecting your hands), laid over a rack in a warm atmosphere and the dried leaves crumbled into dark glass jars. Once dried the nettle loses its sting and the leaf can be handled safely.

The dried herb can be sprinkled quite generously over soups, stews and other dishes. Sieve bought dried nettle as it may contain large pieces of stem.

### Savory
Useful in blends of herbs for salt-reduced diets, savory adds its own unique flavour. Include savory with nettle when seasoning bean casseroles or fish dishes. The savory should be a small amount in proportion to the nettle. (see page 68).

# Adding vitamins and minerals

**M**any herbs will only succeed in giving their full nutritional goodness to your meal if they are picked fresh from the garden, or an indoor pot, and eaten almost immediately. Ideally, chop raw herbs into the dish just before serving. Salads made hours before are never a good idea. All vegetables and herbs begin to lose their vitamin C as soon as they are sliced open or chopped. Cooking them in water will destroy vitamins, and they can lose minerals, particularly if salt is added. So, to make the best of your harvest, eat fresh herbs with your salad. A healthy diet includes a minimum of 25 per cent of raw fruit and vegetables each day, which means at least one salad.

In the time of James I a "grand salad" contained a total of over 30 ingredients, some, admittedly purely decorative. Most modern cooks would find it difficult to name so many, never mind be able to produce them from their own gardens. Some of these old ingredients would seem weird to us today, but we can easily add colour and variety to the usual, "standard salad" of lettuce, cucumber, onion and tomato, without resorting to strange weeds.

Parsley is a familiar herb most often used to garnish foods for special occasions. Try making a sprig or two a regular part of your daily salad together with other herbs recommended in the following pages. Nasturtium, chervil, chives, Florence fennel, pot marigold petals, dill, purslane, salad rocket, salad burnet, mints and sunflower seeds are rightly used as seasonings, garnishes and last-minute additions to yield their full bounty of vitamins and minerals.

Two other herbs however, cannot be eaten raw; these are nettle and elderberry. I hope the recipe section will encourage wary readers to enjoy experimenting with these herbs and come to appreciate their flavours as well as rich nutritional value.

When it comes to adding vitamins and minerals, parsley, nettle, chives and dill stand out from the others as the most beneficial. Read on through the details of each herb to feel more familiar with their natures and then savour the recipes.

## *Chervil*

This is an excellent, vitamin-rich garnish, which is especially useful during the winter months when parsley makes little growth in an open garden situation. Allow the herb to seed itself as a winter ground cover on your vegetable patch for a good supply through the cold months. By spring sowing, these plants will have given of their best and can be dug in, leaving just a few.

Chervil should never be cooked for a long time as a fresh herb and is perfectly suited to adding a light flavouring to cheese or egg dishes as a garnish, or added for one or two minutes at the end of the cooking time. As with parsley add at the last minute to a white sauce to serve with fish. Whether picking the herb to garnish soups or salads, always take the outer leaves, handling the delicate plants gently. Tear the leaves over the dish rather than chopping them.

Dried, chervil is an ingredient in fines herbes.

## *Chives*

The mild onion flavour of chives has been enjoyed for thousands of years. Giant chives are more attractive in the garden, but will not give the same flavour for cookery. Chopped chives partner eggs especially well and really bring scrambled or poached eggs to perfection. Cream or cottage cheese is delicious with chopped chives and their flavour can be added to omelettes with equal confidence. Chive butter (see Preserves page 97) is tasty melted over jacket potatoes and other vegetables just as you serve them. No salad is, of course, complete without a few chopped chives.

By the time you have experimented with them chopped into potato cakes, or cheese scones, or sprinkled chopped chives over vegetable soups as a garnish, you will find no difficulty in keeping your plants constantly harvested. Chives should never be allowed to grow tall and dark as this spoils their flavour. Keep harvesting them and feeding the bulbs regularly.

Drying chives is not particularly successful and loses vitamins. Instead freeze them chopped into ice cube trays or in bags. As chives have a happy habit of multiplying, you may not always wish to keep all the bulbs from divided clumps, for re-planting. The remaining bulbs can be pickled in white wine vinegar in the same way as shallots.

## *Dill*

The balance of vitamins and minerals in dill's feathery leaves and tiny seeds renders it as valuable a herb as parsley. It is helpful to the hair, skin and nails. Chopped dill is a perfect condiment for your salad, both amongst vegetables and as part of the salad dressing. The herb is at its best with cucumber, beetroot, white cabbage and tomato. If eating a tuna or salmon salad, sprinkle dill over the fish. If you cannot add radishes to your salad then dill makes an easily digestible alternative.

With successive sowings, the herb can be harvested through from early summer until the first frosts. The leaves can be dried, but there is an art to retaining the brilliant green colour they should have. Dill herb, also called dill weed, is on sale as a dried herb. The fresh or dried herb can be sprinkled over fish as it is cooking, or added to peas and pea soup. To keep more of the vitamin bounty, freeze dill herb rather than drying it. The leaves can be crumbled while still frozen to save chopping them.

## *Elder*

Elderberries are a rich source of vitamin C for our winter needs. They are ready to gather when the umbels hang down with their weight. Do not eat elderberries raw; they contain anthocyanide pigments which are made safe by cooking. A good harvest of 6.8 to 9kg (15-20lb) of elderberries can be made into syrups, conserves, wines and most conveniently, frozen in cartons. To freeze elderberries, stalk, wash and drain them. Pack into cartons or freeze in single layers on trays before bagging up. These can enrich pies and desserts, mixed with apple or as a single fruit. In recipes elderberries can be substituted for either brambles or blackcurrants. Their rich juice slowly extracted in the oven is delicious sweetened in sauces and the syrup can be diluted as a base for fruit salads of pears, plums and red grapes. Or in winter thickened to form a rich, spicy sauce for pears or apple.

## *Fennel*

There are two distinct varieties of fennel: garden fennel, *Foeniculum offinale,* which is tall and grown for the feathery leaves and seeds; and Florence fennel which is grown as a vegetable for the bulbous root. Both have a similar aniseed flavour. The leaves of either will add vitamin C and potassium to salads. To prepare the bulbs of Florence fennel, discard any discoloured outer layers and tough stalks. Wash and chop the remaining bulb finely, adding about 2 tablespoons of fennel per person for a tasty, easy to digest salad.

To serve as a cooked vegetable, cut the root in half and smear the centre with butter or margarine, wrap in foil and bake in a moderate oven for about 20 minutes until tender. Alternatively, microwave with the two halves prepared as before and placed in a covered microwave dish. Cook on full for approximately 4 minutes until the fennel is tender but not mushy. It is a delicious vegetable with cheese based quiches or fish dishes.

## Marigold

Here, we are talking about good, old fashioned, English pot marigolds, not the French or African varieties. Thanks to a good deal of encouraging publicity for flower cookery in books and magazines, people are becoming more adventurous in including flower petals in salads and fruit salads. One of the prettiest, most familiar and most colourful is the pot marigold or *Calendula*. It is also one of the most nutritious.

The petals do not have a strong aroma or flavour. Begin by chopping a few into salads, egg or cheese dishes, as a gentle introduction to flower cookery. You will soon be using them with confidence. I have even sprinkled pot marigold petals on my breakfast cereal for a bright start to the day.

Their vibrant colour is well suited to cake decorations, trifles and desserts in the form of marigold sugar. Or they can be sprinkled on fresh, or crystallised. Fresh petals can be crisped by floating briefly in iced water before adding to the dish.

## Nasturtium

The spicy flavour of nasturtium leaves never fails to remind me of my childhood, when a large bed of nasturtiums kept a friend and I happily munching through the summer days. Even the dullest salad can be enlivened with a little chopped nasturtium. Successive sowings will provide a steady harvest of young leaves for late spring, summer and autumn.

Nasturtium belongs to the same family as watercress and contains valuable vitamins. The quantity of vitamin C is highest just before the plant flowers. The flowers too have a wholesome value and add a dash of brilliant colour to any dish. A single flower, anchored in a thick slice of cucumber to give moisture, will grace the centre of an elegant salad, or float in a bowl of salad dip or cottage cheese. Add either the leaves or the flowers at the last moment, or they may give an unwanted bitterness to the food. The centre of the flower "trumpet" could be filled with cottage or cream cheese.

Nasturtiums originated in Peru and were introduced into Europe later than most herbs. They quickly became popular in the 17th century as cooks delighted in adding the colourful yellow flowers of the plant closely related to the modern nasturtium, known as "lark's heels", as a garnish.

## Nettle

Nettles have a high content of both vitamins and minerals, with a rich variety of iron, magnesium, potassium and sulphur. Unless you know a safe place to gather them, away from weedkillers and traffic pollution, it is best to plant a nettle patch in your garden. Quite a small area can yield a steady harvest of young growth for the kitchen in spring and early summer, while attracting wildlife and providing other benefits for the vegetables later in the year.

Wearing rubber gloves will give plentiful protection while gathering the young tops with four to six leaves. These are washed, and damaged leaves discarded, before being boiled in (15-30 ml) 1-2 tablespoons of water in a thick-bottomed pan until tender. Cooked nettles have no sting. Remember to gather four times as much volume as you need since nettles are dramatically reduced in size as they cook.

Nettle soup is an old favourite, or try the nettle pancakes in the recipes. Nettle puree can be frozen for use later in the year. For new recipes substitute nettle where you would otherwise use spinach.

## Parsley

I always feel sad at the end of a buffet meal, when I see a row of plates left on the table stripped bare of sandwiches and with forlorn, limp sprigs of parsley remaining. The iron content of parsley, quite apart from the vitamin C when it is freshly picked, means we cannot afford to throw such goodness away.

Old herbals tell us that in ancient Rome the gladiators were fed on parsley before being sent into the arena. No doubt the extra iron was an added bonus to the wounded victor.

There are so many opportunities to use parsley that little and often is a natural, healthy way to enjoy it. No salad is complete without a generous sprinkling of the herb, with the Italian, or, as it is also known, French parsley, giving a slightly peppery flavour compared to the curled. Either can be included in potato cakes, fish cakes, the famous parsley sauce, flans, omelettes, fish and pulse dishes and much more. Dried, it is an essential ingredient in bouquet garni and mixed herbs.

Parsley can be frozen for winter use, or a few first-year plants potted up and taken indoors to grace the window sills. Take care not to include seeds when harvesting from second-year plants as these contain a high concentration of apiol and can cause miscarriages.

### Purslane

This herb adds a new dimension to salads with lush, succulent leaves adding a flavour reminiscent of "mange-tout". The cooling effect is helpful to the digestion, particularly with "hot" ingredients, such as radishes and onions. Galen first recommended it in this role thousands of years ago. Purslane was particularly popular from the 16th to the 18th century as an essential salad ingredient. It was so regarded during this time that large quantities of the older stems and leaves were washed, part-dried and pickled for winter use.

Nowadays we are more likely to appreciate the herb for its valuable vitamins and minerals, than using the rosettes of leaves to frame a decorative garnish of borage flowers. If buying seed for summer purslane in salads, check these are for edible plants, some new varieties are intended for their flowers only. (see page 53)

### Salad burnet

This is such a pretty herb to grow and scatter as a garnish. Salad burnet was a great favourite in the knot gardens of Tudor times and was served over salads and floated in wine cups. One or two tablespoons of the graceful leaves can be mixed in with a little mint in a salad to accompany fish, or the herb can be added with parsley and chives. The best French and Italian salads once included salad burnet, then known as pimpinella. Late spring and into early summer is the time to appreciate the young growth of leaves, before the plant flowers. Regular harvesting can be carried out to stop flower growth, in which case the leaves may be gathered through the summer and autumn and even into a mild winter.

Although salad burnet can be chopped over cooked vegetables or made into herb butter to melt over them as they are served, it is not cooked with the vegetables. Use always as a fresh, nutritious garnish. The flowers, while they resemble raspberries are not eaten but can make a very attractive table decoration.

### Salad rocket

A stronger flavouring than salad burnet, this herb has gained steadily in popularity in recent years. It is now commonly on sale with other salad ingredients and it is a great joy to welcome it back from relative obscurity. The younger leaves have a milder flavour, while the older ones add a spicy bitterness to salads. The herb once had a reputation for being aphrodisiac and concerned writers of the times recommended eating it with lettuce and purslane to counteract this.

Like purslane, salad rocket has been pickled for winter use. It may also be cooked along with other green vegetables, or used to give a distinctive flavour to sauces. Straight from your salad patch however, salad rocket will add a valuable store of vitamins and minerals to your meal.

### Sunflower

No herb has enjoyed so much attention, research or publicity in modern times as the sunflower. We are all familiar with the healthy reputation of sunflower oil and fats, but perhaps think less of the source of the oil - the seeds.

These are deliciously nutty in flavour when lightly toasted under the grill for a few minutes. They can be sprinkled over salads or cereals, or used in crunchy toppings to some desserts. They make biscuits and fruit bars crunchy and tasty and can be eaten alone as a snack to replace sweets.

Rich in minerals, especially calcium, and containing zinc, potassium and magnesium, sunflower seeds can also give their exceptional goodness when sprouted in the same way as alfalfa. The sprouted seeds can be sprinkled over salads or accompany salad vegetables in sandwiches.

One of the first uses for the sunflower when it was introduced from Peru (then called the marigold of Peru), was to give edible flowerbuds. The small flowerbuds can still be scattered over salads as a decorative garnish.... but I think the seeds will be found more enjoyable.

# Herbal sweeteners

WHETHER you would like to reduce the amount of sugar in your diet to help you to lose weight, for the sake of your teeth, or for your general health; a herbal sweetener has to be good news. Ready-prepared foods contain a lot of hidden sugar; some tinned vegetables and fruit, canned drinks, drinking chocolate, soups, yogurts, ice cream, jams and sauces contain high amounts. There has been a great interest in sugar-free cookery and providing artificial sweeteners, honey can be very useful, but does contain 75 per cent sugar, although of a more digestible kind. Carob powder has also gained favour as it has less sugar than chocolate and more fibre.

No modern herb garden would be complete without a sugar saver.

### Angelica

This herbal sweetener, unlike sweet cicely, unfortunately does raise the blood sugar level and so is not suitable for diabetics. Simply to reduce the amount of sugar in a dish, however, use angelica leaves or small stalks. For anyone who does not like the taste of aniseed, angelica makes a very acceptable alternative to sweet cicely. It is a majestic, distinctive herb and has a unique, slightly musky flavouring which is added to wines. Angelica is the perfect herb to cook with rhubarb, and some old recipes for rhubarb jam include the stems.

Other acidic fruits such as gooseberries and plums will benefit from the sweetening qualities of angelica as they are cooked. When making marmalade, try adding the leaf or stem of angelica to make an exceptional preserve. The herb can also be added, fresh or candied to desserts with oranges and lemons.

Most people have only tasted the commercially prepared crystallised stems. This is a pity as I have never bought any which tasted as rich and fragrant as the home-candied angelica. This is definitely a "sweet" to make at home and chop into cakes, icings and desserts.

Angelica tea made from the leaves can also be used as a special flavouring with delicious results. Do not take the tea or syrup while pregnant.

### Sweet cicely

Sweet cicely is a very special herb which can reduce the sugar needed by more than half when included in fruit desserts. The leaves are available from early spring until the first frosts. Through the centuries they have been chopped into sauces and fruit dishes. When dandelions and other tart greens were eaten, "sweet cis" helped to make them more palatable.

The herb is recommended for diabetics and can be used alone as fresh, chopped leaf to sweeten fruit salads, or even sprinkled over breakfast cereals when sugar is not allowed. Fruit drinks will be a little sweeter with the chopped herb floating in the jug. Sweet cicely can also give a healthy sweet seasoning to home made tomato sauces.

Sweet cicely dried well below 40°C (104°F), retains its green colour and aniseed flavour. A small patch of the herb will give you several harvests during the year for drying even after the herb flowers.

The main use for the leaves is to sweeten stewed fruit as it is cooking. For the fresh herb, two-three full leafy sprays will be needed to 0.45kg (1lb) of gooseberries, plums, rhubarb or apple. With dried leaves, a handful can be added to the stewing fruit together with approximately half the normal amount of sugar. With apples or plums, experiment with less than half. The fresh sweet cicely can be removed when the fruit is cooked and before it is used as a pie or crumble filling.

The circlets of tiny cream florets are followed by long, green seed pods, pointing skywards. The green seeds were once gathered to add their aniseed flavour to salads and served in a dressing. They may still be appreciated in pickles. The root too was boiled, sliced and served in vinegar. It can also be harvested in autumn and candied for inclusion in marmalades, jams and sweets. (see Herbcraft Naturally).

Culpeper recommended the herb for the elderly, saying, "It is so harmless, you cannot use it amiss". This last comment has been repeated about sweet cicely over hundreds of years. Above all, it is a safe, well-tested herb which you can feel happy to use as often as you please.

# Flowers in cookery

THE return of flowers to modern cookery after a long absence offers us many opportunities for creative recipes and impressive garnishes. When we read of wonderful Elizabethan dishes served at feasts, garlanded with flowers, we perhaps have difficulty in imagining them. Now we can experiment on a smaller scale to appreciate the skill and flair of a natural garnish.

Not all the flowers in your garden will be edible, however, and one or two important points in preparation should be noted before you begin to explore this culinary art. Those flowers which I particularly recommend from my own experience are -

*Gallica* or *Damascena* rose petals, clove pinks, borage, chives, violets, pot marigold petals (**never** French or African marigolds) nasturtium, heartsease, elderflowers, dill, fennel, red bergamot, mint, lavender, primroses and cowslips (**not** the American varieties).

I hope you won't be using any chemical sprays in your garden, but if you are gathering flowers for cookery do check no-one else has been spraying recently near your harvest. For instance, roses grown along a boundary fence may have been affected by a spray used in your neighbours garden.

Pick flowers on a dry day when they are either in bud or newly opened. Full-blown flowers are already past their best as far as fragrance and flavour are concerned. Insects should be gently washed away in cold water. Always remove any green parts from flowers to be eaten and cut away the white "heels" from the base of the rose and clove pink petals as these will make the flowers taste bitter.

If the flowers are to be dried, crystallised or used in preserves such as vinegar, syrup, honey or jellies, the best time of day to pick them is mid-morning. At this time the dew has dried and the sun has not yet drawn out the essential oils.

For jams and jellies, clove pinks, rose petals, lavender flowers, violets and elderflowers are the most commonly used. Rose-petal jelly made from richly perfumed damask roses is both a treat and a restoring tonic to anyone who has been ill for some time. A smaller amount of rose petals can be added to strawberry jam to enrich the flavour. No gooseberry jam or jelly would be the same without the inclusion of elderflowers in the recipe, and more unusual combinations can be as successful. Lavender flowers may be tried with limes in preserves, or mint flowers with apple instead of the leaves. Flower jellies having an apple base were once filled with a delicious assortment of edible blooms: borage, clove pinks, pot marigold petals and heartsease all mixed together.

Flower vinegars are a quick and easy way of capturing summer fragrances and flavours. See the recipes for a white wine vinegar coloured red with bright nasturtium flowers, or elderflower vinegar, so perfect for salad dressings. Lavender and rose vinegars are the most fragrant. Honey can also be infused with flower fragrances and flavours; try rose petals, clove pinks, or lavender.

Flower sugars were old favourites. These can make fascinating cake-icings as the sugar is coloured with red rose petals, lavender, pot marigold petals, violets or the more vibrant clove pinks. Other desserts can be turned into gourmet dishes with the simple addition of herb syrups or crystallised flowers. The latter are lovely set with ice creams, sorbets, yoghurt or custards. Flowers can also be set into trifles and jellies as magnificent centrepieces for any party.

Once you begin to relate flowers to your favourite recipes, ideas for new combinations will flow. In spring, violets add welcome colour to simple side-salads, such as watercress and cucumber. In almond and rice puddings they echo recipes of ceturies ago, while crystallised to decorate cakes and chocolates they are perfect for Mother's Day presents or Easter cakes. Primroses and English cowslips can also bring a breath of spring as decorations. Sadly, few gardens have sufficient for the elaborate puddings and wines which used to be made from these flowers. Those in the wild are protected and it is hoped will be left alone to grow again in numbers.

Later in summer borage flowers are the prettiest flower decorations for salads and sweets, such as chocolate mousse. They are rivalled only by the sweet heartsease, equally enchanting amongst sliced hard boiled egg, or on a cream topping. Striking in a different way is the red bergamot; a single flower is all that is needed set in the centre of a quiche, a bowl of creamy dessert or on a cake as the ultimate decoration.

Dill and fennel flowers make a pretty garnish for fish dishes and savouries. Perhaps the most versatile is the pot marigold which was once sold in grocers for winter stews and soups. The fresh or dried petals are a colourful addition to salads, rice dishes, egg and cheese recipes, custards, dips and omelettes. They can also be added to cakes and biscuits.

If variety is the spice of life then flowers are the perfect ingredient for every meal!

## A touch of Lemon

LEMON-FLAVOURED and scented herbs are an especial favourite in many gardens. The familiar lemon balm is sadly rarely appreciated as a culinary herb and deserves to be used far more. The flavour is subtle in ice-cream, the fillings of baked apples and sauces to accompany fish. For a stronger tang the herb can be mixed with lemon thyme for sweet, or lemon basil for savoury recipes. Either the two herbs can be infused together to make a strong, flavouring tea which can be added to cakes or desserts, or they can be chopped together in savouries. Lemon mint is another herb as yet little known and easy to grow.

Lemon verbena and lemon-scented geraniums are the most powerful flavourings, each with their individual qualities. The leaves of scented geraniums can be laid in cake tins to infuse the sponge mixture with their distinctive flavour and fragrance as it cooks. They make beautiful fragrant jellies with just one large leaf added to each jar of apple preserve. For cakes, ice cream and desserts, lemon herbs are ideal. They also provide a perfect finishing touch to cooling fruit drinks or herb teas.

# *Recipes*

**Note:** Follow either the imperial or the metric measures in the recipe, as they are not interchangeable.

## Starters
### *Grapefruit in Ginger*
3 grapefruit
2 large bananas
4-6 sticks of celery, preferably from the heart
A few unblanched almonds
1 sprig of applemint
6 small sprigs of gingermint
3 glace cherries (optional)
Cut the grapefruits in half, making a decorative jagged edge. With a grapefruit knife, remove the flesh of the fruits over a large bowl. Add the finely chopped celery and banana. Spoon the grapefruit juice over the fruit. Wash and finely chop the gingermint and applemint leaves and stir into the mixture. Leave to stand for 10-15 minutes. Spoon the filling into the grapefruit halves. Sprinkle with fine slivers of almond and decorate in the centre either with a half glace cherry in each, or a sprig of gingermint. Chill for 10 minutes before serving. Serves 6.

### *Herb filled Mushrooms*
170g (6oz) mushrooms
1 clove garlic
3 plum tomatoes
1 small onion
1 teaspoon basil
1 sprig of hyssop
1 tablespoon chervil
$1/4$ teaspoon celery salt
2 dessertspoons chopped fennel
$1/4$ teaspoon ground coriander
2-3 dessertspoons white wine.
Finely chop the onion and sauté for 2-3 minutes. Add the crushed garlic and continue cooking gently, while dicing the fennel. Chop 2 mushrooms with a few stalks and add these with the fennel and chopped plum tomatoes. Stir while cooking for 2 minutes. Pour in the white wine. Strip the leaves from the hyssop and chop these with the basil. Season the vegetables with these herbs, celery salt and ground coriander. Leave over a gentle heat, stirring from time to time until almost all the wine has been absorbed. Sprinkle in most of the chopped chervil, saving a little for decoration. Fill the washed or peeled, de-stalked mushrooms. Either serve raw on a bed of lettuce, or bake at 180°C (350°F) for 8-10 minutes before serving.

## Lovage and Mushroom Soup

2 large onions
100g (4oz) mushrooms
1 heaped dessertspoon cornflour
300ml (½ pint) milk
900 ml (1½ pints) stock
18g (¼oz) margarine
3 tablespoons chopped lovage

Sauté the chopped onions in the margarine until soft. This will take about 4 minutes. Add the chopped lovage leaves and sauté again while peeling and slicing the mushrooms. Add the prepared mushrooms and sauté again for 3-4 minutes. Stir in the cornflour and return briefly to the heat. Pour in the boiling vegetable stock. Simmer for approximately 30 minutes. Cool slightly. Liquidise and add the milk. Return to a gentle heat and serve garnished with chopped chervil or watercress.

## Fennel and Pea Soup

18g (¾oz) marg
2 medium bulbs fennel
1 clove garlic
1 medium potato
100g (4oz) peas
150ml (½ pint) milk
generous ½ teaspoon savory
½ teaspoon herb pepper
1.2 litres (2 pints) stock

In a large pan melt the margarine over a moderate heat. Sauté the fennel chopped into small cubes, peeled, cubed potato and peeled, crushed garlic for a few minutes, until soft but not brown. Stir. Cover the pan and continue to cook the vegetables over a low heat for 15 minutes, stirring from time to time. If using frozen peas, cook these first. Add the peas together with the boiling stock and seasoning when the fennel is soft. Bring back to the boil and simmer for a further 10 minutes. Cool and liquidise. Add milk and reheat. Serve garnished with a little fennel leaf or watercress.

# Main Courses and Salads
## Savoury Nettle Pancakes

*Pancake mixture*
100g (4oz) plain wholemeal flour
2 eggs
300ml (½ pint) milk
Filling
1 large onion
2 medium tins plum tomatoes
2 large carrots
450g (1lb) cooked nettle
oil for frying
seasoning
Worcester sauce (optional)

Beat the eggs and milk together with the sieved flour, or mix in a blender. Leave to stand. Dice the onion and slice the prepared carrots finely into rings. Strain 8 plum tomatoes from their juice. Fry the diced onion and carrot rings gently in a little oil until the onion is golden brown and the carrot is beginning to crisp. Add the plum tomatoes and drained nettle. Stir well, season with salt and pepper (for herb pepper and salt substitute see preserves page 98) and a dash of Worcester sauce if liked. Fry for 2-3 minutes longer to heat through. Drain and keep hot.

Fry the pancake mixture in a little of the vegetable juices, adding more oil if necessary. Fill four cooked pancakes with the nettle and vegetables and roll. Place on a pie dish and bake in a pre-heated oven at 190°C (375°F) for 10-15 minutes. Serve with the tomato sauce below.

*Tomato sauce.*

Liquidise any remaining plum tomatoes with the juice. Pour into an enamel pan, adding 1 teaspoon lemon juice, ½ teaspoon chopped basil, 1 dessertspoon sweet cicely, and a good pinch of herb pepper. Heat gently for about 5 minutes.

### *Herby salad*

1 medium-sized lettuce, washed and shredded.
Other salad vegetables as available: fennel or cucumber, celery, radish, carrot, salad rocket or cress.
2 heaped tablespoons chopped fresh herbs: parsley, mint, chives, purslane, lemon balm and lovage.
Edible flowers shredded: pot marigold petals, clove pinks (white heels removed), whole borage flowers, 1 nasturtium flower for the centre.
Prepare salad vegetables and arrange on a bed of lettuce. Sprinkle the shredded petals and whole borage flowers over the salad. Anchor the stalk of the nasturtium flower in a slice of cucumber and set in the centre.
Salad Dressing 1½ tablespoons olive oil, ½ tablespoon elderflower or nasturtium vinegar. Mix and season with lemon herb pepper (see preserves, page 98).

### *Rosemary potato cakes*

450g (1½lb) potato
50g (2oz) cheddar cheese
½ teaspoon ground rosemary
1 dessertspoon chopped chives
a little milk
margarine or butter to taste
a pinch of salt substitute
1 egg (optional)
Mash the potatoes with margarine and milk. Combine with the grated cheese and herbs while still hot. Form into cakes, adding a little beaten egg to bind if necessary. Leave to firm for 15 minutes before frying or grilling.

## Fennel flan

170g (6oz) plain wholemeal flour
1 medium onion, chopped
1 level teaspoon mixed herbs
2 eggs
85g (3oz) vegetable fat
1 tablespoon oil
85g (3oz) grated cheese
150ml ('/4 pint) milk
1 medium bulb of Florence fennel.

Rub the fat into the flour, adding a little water as necessary to make a pastry case. Line the pie dish and bake this blind for 10 minutes at 190°C (375°F). Meanwhile, sauté the chopped onion in the oil for 2 minutes. Add the finely chopped fennel and continue cooking until this begins to soften. Spoon the onion and fennel into the partially cooked pastry case. Sprinkle over the grated cheese and mixed herbs. Beat the eggs and milk together and pour over. Return the flan to the oven for a further 30-40 minutes, until it is golden brown and well risen.

Alternatively the onion may be omitted and broccoli and peas added instead.

## Savoury rice

1 small carrot
1 large onion
225g (8oz) easy cook rice
600ml (1 pint) vegetable stock
1 clove garlic
'/2 cup peas
2 tablespoons mixed peppers
1 small courgette
2 teaspoons chopped basil
1 top of rosemary
2 teaspoons chopped parsley
1 large bay leaf
1 tablespoon oil
3 sticks celery or 3 tablespoons chopped Florence fennel
1 tablespoon chopped marigold petals

Chop the onion finely and sauté in the oil for 2-3 minutes. Add the peeled and chopped garlic and continue cooking. Add finely chopped celery, carrots, courgette and peppers. Sauté until the vegetables begin to soften. Add partly cooked peas and rice. Sauté for 4 minutes, add herb seasonings and pour over the boiling vegetable stock. Cover the pan and leave on a gentle heat for 10 minutes, then continue simmering without the lid until the stock is almost gone, approximately another 10 minutes.

### Sage cheese and bean salad

1 small tin red kidney beans, drained
several raw chopped mushrooms
florets of raw cauliflower
shredded white cabbage or iceberg lettuce
1 small carrot, grated
1 small onion, sliced into rings
celery, chopped

Make a salad dressing with equal parts of salad cream, basil chopped in oil and savory herb vinegar. Add two pinches of mustard powder. Blend in the salad bowl and toss the salad ingredients in the dressing.

*Sage cheese*. This needs to be prepared a *few hours in advance*. Stir 6 washed and torn sage leaves into a 225g (8oz) tub of cottage cheese. Leave covered in a cool place for several hours. Serve.

### Salad potatoes

680g (1½lb) new potatoes
25g (1oz) margarine
4 generous tablespoons mayonnaise
25g (1oz) cornflour
300ml (½ pint) milk
3 heaped teaspoons each of chives, dill and lovage.

Scrub and boil the new potatoes until tender. Melt the margarine over a low heat. Stir in the cornflour and add the milk gradually. Stir over a gentle heat until thickened and smooth. Bring to the boil, stirring, and simmer for a few minutes. Cool. When cold add mayonnaise, season if liked and stir in the chopped herbs. Pour over diced cooked potatoes.

### Rosemary whiting

whiting for 2 people
400g (14oz) can plum tomatoes
1 medium onion
good pinch lemon pepper (see Preserves page 98)
1 tablespoon fennel herb vinegar or white wine
1 teaspoon chopped rosemary or ½ teaspoon ground rosemary
a little margarine
1 tablespoon oil.

Strain the tomatoes and lay these in the bottom of a casserole dish. Slice the onion and fry gently in the oil until soft. Arrange the onion slices over the tomatoes and season with lemon pepper. Sprinkle with the rosemary and tablespoon of fennel vinegar or wine. Lay the washed fish on the sauce, brushing it with a little melted margarine. Cover and bake at 150°C (300°F) for 40 minutes. Remove the lid for the last few minutes of cooking.

*Picnic eggs*

6 hard boiled eggs
2 tablespoons grated cheese
2 tablespoons oil
½ tablespoon lemon juice
1 heaped teaspoon mayonnaise
1 tablespoon pot marigold petals
2 tablespoons chopped herbs - made up of parsley, chives, lemon thyme and marjoram. Heartsease flowers and pot marigold petals or variegated lemon balm leaves to garnish. Heat the pot marigold petals and lemon thyme in the oil for 5 minutes over a low heat. Allow to cool. Strain, mix 1 tablespoon of the herbal oil with the cheese. Chop the remaining washed herbs and mix in. The proportions of each herb are a matter of taste. For a sweeter recipe add mainly parsley and marjoram. To give the mixture more of a tangy flavour add extra chives. Set aside while hardboiling the eggs. Shell and halve the eggs, remove the yolks and mash. Add the mayonnaise and lemon juice. Common thyme can be used instead if wished. The joy of this recipe is that it is always slightly different in flavour. Let the mixture stand for 10 minutes before replacing the filling into the egg whites. Garnish with heartsease flowers and pot marigold petals.

## Cheese dips
### Parsley cottage cheese

225g (8oz) cottage cheese
2 tablespoons French parsley
1 teaspoon chopped hyssop
2 teaspoons chopped oregano
1-2 cloves of garlic, crushed.
Wash and chop all the herbs. Peel and crush the garlic, using a garlic press and add to the herbs. Stir the mixture into the cottage cheese and leave to stand for at least 15-20 minutes before serving.

### Lovage cream cheese

225g (8oz) cream cheese
4 large leaves of lovage
1 teaspoon chopped French parsley
pinch lemon herb pepper
1 heaped tablespoon chopped fennel leaf
Wash and chop all the herbs. Stir into the cream cheese and leave to stand for 15-20 minutes before serving.

## Desserts
### Elderflower and gooseberry whirl.

2 heads elderflowers (in perfect condition)
450g (1lb) gooseberries
100g (4oz) brown sugar
300ml (½ pint) water
6 tablespoons evaporated milk
a few chopped walnuts
grated chocolate and fresh cream to decorate.

Dissolve the sugar in the water in an enamel pan. Bring slowly to the boil. Add the topped and tailed gooseberries and the washed elderflower heads. Cook over a low heat for about 10 minutes, until the gooseberries are soft. Remove the elderflowers and strain. Set the gooseberries to cool. When cold, liquidise the fruit with the evaporated milk. Pour into glass dishes, top with whirls of fresh cream, sprinkling with the walnuts and grated chocolate. Chill. (serves 4).

### Rosemary and rhubarb crumble

450g (1lb) rhubarb
85g (3oz) raw cane sugar ground with ½ teaspoon dried rosemary,
(or use ready ground herb).
*Topping* - 135g (5oz) self raising wholemeal flour
50g (2oz) margarine
50g (2oz) raw cane sugar
25g (1oz) sesame seeds
25g (1oz) finely chopped walnuts or hazelnuts.
Cook the rhubarb gently with the sugar and rosemary in a little water. Drain and spoon into a casserole dish.
*Topping:* Rub the margarine into the flour, saving a little for the top. Stir in the remaining dry ingredients and pour over the fruit. Dot with saved margarine and sprinkle with a few sesame seeds. Bake in the centre of a moderate oven at 180°C (350°F) for approximately 45 minutes, until golden brown.

### Fruit salad

2 peaches and 2 nectarines, or 4 peaches
2 apples
1 pear
4 dessert plums, peeled if the skins are bitter
1 dessertspoon chopped gingermint
1 dessertspoon chopped sweet cicely
1 or 2 flowers of clove pinks or borage for decoration
approximately 150ml (¼ pint) elderflower or clove pink syrup
(see preserves page 101)
Peel fruit or leave the skin on according to taste. Core fruits and chop into the base of flower syrup in a bowl. Stir to make sure the fruit is thoroughly coated with syrup. Add chopped herbs and clove pink petals with the heels removed. Chill slightly before serving.

### Peach and rose ice cream

1 medium tin peaches in fruit juice
or 2-3 peaches
1 tablespoon rose petal jelly (see page 102)
2 dessertspoons rose water
1 dessertspoon rose sugar
1 large egg
150ml (5floz) soya cream (or double dairy cream)

Liquidise the peaches and rose ingredients. Heat in the microwave for 2 minutes on 8, or bring to a simmer on the stove. Pour over the beaten egg, beating all the time. Stir in the whipped soya cream. Pour into a rigid container and put in the freezer until it starts to freeze around the edges. Remove and stir well. Add cowslip flowers in winter or chopped rose petals with the white heels removed, in summer. Return to the freezer. For a special occasion turn the ice cream out of the dish and decorate with rose sugar and crystallised petals.

### Elderberry cheesecake
225g (8oz) digestive biscuits
100g (4oz) soft margarine
1 tablespoon brown sugar.
*Filling.*
1 egg
1 tablespoon icing sugar
225g (8oz) cottage cheese
2 level teaspoons gelatine
75ml (3floz) whipping cream
50ml (2floz) milk
1½ tablespoons lemon curd
225g (8oz) elderberries
1½-2 tablespoons of water
crystallised flowers for decoration.
Grind or crush the biscuits to fine crumbs. Melt margarine and stir in the biscuit crumbs and brown sugar until well coated. Press down to line a 25cm (10 in) flan case. Leave to set hard. Bring the elderberries to the boil with 1½ tablespoons water. Simmer for 2-3 minutes and set aside to cool. Separate the egg. Whisk the white until stiff. In another bowl, whisk the egg yolk, icing sugar and lemon curd. Blend the cottage cheese with a little of the cream and milk. Whip 50ml (2fl oz) of the cream until stiff. Dissolve the gelatine in 2 tablespoons of hot water. Combine the gelatine with the cheese and egg mixtures and fold in the egg white and cream. Spread elderberry on base. Pour over filling. Chill for 2-3 hours before serving and decorate with crystallised flowers.

## Cake and Biscuit recipes
*Marigold "fairy" cakes*
85g (3oz) pot marigold sugar
85g (3oz) margarine
1 large or 2 small eggs
35g (1½oz) ground almonds
1 tablespoon pure orange juice
1½ tablespoons pot marigold petals (opt)
100g (4oz) self raising flour
icing sugar
rose-water
crystallised flowers
If you do not have pot marigold sugar already made, put the pot marigold petals into a grinder with the sugar for a few seconds. Otherwise use 85g of sugar. Cream the margarine and pot marigold sugar. Add the beaten egg with a little of the flour. Stir in the

ground almonds. Finally mix in the pure juice alternately with the remainder of the flour. Spoon into bun cases and bake at 180°C (350°F) for 15-20 minutes, until golden brown.

To decorate, mix a little icing sugar with rose-water and ice each bun, setting a crystallised flower on the top.

## Rose petal tarts

Shortcrust pastry
100g (4oz) flour
38-50g (1½-2oz) sunflower fat
a little rose-water
rose-petal jam
85g (3oz) margarine
85g (3oz) rose sugar
25g (1oz) ground almonds
85g (3oz) self raising flour
1 egg
1 dessertspoon of rose-water.

Mix the pastry, roll it out and line the bun tins. Place ½-1 teaspoon of rose-petal jam in each tart. Cream the margarine and sugar until light and fluffy. Add the lightly beaten egg with a little of the flour. Mix in the ground almonds and the remainder of the flour, alternately with the rose-water.

Spoon the mixture over the jam in the tarts. Bake at 180°C (350°F) for about 15 minutes. For special occasions, dot with icing and decorate with crystallised rose petals.

## Rosemary buns

85g (3oz) margarine
2 eggs
25g (1oz) candied peel
100g (4oz) self raising flour
85g (3oz) raw cane sugar ground with 1 teaspoon dried rosemary, (or add 1½ teaspoons ground rosemary)

Cream the margarine and sugar until light and fluffy. Add the eggs one at a time with a little flour. Gradually fold in the remainder of the flour, followed by the finely chopped candied peel. Turn into bun tins and bake at 180°C (350°F) for approximately 15 minutes.

## Sunny apricot bars

100g (4oz) dried apricots
50g (2oz) raisins
100g (4oz) oats
50g (2oz) ground almonds
2 dessertspoons rose-water
4 teaspoons honey
50g (2oz) wholemeal flour, egg to mix
sunflower seeds (sesame seeds or chopped nuts could also be used as a coating)

Mix all the dry ingredients, chopping the apricots finely. Add the rose-water carefully and mix. Next add the honey, bringing the mixture to a soft dough consistency with the egg. Shape into about 18 bars, approximately 1cm (½in) thick. Roll in sunflower seeds to coat.

Bake on a greased baking tray at 170°C (325°F) for 10-12 minutes, until golden brown. When cold the bars can be covered with chocolate or melted carob.

## *Peppermint oaties*

100g (4oz) margarine
85g (3oz) sugar
85g (3oz) oats
1 small egg yolk
200g (7oz) self raising wholemeal flour
3 tablespoons finely chopped peppermint leaf infused in 3 tablespoons of boiling water.
Cream the margarine and sugar. Add the egg yolk and strained peppermint infusion (which should have stood for 5-10 minutes). Stir in the flour and oats. Form into small squares or rounds, about 1cm ($\frac{1}{2}$ in) thick. Bake on a greased baking tray for about 10-12 minutes at 170°C (325°F). When cool coat on one side with chocolate if liked.
*Note:* - The strength of peppermint flavour varies with the climate and maturity of the plant. Extra flavouring may be needed early in the year. Add 1 drop of essential oil of peppermint together with the infusion.

## *Rose biscuits*

100g (4oz) margarine
85g (3oz) rose-sugar
170g (6oz) self raising flour
2 teaspoons rose-water
1 small egg yolk
a few chopped almonds or hazelnuts
Optional: 1 drop essential oil of rose geranium
Cream the margarine and sugar. Add the egg yolk and rose-water with a little of the flour. If using, carefully add just 1 drop of essential oil to the mix and beat well. Steadily add the remainder of the flour last. Form the biscuit dough into a roll and cut into slices about 1.2cm ($\frac{1}{2}$-$\frac{3}{4}$ in) thick. Coat the biscuits with chopped nuts if liked, and bake on a greased baking tray at 170°C (325°F) for about 10 minutes.

## *Lemon loaf*

50g (2oz) margarine
170g (6oz) caster sugar
$\frac{1}{2}$ cup milk
1 egg
5 sprigs lemon thyme
5 sprigs lemon balm
grated rind of 1 lemon
225g (8oz) self raising flour.
Heat the chopped lemon balm and lemon thyme in the milk until almost boiling. Stand to cool. Cream the margarine and sugar until light and fluffy. Add the grated lemon rind and beaten egg, together with a tablespoon of the flour. Fold in the remaining flour alternately with the strained milk. Bake in a greased and lined loaf tin at 180°C (350°F) for about 50 minutes.

When cool, glaze with a little icing sugar mixed with lemon juice.

### Caraway Madeira

100g (4oz) margarine
100g (4oz) sugar
2 eggs
1 teaspoon grated lemon rind
milk to mix
225g (8oz) self raising flour
1 dessertspoon of caraway seeds and a few for decoration.

Cream the margarine and sugar. Beat the eggs and add with a little of the sieved flour. Add the remainder of the flour gradually with milk to mix and the grated lemon rind. Stir in the caraway seeds last. Spoon into a 22cm (9in) round cake tin, greased and lined. Sprinkle with a little sugar and a few caraway seeds before putting it into the oven. Bake at 170°C (325°F) for about an hour. The oven may need turning down after 40 minutes.

### Minted fruit slice

225g (8oz) dried fruit, (including 50g (2oz) chopped dried apricots)
6 tablespoons apple juice
170g (6oz) shortcrust pastry
5 good sprigs mint
a little milk
sugar

Simmer the dried fruit in the apple juice in an enamel pan for about 10 minutes, with the chopped mint. By this time the fruit should have absorbed the juice and mint flavour. Roll out the pastry, dividing it into two. Lay one half on a baking tray and spread with the minted fruit. Cover with the second layer of pastry. Brush the top with milk and sprinkle with a little sugar. Bake at 190°C (375°F) for 10-15 minutes. Cut into slices while still warm.

### Peppermint and chocolate chip buns

85g (3oz) margarine
85g (3oz) sugar
2 tablespoons fresh peppermint
2½ tablespoons boiling water
25g (1oz) plain chocolate
100g (4oz) self raising flour
1 egg

Chop the peppermint leaves finely and add the boiling water. Leave in a covered cup to infuse for 10 minutes. Cream the margarine and sugar until light and fluffy. Add the egg with a little of the flour and mix. Strain the peppermint infusion into the mix gradually, pressing the leaves dry and adding the remainder of the flour at the same time. Lastly, stir in the flaked or grated chocolate. Spoon into bun tins and bake at 180°C (350°F) for about 15 minutes. (Makes approximately 12).

*Note:* The strength of peppermint flavour increases according to the climate towards midsummer. Extra flavour may be necessary earlier in the year. 1-2 drops of essential oil of peppermint can be added in place of the leaf.

# Cooling summer drinks
## *Summer punch*
450ml (³/₄ pint) red grape juice
150ml (¹/₄ pint) dry ginger ale
300ml (¹/₂ pint) pineapple juice
150ml (¹/₄ pint) grapefruit juice
600ml (1 pint) lemonade, or to taste
clove pinks, borage flowers, 4 good sprigs of gingermint, 4 sprigs of lemon balm (or variegated lemon balm).
Mix the fruit juices together, add washed and bruised gingermint and lemon balm. Chill for 20 minutes. Add dry ginger ale and lemonade just before serving, removing the steeped herbs and adding a further sprig of each to decorate, with borage flowers (backs removed) and clove pink petals or small clove pink flowers with the stems and heels removed. Add ice cubes and serve.

## *Balm punch*
750ml (1¹/₄ pints) lemon balm tea made by pouring boiling water over 6 good sprigs of lemon balm
300ml (¹/₂ pint) pineapple juice
600ml (1 pint) lemonade
sweet cicely leaves, borage flowers and a sprig of lemon balm to decorate.
Make the lemon balm infusion by pouring boiling water over the washed and torn leaves and stems. Leave the infusion to go cold. Strain into a punchbowl and add the pineapple juice. Steep 3 or 4 sweet cicely leaves (torn) in the punch while chilling for 10-15 minutes. Remove these and add the lemonade just before serving. Decorate with borage flowers and a sprig of lemon balm. Serve iced.

## *Herb teas*
There is surely a herb tea which is right for every need and occasion. Whether it is taken at the end of a meal, with an afternoon slice of cake, simply to refresh, or to aid sleep, herb tea is a healthy drink.

In summer, the cooling, sweet fragrances of lemon balm, peppermint or chamomile will soothe and refresh. For those who enjoy sweet teas, sweet cicely, limeflower and fennel offer both after-dinner digestive properties and a mild, soothing action. When the rain lashes at the windows and something with a warming flavour is required, perhaps to ease summer colds, thyme, lemon thyme or nettle will be enjoyed. An occasional cup of rosemary tea will warm you right through, although this is not a remedy to take in quantity. Teas to drink at bedtime to quiet restless thoughts are bergamot, chamomile, thyme, lemon balm, or limeflower. While next morning a cup of lemon thyme, peppermint or nettle, will wake you.

When making herb teas, remember the flavour of a tea made from the fresh herb can be milder and, sometimes, quite different from that made with dried. In general twice the amount of fresh herb is used to dried. With large-leafed herbs a sprig of 4-6 leaves of young growth is right per person, although the strength of flavour of some herbs requires a different amount. Scented-leaf geraniums are powerfully flavoured and a single medium-sized leaf in the bottom of a cup will be sufficient. Rosemary is also powerful and will need to be pounded with a rolling pin before pouring on the boiling water. Lemon verbena is another which can be quite strong. One teaspoon of dried herb per person is a good general guide. Chamomile flowers can be a little difficult to measure, but again a teaspoon per cup.

Herbal tea bags are useful to carry on journeys; simply ask for a pot of hot water to infuse them. Those most commonly available from wholefood, healthfood and delicatessen shops are: chamomile, fennel, peppermint, rose hip, lemon verbena, limeflower, nettle and wild strawberry. Herbal tea blends for early morning, after dinner and bedtime are also on sale.

Of course it is more enjoyable to make up your own tea blends, once you are accustomed to the flavours. Lemon verbena or lemon thyme can be given a "softer" tone by the addition of lemon balm and a little lemon peel. Rosemary will spice rose hip, but don't add too much, or it will become dominant. Lavender flowers can be added to limeflower. Mint, again in a small quantity, can bring nettle tea to life. Once you find a blend you really enjoy then dry the ingredients so that you can mix these at your leisure and even give jars of unique herb teas to your friends.

Gift jars of herb teas should, of course, always bear the basic instructions for making the tea. Always use non-metal teapots, as metal can taint the flavour by reacting with some herbs. Warm the pot first, tearing in the washed fresh herb, or spooning in the dried, then pour on boiling water. Leave to stand for four or five minutes with most herbs. The exception is chamomile which is ready in three minutes and can be unpleasantly strong after five. Strain, preferably through a nylon strainer, and add a slice of lemon if liked, particularly with lemon teas. Do not add milk or sugar. If necessary always sweeten with honey. Bergamot tea is usually made with the leaves, but flowers can be added. Bergamot milk can be made as a night drink with 150ml (¼ pint) of boiling milk poured over ½ tablespoon of the herb. More information on individual herb teas can be found in the sections on Compassionate herbs for stress (see pages 112-114) and Medicinal herbs, (see pages 146-147). Consult note on pregnancy 161. **If using newly bought fresh herb for tea, check this is pesticide free.**

### Savoury Preserves

Once every household would have pantry shelves well stocked for winter with herb pickles, jellies and seasonings, herb cheeses and syrups which could be diluted to make drinks, taken by the spoonful for coughs, or used as flavourings for desserts. Crystallised flowers or angelica stems, and flowers pounded with sugar to form conserves, were added luxuries.

Today we can buy fruit and vegetables out of season and have tinned and frozen goods readily available, the need to prepare for a long season of plain food is no longer felt. Even so, the satisfaction and pleasure in bringing out a bottle of rose syrup, home-made mustard, or pot of savoury herb jelly when visitors come unexpectedly, or a friend is in need of a cheering present; makes the extra effort worth while. Your store cupboard can be filled gradually as herbs are harvested from early summer on into autumn. Along with the delicious jellies and vinegars, and beautifully preserved crystallised flowers, you will have captured memories of sunny days in your garden.

### Herb vinegars

Herb vinegars are the easiest preserve to make. All you need beyond the herbs of your choice is a supply of white or red wine vinegar and airtight bottles. It is fun to experiment with different herbs and blends of herbs in small bottles to find your favourites before making larger amounts. Those herbs which are most popular in vinegar are tarragon, fennel, mint, basil and garlic. Savory, marjoram, bay, thyme and rosemary offer more flavours to try. If you prefer to blend herbs, then refer back to the list of herb strengths, (see page 68) for guidance in the proportions. Powerful herbs such as rosemary or mint should be partnered with twice the amount of mild herb or herbs. Marjoram, lemon balm and parsley will all be useful as "supporting" herbs.

The leaves should be freshly picked, washed free of insects and bruised to dry between layers of kitchen paper-towels before adding to the vinegar. Pour a little of the liquid out of full bottles and then keep adding sprigs of herb until the bottle appears to be filled. The exceptions to this rule are the powerful herbs, rosemary and garlic. Four to six sprigs of rosemary will be sufficient and four or five cloves of garlic to each pint of vinegar, will create a strong flavour.

Some recipes recommend pouring warmed, but not boiling, vinegar over the herbs. As long as the weather is sunny and warm, this is not necessary. Simply set the bottles of herbs in vinegar on a sunny windowsill with their tops tightly applied. Shake the bottles each day as you pass and after two to three weeks test the vinegars for flavour and fragrance. If they are satisfactory, strain out the herbs and return the vinegar to the bottles with a single sprig of the herb as decoration. Always label herb vinegars. If you would like a stronger flavour, repeat the process with fresh herbs.

Flower and seed vinegars can also be made. For salad vinegars I like the bright red and orange nasturtium flowers which give their colour to the vinegar.
A combination of nasturtium flowers with 1 tablespoon each of basil, parsley and Greek oregano, with 4 bay leaves (torn) gives a spicy "zing" to the vinegar. Another vinegar for salads is elderflower. Remove the florets from the stalks and pack these into a pottery or dark glass jar until it is full. Slowly pour over the white wine vinegar, allowing it to seep gradually into the flowers until they are saturated. Cork and leave in a warm place out of direct sunlight for five or six days before straining. Rose petals, violets, lavender and deeply shaded clove pinks will all give their colours and fragrances to vinegars which may be used in sweet as well as savoury recipes. With cider vinegar as a base these flowers make a vinegar also suitable as a cosmetic hair rinse or skin toner.

To prepare seed vinegars gather the seeds on a dry day and scald them with boiling water first, to remove any insects. Pound 1-2 tablespoons of coriander, dill, fennel or aniseed before adding them to a pint of vinegar. You may like to use a smaller quantity of caraway or lovage. Steep as for leaf vinegars and strain.

### Herb oils

Recent advice from the Ministry of Agriculture, Fisheries and Food is against making herb oils at home. This follows cases of botulism caused by oils containing herbs or vegetables. The absence of air and likely temperature during storage may encourage the spores of the bacteria responsible to grow. Commercially made oils are specially acidified for safety. This is not practical for home use.

### Herb butters

Incorporate chopped fresh herbs into creamed butter. If the herb butter is to be served with fish, a teaspoon or two of lemon juice can also be added. Again, refer to the chart of herb strengths (see page 68) to judge the correct amount of herbs. The finely chopped leaves from a single 10cm (4 in) stem of rosemary can be sufficient in 50-85g (2-3oz) butter. A dessertspoon to a tablespoon of mild herb should be added to the same quantity. Shape the herbed butter into a long roll which can be cut into neat pats later. Return to the fridge until needed. Herbs which are a delight to use include - chives, mints, parsley, chervil, tarragon, basil, marjoram, fennel, garlic, pot marigold petals, rose petals, rosemary, sage and savory.

While savoury herb butters are most used with appetizers, on vegetables about to be served, for grilling and so on, flower petal butters can also be spread in scones and used as an ingredient in cake fillings.


### *Lemon herb pepper*

Pepper can also be flavoured with herbs; the resulting aromatic blend gives seasoning a whole new meaning. It should be remembered that this recipe is more pepper than herbs, so do warn unsuspecting visitors who may expect it to be the other way around. The proportions of peppercorns to herb can of course be altered, according to your taste. Herb pepper is delicious as a seasoning for sauces, omelettes, scrambled egg, soups, stews and savouries. This pepper is designed to be especially suited to egg, cheese and fish dishes; other peppers can easily be made with herbs suited to meats.

4 teaspoons black peppercorns
4 teaspoons white peppercorns
1 teaspoon grated dried lemon rind
2¹/₂ dessertspoons each of chervil, marjoram and lemon balm.

Grind the peppercorns in a coffee grinder, or pound with a pestle in a mortar. Add the herbs and grated lemon rind and grind or pound until fine.


### *Salt substitute*

5 dessertspoons lovage
5 dessertspoons parsley
3 dessertspoons nettle
2 dessertspoons dill weed

Mix the dried herbs and grind together before storing in a dark, screw-top jar. A salt pot with large holes can be used.


### *Bouquet garni*

A bay leaf, a sprig of parsley, a sprig of thyme and a small sprig of rosemary are the most essential ingredients in a bouquet garni. You can, however, add to these to suit your taste. Lemon peel or tarragon may be enjoyed. Make small muslin sachets, either stitching the dried herbs inside or leaving drawstring tops so that small bunches of fresh herbs can be inserted and the sachet re-used.


### *Mixed herbs.*

A traditional mix - to equal parts of thyme, marjoram and savory, add a double quantity of parsley. A simple blend, this is worth the trouble to make as the flavours will be far superior to a bought version.

### Fines herbes
Another traditional herb blend used mostly in omelettes. Better fresh than dried, chervil, parsley, chives and tarragon are mixed together.

### Soup herbs
The other ingredients should influence your choice of herb seasoning. However, a good all round soup mix will always contain lovage.

2 dessertspoons lovage       1 dessertspoon parsley
1 dessertspoon thyme       $\frac{1}{2}$ dessertspoon basil
$\frac{1}{2}$ teaspoon celery salt
Grind together and store in a dark, screw top jar. Add 1 dessertspoon to $2\frac{1}{2}$ pints of soup.

### Herb mustard
25g (1oz) black mustard seeds
25g (1oz) white mustard seeds
$\frac{1}{2}$ teaspoon celery salt
$\frac{1}{4}$ heaped teaspoon lemon herb pepper as above
2 teaspoons dill seed
approximately 7 teaspoons fennel vinegar
approximately 7 teaspoons liquified thyme honey
Grind the mustard seeds and dill seeds together, leaving some in largish pieces rather than as a fine powder. Season with celery salt and herb pepper. Keep adding the vinegar and honey alternately until a smooth consistency is reached. (Sufficient to fill a good sized mustard jar). Use to flavour fish.

### Herb mustard 2
25g (1oz) black mustard seeds
25g (1oz) white mustard seeds
$\frac{1}{2}$ teaspoon celery salt
$\frac{1}{4}$ teaspoon herb pepper made as above with parsley, tarragon and basil
2 teaspoons coriander seed
approximately 7 teaspoons tarragon or basil vinegar
approximately 7 teaspoons liquified honey
Grind the mustard seeds with the coriander seeds and make up as above. Use with meat.

## Sweet Preserves
### Crystallised angelica
For several years I tried recipes for crystallised angelica that seemed to involve a lot of effort over a number of days with mediocre results. Then I found a recipe over a hundred years old which, with a few adjustments, produced excellent results every time.

    The best stems to harvest are those about the thickness of your little finger. These may be leaf or flower stems and can be gathered from early summer onwards. Cut the stems into short lengths, no longer than your little finger and simmer them with a little water in an enamel pan. Once they are sufficiently tender to allow a fork through them, drain the stems and peel away the paper thin film of skin around each stem. This is time-consuming but crucial to the success of the recipe. Return the peeled angelica to the pan and bring back to the boil, simmering for five minutes. Dry on paper-towels.

Weigh the dried stems and set these in layers with an equal weight of white sugar, in a covered casserole dish. Leave this in a cool place for 2 days. By this time the sugar will have dissolved into a syrup around the stems. Return the syrup and angelica to the pan and bring to the boil. Simmer for 5 minutes. Drain and cool. Sift more sugar over the stems and dry on a dish in an open oven with the temperature no higher than 50°C (120°F). While still supple, but outwardly crisp, store between layers of greaseproof paper in jars or rigid, airtight containers, in the dark.

## Crystallised flowers

Flowers can easily be candied by dipping them in beaten egg-white and sugar. If you wish to keep your harvest for several months through the winter, however, I would recommend using gum arabic and rose water.

The rose water should be clear and is available from foodstores. Always use fresh rose water in uncooked recipes. Gum arabic bought from pharmacies is of high quality and expensive. A cheaper, more suitable form is available from stores selling cake-icing accessories.

Pour one tablespoon of rose water into a small bottle with a wide neck and add one teaspoon of powdered gum arabic. Replace the top firmly before shaking the bottle for a minute or two to dissolve the gum arabic. Always add the powder to the liquid or it will not dissolve fully.

Each flower, which of course should be edible, is best treated as soon as possible after picking. Gather the flowers in late morning choosing those which are newly opened, and in perfect condition. Dip first in clear water to remove any insects and dry gently on paper kitchen towel. Cut away stems and green parts, also the white heels of rose and clove pink petals. Immerse the flowers completely in the gum arabic solution by dropping them into the bottle. A fine clean paint-brush or a spoon handle can be gently used to retrieve them one at a time and set them down on a layer of fine white sugar. Sprinkle more sugar over the flowers to coat them, gently removing any soggy lumps in the heart of the flowers. Place on a layer of greaseproof paper on a cake rack to dry in a cool oven with the door ajar. When they are hard to touch, store them in layers between greaseproof paper in jars or rigid containers.

Flowers to crystallise:- borage, heartsease, violets, primroses, English cowslips, small pansies and rose, clove pink, and pot marigold petals. Small leaves of spearmint, pineapplemint, gingermint and green peppermint can be prepared in the same way. Black peppermint tends to be very strong if tasted, rather than left merely for decoration!

## Herb sugars.

These can be a very attractive, as well as a fragrant and delicious addition to cakes, butter icings or home made ice-cream. Herb sugars can also be sprinkled effectively over cakes and desserts as decoration.

Deeply coloured clove pinks, dark red petals of *Damascena* and *Gallica* roses, pot marigold petals and dried lavender flowers will all give colourings, although the lavender is pale. Other herbs, such as rosemary, lemon thyme or scented geranium leaves can be added in much smaller proportions and treated rather differently.

For coloured flower sugars add half to one and a half times the amount of herb to sugar. With the exception of lavender, fresh herb petals should be used, with the white heels removed from the clove pinks and roses. All green parts of the flowers are removed also. The fresh, washed and dried petals are either pounded with the sugar in a mortar or placed in an electric grinder for a few seconds to achieve a finer result. Home-dried lavender is best processed in a grinder. Spread the coloured sugar on foil and set it in a warm oven with the door ajar. (The temperature should not be above 50°C (120°F). Store in dark glass screw top jars until needed.

Flavoured sugars can be obtained by adding one or two sprigs of rosemary or lemon thyme, or one or two scented geranium leaves to a 45kg (1lb) jar. Wash, dry thoroughly and tear or pound the herbs before adding. Leave sealed for several days before use.

## Herb honey

Honey has been heated with herbs for medicinal purposes for hundreds of years. Whether you wish to add herbs such as thyme, horehound or sage to relieve coughs and sore throats, or rose petals for a delicious tonic, the method is simple. Pour the honey into a thick bottomed pan and heat gently. Stir in the washed and bruised herb and continue to simmer for 20 to 30 minutes. Do not allow to boil. The amount of herb varies according to its strength. Rosemary, sage or horehound should be added cautiously until you have experienced the flavour. Begin with only three small sprigs, adding up to 2 tablespoons of chopped green herb. With rose petals you can be more generous, adding as much as three quarters of a cupful to 0.45kg (1lb) of honey.

Pour the warmed honey into a casserole dish and leave covered in a cool place for four to five days. Re-heat, being careful once more not to boil the honey. Simmer for 20 minutes and then return to the original, sterilized jar. Rose honey can also be made by adding rose water to heated honey. This is quite common in early recipes. About 300 ml ($^{1}/_{2}$ pint) of rose water could be added to 0.45kg (1lb) of honey. Some liquid pectin or lemon juice will then be needed for extra thickening. A third method is simply to layer honey and *Gallica* rose petals in an earthenware casserole. Always begin and end with a layer of honey. Stand the covered casserole dish on a sunny windowsill for a week, turning it round occasionally. Strain out the petals and return the honey to clean jars.

## Herb syrups

Several methods of making herb syrups appear in old recipe books. Generally, either a syrup of boiling water and sugar was made and then poured over the petals which were later strained from the mixture, or the herb might be boiled in water first and the sugar added to this later. With delicate flower petals such as violets, cowslips, roses, borage, lavender and clove pinks, pour boiling water over the petals and stand overnight before straining and heating to dissolve in the sugar. Rose petal syrup, was sometimes made by adding 0.45kg (1lb) of fine sugar to each 300ml ($^{1}/_{2}$ pint) of rose water. With the sugar dissolved, the juice of half a lemon was added before bottling.

Clove pink or gillyflower syrup can be made as follows. Take 35g (1oz) of petals and remove the white heels from the base of the flowers along with the green parts. Put the flowers into a pan and pour over 425ml (15floz) of boiling water.

Leave to stand for 25 minutes. Add 150ml (5floz) of rose water and simmer gently for 10 minutes. Leave to steep overnight. Strain and heat gently, adding 275g (10oz) of sugar. Pour into sterilized bottles. Refrigerate once opened.

The most popular syrups have always been rose, rosehip, nettle, elderflower, elderberry and pink or carnation. To these could be added angelica, lavender, cowslip and sweet cicely. Rose, rosehip, nettle and elderberry were often taken medicinally as well as used for flavourings. They can equally well be diluted as drinks and used in other ways.

Syrups make delicious bases for fruit salads. They may be poured over vanilla ice cream or thickened as sauces. Simply diluted with water or lemonade, they make refreshing drinks. If they are to keep for any length of time, however, the yeasts present in the herbs must be killed. This can be done either by lowering their temperature drastically, or by heating. Once the syrup has gone cold it can be poured into small rigid containers and placed in the freezer. Always leave space for the liquid to expand beneath the lid. Syrups do not freeze completely, but will keep perfectly in this semi-solid condition. To sterilize bottled syrups, first set the tops or corks in boiling water for 15 minutes. Do not fill the bottles beyond the base of the necks and place the sterilized tops on the bottles. These are then stood on a metal tray inside a large preserving pan and water is poured in up to a little above the level of the syrup. Once bubbling, it should come to the base of the tops. Bring slowly to simmering and simmer for 20 minutes. Remove the bottles to cool. Always refrigerate opened bottles as you use them. Alternatively if almost empty spirit bottles which have not been washed out are re-used for storing syrups, the effect of the alcohol residue will mean the syrups keep perfectly well in a cool cupboard until opened.

## *Elderflower and lemon balm syrup*
25 heads of elderflowers in perfect condition
leaves stripped from 6 young sprigs of lemon balm
550g (1¼lb) granulated sugar
1.2 litres (2 pints) water.
Gather sweet smelling elderflowers on a dry day. Remove the florets from their stalks and place, with the washed lemon balm leaves in an enamel pan of cold water. Simmer gently for 40 minutes, adding water as necessary to maintain the quantity. Strain, pulping the flower heads to release all the liquid. Return to the cleaned pan, adding the granulated sugar to the slightly reduced quantity of herb infusion. Heat gently as the sugar dissolves and simmer for 10 minutes. Cool and freeze or bottle.

## *Herb jellies*
Herb jellies are a great favourite, with mint perhaps as the most well-known. Often these are made by cooking apples to pulp and straining the resulting liquid through a jelly bag overnight, to use as a base. The recipes below show a different method, with fruit juices and a herb infusion giving the flavour, while sugar and liquid pectin provide the setting qualities. All manner of interesting and new combinations can be made. I have given two examples, one sweet and the other tangy. With these as starting points, other recipes can easily be worked out, keeping the proportions of herb infusion, fruit juice or juices and sugar.

## *Rose Petal Jelly*
This is one of two methods given in Herb Sufficient, this one can be made in winter and requires fewer roses. The combination of rose water and heavily fragranced rose sugar makes this a favourite, but you may feel the absence of petals leaves the need for a drop of food colouring.

425ml (15floz) rose water | Juice of half a lemon
100ml (4floz) liquid pectin | 225g (8oz) rose sugar
675g (24oz) granulated sugar | few drops of red food colouring

Pour the rose water into an enamel or preserving pan. Add lemon juice. If the rose sugar is in quite large granules, grind this first. Add both sugars slowly over a low heat, stirring well. Once the sugar has dissolved bring to the boil and stir in the liquid pectin. Boil rapidly for 2 minutes. Remove from the heat and skim if necessary. Add a few drops of food colouring to bring the pink jelly to a deep red if liked. It is safer to drip the colouring onto a spoon first to avoid adding too much. Prepare 4 jars and pour the cooled jelly into the warm jars. Seal and label.

### *Lemon thyme and grapefruit jelly*
3 cups sugar
$^{1}/_{2}$ cup herb infusion
1 cup grapefruit juice
100ml (4 fl oz) liquid pectin.

Pick a good handful of lemon thyme. Strip most of the leaves from the stems to use, leaving only the tops which are covered in leaves, when measuring. You will need 4 tablespoons of fresh herb. Put the herb into an enamel pan and pour over 1 cup of boiling water. Simmer this over a gentle heat for about 10 minutes, until the liquid is reduced by half. Meanwhile, put the sugar and grapefruit juice into a large preserving pan and then add the herb infusion. Bring this slowly to the boil, making sure the sugar is dissolved, before turning up the heat. Once it is boiling, add the liquid pectin and stir well. Bring back to the boil and boil rapidly for 2 minutes. Skim if necessary. Pour into sterilized jars while still warm. Seal as for jam.

This is a tangy jelly, quite delicious!

## Compassionate Herbs for Stress

**A** personal retreat from the world where we can unwind amongst the gentle and refreshing fragrances of the herb garden, is a sanctuary many have longed for, and the fortunate have achieved.

Precious time spent breathing in the rich perfume and soft glow of evening primroses in the moonlight of a summer garden, will soothe the tired mind in readiness for sleep. Relax and gather sprigs of lemon thyme, lemon balm or bergamot as you return to the house for a mildly tranquillizing nightcap.

The fresh harvest from such a garden offers herbs to enrich healthy salads with anti-stress vitamins and minerals. Dried, the fragrant herbs can be blended into a pot-pourri filled with the peace of a lazy summer's afternoon, to transport your thoughts to serenity in the dark winter days. While herb pillows may help to ease your weary body at night, restful bath sachets of home-gathered and dried herbs can calm you to cope with the stress of the day.

Too much stress is felt by everyone at times. We can all lighten our load by helping our body through diet, healthy sleep patterns, soothing fragrances which act on mind and body, and spending time in our own garden of serenity.

## Thoughts on Stress

**A** LTHOUGH stress is felt to a varying degree by everyone, it remains very much a personal problem. Someone once defined stress as the difference between one's expectations of life and what, in reality, happens. A simple change in our expectations of ourselves, in how much work we actually need to pack into a day, for instance, can be constructive or destructive. Our expectations of others, in their behaviour towards us, is even more complex.

We all know that the death of a close relative or friend, a divorce or separation, having a baby, losing or changing work, and moving house are major sources of stress in our lives. Our daily level of tolerance dictates how well we cope when we feel threatened by events. It is difficult not to notice that some people seem to sail through experiences that prove extremely stressful to others. While our outlook on life in general is a key factor, other elements in our daily round may help to tip the balance.

Our bodies are subjected to many regular sources of stress. Pollution in the air, synthetics and chemicals in clothing, furnishings and cleansers, unnatural light and noise levels can all affect us.

Important factors in our diet are easier to control. Drugs such as caffeine, processed foods containing chemical additives and colourings or preservatives, are far easier to avoid than formerly. Canned fruit and vegetables with no sugar or salt are available, but it is even better to eat more fresh vegetables and fruit in salads. Herbs are natural, healthy flavourings and preservatives, offering their own content of vitamins and minerals, sweeteners and colourings. Drinking large quantities of coffee and tea actually adds to the daily stress your body has to cope with. Coffee, in particular, raises the blood pressure. Changing to herbal teas, even only at night and in the morning will help you towards a healthier life.

Poor sleep is another area where herbs can give of their best. We all know that a disturbed night's sleep makes the following day more difficult to cope with. Several such nights in a row can prove disastrous. A relaxing herbal bath, a sleep pillow, a walk in the herb garden before bed, followed by a soothing cup of herbal tea, or a few drops of essential oil on a burner in your bedroom, can all be helpful.

*Lemon verbena*

(Top right) *Oregano*

(Right) *Sweet cicely*

(Below right) *Pineapplemint*

*Bergamot*

# Herb cultivation

*Salad burnet*

(Top left) *Cowslip*

(Left) *Elder*

(Below left) *Sage*

*Scented geranium*

*Winter savory*

(Top right) *Comfrey*

(Right) *Violets*

(Below Right)
*Green santolina*

*Germander*

# Compassionate herbs for stress

*Biennial clary sage*

*Variegated lemon balm and 'sops-in-wine'.*

**(Right)** *'York and Lancaster' rose*

*Fragrant bank of Thyme, Chamomile, Pennyroyal, Mint.*

# Herbs in cookery

*Desserts, jellies, sugars, stuffed mushrooms and savoury rice.*

*(Left) Marigold sugar*

**(Below)** *Marigold 'fairy' cakes decorated with crystallized flowers.*

Of course you don't have to wait until bedtime to enjoy a cup of tranquillizing tea or the fragrance of a lavender based pot-pourri. Working in a herb garden is one of the most relaxing occupations I know. I hardly think of it as work, for as I weed or clip low hedges of aromatic herbs, I find myself brushing against them and releasing delicious perfumes. A herb garden is surely the very best place to unwind quietly, away from the pressures of the day.

Even in the depth of winter, the dried herbs, gathered and blended for sachets, pillows or sweet tussie mussies, can fill your imagination with the soothing aura of your own special garden 'retreat'

## The serenity garden

**A** serenity, or meditation garden should be planned so that it is graced with charm and interest in every season, for we cannot always predict when we will need this retreat most. In warmer climates, a sunny afternoon in winter should find the garden enlivened by flowers and variegated foliage. There is nothing less cheering than a sad plot of bare earth with a few scrubby plants clinging to life, apparently against all odds.

Winter pansies will bring colour, and - in the language of flowers - loving thoughts to your serenity garden. They will keep on blooming for months, beginning as the winter honeysuckle comes into flower at Christmas or soon after, and continuing until the snowdrops, crocus, primroses, violets and rosemary are bursting with vibrant life. Violets, lungwort and primroses cluster at the edges of the path, while the fragrance of winter honeysuckle invites you to linger a little on the seat whether the sun is warm or not. The honeysuckle continues flowering for several months, by which time the rosemary bushes are heavy with their delicate blue-lavender flowers, drawing the first bees.

The miniature yellow tulips confirm spring in my closed knot like golden stars, almost flat to the ground. They pick out a bright pattern between the low hedges of dark germander and silver cotton lavender. Before the tulips are gone, the cowslips within the knot and in the outer borders, are nodding their yellow bells of flowers in the breeze.

On into early summer the thymes are showing the promise of a mass of flowers. The golden and silver thymes flower first, with the common thyme, to be followed a little later by the lemon thymes, kept tumbling with the sheer enthusiasm of the bees. Orange and yellows predominate in the summer serenity garden with tall evening primroses and the lower pot marigolds spreading in profusion wherever I allow them. Here and there splashes of blue borage, mauve, yellow and cream heartsease and the deep pink of oregano, add new notes to the rhapsody.

As the weeks pass, purple and red bergamot and yellow St John's wort catch the eye while still the evening primroses tower above.

All through the year as some herbs die down others take their places. The sunflowers catch the glory of autumn sunlight and the holly hedge appearing as herbs are cut down, reminds us of the joys of Christmas ahead; the closed knot with its symbolic lover's knot pattern, remains. Clipped neatly, with a succession of flowers from tulips, cowslips, thymes and fragrant pinks, it symbolises the eternal triumph of love over evil.

The contrast of the careful order against the abundance of flowers and forms in the outer beds reminds us of the central heart of peace and quietness in each one of us. The bay tree at the centre has always been appreciated as a protective tree, keeping lightning, witches and other evils away. It was once believed a bay tree predicted misfortune by dying. A healthy tree can be seen as a reassurance that all will be well, however dark the way ahead may appear.

## Chamomile

Our ancestors enjoyed whole paths and lawns of chamomile so that a walk in the garden gave them the sweet, heady scent of the herb as it was trodden underfoot. Chamomile lawns, and chamomile seats graced herb gardens, providing soothing, health-giving retreats from living conditions which were often polluted with less desirable odours. The fragrance of chamomile was recommended for patients suffering from consumption and they were advised to spend time each day breathing in the cleansing scent. The herb has soothing, anti-allergenic properties which also ease histamine-induced reactions such as hay fever and allergic asthma.

Even if you do not have the space for a chamomile lawn of any size, a small patch, perhaps close to the seat in your garden of serenity will give you the opportunity to set foot on the feathery green covering and enjoy the perfume. There is no harvest of lawn chamomile as such, although it does need trimming several times in the year. The true harvest comes from walking on it, which also helps the herb to grow healthily. The cultivar *treneague* is the best for making lawns, (see Planning a herb garden, page 17).

A further use for small patches of chamomile lawn is to provide stepping places in a wide bed or closed knot, to enable you to reach herbs easily. However this should be amongst low-growing herbs as chamomile needs sunlight.

## Evening primrose

One of the best known applications of evening primrose oil is in treating pre-menstrual tension. The oil cannot be prepared at home however, and so the best contribution the herb can make to your serenity is in the garden. Its rich, delicious perfume can fill the air as dusk draws on into the night.

Walking in the garden at the end of a long, tiring day and sitting out on a warm night quietly thinking, surrounded by these tall "guardian angels" brings an inner peace. Surely this is the perfect preparation for a restful night's sleep. The flowers, which can appear limp during the heat of the day, rather like a balloon which has lost its air, fill out at dusk. By moonlight they seem almost to be glowing lanterns, hanging alongside the stems.

This soft, phosphorescent effect is best appreciated if they are planted in a semi-circle, partially enclosing a seat. Resting amongst them you can bask in the idyllic perfume which brings to mind a blend of roses and beautiful, heady, old-fashioned pinks.

As week follows week through the summer, the evening primroses will continue to flower from early June through until September. Only those who never venture into their gardens at night could fail to find them compassionate companions during this time. What better way of tempting anyone to sit quietly in the darkness, looking up at the stars, or around the moonlit garden, than to grow evening primroses.

## Scented geraniums

A pot of rose — or lemon scented geraniums makes a perfect present to anyone who is ill and confined to the house, or to a friend passing through a stressful time in their lives. I would hate to be without my winter windowsills lined with these pretty and fragrant plants through the dark and gloomy days of bad weather.

The leaves can be saved as they fall from the plant to include in fragrant and soothing pot-pourri or pillows. Even when they have turned brown they will have lost none of their rich perfume, which is so distinctive. Set next to an open window, they also help to repel flies, reducing at least one source of annoyance and irritation in the household.

Fresh leaves can be used in cookery when they give a fragrant flavour to jellies and cakes; one which makes you want to shut your eyes in order to enjoy it to the full. A truly soothing experience. They can also add unusual, delicate flavours to summer drinks and herbal teas. The flowers are small, but make a pretty garnish.

Through the summer months, while there is no danger of frost, scented geraniums will give a profusion of new growth, released from their pots and set into beds in the serenity garden. Or they can be planted in tubs or urns and placed at either side of a seat or your house door. If the leaves are brushed as guests enter, this will give a pleasant cloud of fragrance.

## *Heartsease*

The joy of my garden, summer and winter alike, heartsease seems to flower and just go on flowering. In a mild winter their sunny faces will lighten the dullest day with a touch of "magic". Heartsease is a member of the *Violaceae* family, closely resembling both small pansies and violets.

The *Viola tricolor arvensis* has predominantly yellow and white flowers, on taller stems than cultivated small pansies and these can be intermingled with *Viola tricolor vulgaris,* which has more of a violet colouring in the flowers. Many variations will soon appear in your garden to delight you with some new discovery when you least expect it.

It is fun to create a pressed flower picture using as many differently shaded flowers as you can find. Heartsease are also perfect for pressed flower cards to share sympathy with a friend or to wish them better health. A personal message will make the card a treasured gift. Some of the common names for heartsease could well be written beneath the flowers on a card or picture. Several are just made to bring a smile to a sad friend. "Tittle-my-fancy", "Cuddle-me", "Call-me-to-you", or "Kiss-her-in-the-buttry". On a religious note, heartsease was also known as "Trinity Herb" and perhaps the most sweetly nostalgic is "Three-faces-in-a-hood".

The best known name of "heartsease" expresses the character of the herb beautifully, however. The herb has been prescribed homoeopathically for a weak heart and for skin complaints. In herbal medicine is still given for skin problems of a nervous origin, such as eczema.

I feel sure as a herb to turn thoughts to happy times, it will be valued as much in the future as it has been in the past.

## *Pinks*

So many pretty, old-fashioned pinks are well suited to a serenity garden, whether the area is large or small. There are low growing varieties to edge paths, add silver foliage and delicate flowers between the hedges of a closed knot, or fill tubs, pots and troughs within a formal setting. Slightly taller pinks are happy to "tumble" down banks of earth amongst rocks and low shrubs, or appear as attractive islands of silver on a scented bank of thymes, chamomile, and pennyroyal.

Their fragrances vary from the heady, spicy pinks such as the Elizabethan "sops-in-wine", to the rich yet subtle "salmon flake" with soft, pink markings. The flowers vary even more: some are plain in colour, large and double, while others are petite with intricate patterns as complex as a butterfly's wing. The choice of pinks is a personal matter. Some you may find exciting rather than soothing, although their perfumes are relaxing to all.

In a larger bed the taller pinks and carnations will need support and could be placed next to a low fence to good effect. "Dad's favourite" is guaranteed to delight all who see it and flowers over quite a long period in midsummer with maroon edged petals to white flowers.

Clove pinks were once commonly eaten sprinkled on salads, made into conserves or floated in wine cups to raise the spirits. These charming flowers are now being revived as ingredients in summer dishes and can be grown from seed. They will add romance to even the simplest fruit salad or party drink. It is these little touches which can raise the quality of life, bringing a quiet satisfaction and contentment.

## Rose

The very presence of the heady perfume of roses is soothing, turning our thoughts towards pleasure rather than pain. The Roman idea of lying on a literal "bed of roses" with thick layers of rose petals on their couches must have been bliss indeed.

To gain the most from fragrant climbing roses, train them up the house wall to frame a bedroom or sitting room window. If you have a quiet seat in the garden where an arch can be set above it, then a beautiful rose arbour can be made. This is the perfect place to sit quietly meditating. The heavily perfumed damask roses can give lasting fragrance.

"Madame Hardy" is an old, double white rose to be recommended, along with "Belle amour", an Alba-damask hybrid, with coral pink flowers and a spicy perfume. "Maidens blush" is a pretty, pink, fragrant rose which grows alongside the covered way in my "Elizabethan" garden. It dates back to the 15th century. *Gallica officinalis,* the red, "apothecary's rose" is there too, while the prolific white, *Rosa alba* covers the arbour of the chamomile seat. *Rosa mundi* adds a glory of striped roses, deep cerise and white, and the "York and Lancaster", *Damascena versicolor* bears large pale pink and white roses which frame the entrance of the covered way. The *Albertine,* my father's favourite rose, is a mass of fragrant blooms in summer, gracing the astrology garden.

All of these give rosebuds and petals for soothing fragrant mixtures. The apothecary's rose or a heavily scented red damask are the best for cookery. Rose conserves of the petals pounded with sugar, or in a jelly or honey, have all been eaten in the past to soothe jagged nerves and revive patients during a long convalescence. Rose vinegar, made by steeping the red petals in white wine vinegar on a sunny windowsill, (see Recipes page 96) can relieve throbbing headaches caused by being too long in the hot sun. Dried rose petals form the base of so many delicious pot-pourri and sachet blends, I cannot imagine making up soothing recipes without them. Even when lavender is the dominant fragrance, rose is often present as a lower note in the aromatic scale.

The rose, too, is a traditional messenger of love. What more could we wish for?

## Rosemary

This is a herb which has ever been associated with protection and remembrance. It is was once always to be found both at celebrations such as weddings, christenings and Christmas and those times when spirits are low, in sickness and bereavement. For many centuries it was the most popular herb for protection against disease or evil spirits. Many fears must have been eased by the comforting presence of rosemary as rumours of plague and other infections spread alarm. Sprays of the herb can be given as a sign of love, friendship or simply good wishes. Flowering rosemary was once considered to be the perfect bridal head dress.

Although rosemary is essentially a herb which stimulates, it too has a place in easing stress. The oil is healing for over strained muscles and is also used to treat depression and loss of memory. Rosemary oil should not however be used by anyone suffering from epilepsy.

The herb is traditionally connected with restoring memory, speech, and sensory perception after strokes. It is a herb to jolt you back from the depths of fatigue, to feel able to cope once more with the pressures of everyday life.

Rosemary tea has revived me on numerous occasions to finish a long project. The tea should also be avoided by epileptics, and anyone suffering from high blood pressure or hot flushes. It should not be taken during pregnancy.

I also include rosemary in sleep pillows where it acts with the other herbs present to clear the head and ease the mind, ready for sleep.

### St John's wort

This pretty herb, a mass of golden stars when in flower, is a pleasure to grow. Its habit of spreading with a forest of tiny seedlings, need be no problem, so long as the many flowers are harvested to make a soothing medicinal oil you will treasure. For details of the oil, see Medicinal (page 142). This is a most effective burn treatment. Recent warnings about taking St. John's wort herb internally alongside other medication do not apply to use of the oil.

St John's wort also has a medicinal use as a tranquillizer, which gives it a well-earned place in the serenity garden. The herb is taken regularly as a tea over a period of several weeks, for anxiety and depression. However it should not be administered in this way without medical supervision. If you are already taking St. John's wort in addition to drugs, do not stop taking the St. John's wort without consulting your doctor first. The strength of the treatment he or she is prescribing may have to be changed at the same time (see also Medicinal page 155).

For this reason its main value towards serenity is as part of your garden and in the use of the oil which is also valuable in healing nerve injuries. The rich folklore which has grown up about this herb also reminds us of its protective role against evil spirits. As we find so often, this indicates both a herb with powerful properties and one which can be put to good use by a herbalist.

## Eating for serenity

THOSE minerals which have a particularly helpful effect on your nervous system are potassium, calcium and magnesium. Nettle contains all three, together with iron. Although nettle is obviously not suitable as a salad herb, don't forget you can sprinkle dried nettle as a seasoning for almost any dish.

Dill offers potassium and calcium. It has the added bonus of helping you to digest salad vegetables which may be a problem to some people, particularly cucumber and radish. A little fresh dill chopped onto salad or into sandwiches will also sweeten your breath. A sprinkling of pot marigold petals is a colourful, attractive garnish. In previous centuries, chopped flower petals and whole flowers enlivened salads rich in many ingredients. It is time we returned to such luxury! Borage flowers are also decorative, offering a precious tiny dose of courage to face life with a smile. Although the young leaves have a high content of potassium and calcium, they are no longer recommended as a salad herb. A few now and then may be safe, but the alkaloids present could be harmful in larger doses. Applemint and spearmint, together with lemon balm leaves, salad rocket and purslane, can also be chopped into a salad in small quantities. The flavour of mints can easily be overpowering and so use with discretion. Mints are however, perfect with a potato salad.

Sunflowers need a fine autumn for the seeds to ripen, but they can be a successful crop in fields and gardens. Do buy sunflower seeds if you are not already growing them for fun, and sprinkle them onto your salads or nibble as a toasted snack. Toasting brings out the nutty flavour which makes them irresistible. They are rich in calcium, magnesium and potassium, iron, zinc and B vitamins.

Garlic is a must in any healthy diet. It should be eaten regularly to help in preventing stress diseases such as heart problems and hardening of the arteries, to say nothing of its other many virtues.

Read the backgrounds of each herb in easing stress and refer to Herbs in Cookery (see pages 84-103) for recipes. You'll enjoy them!

## *Borage*

An old Greek proverb, "I, borage, bring always courage", is an early reference to the cheering properties of this attractive, popular herb. The Romans believed it could make men joyful and added it to their wine cups. In later times knights setting out for the Crusades might be given a parting stirrup cup with borage flowers floating in the liquor to give them courage for their journey and all it might entail. Competitors in tournaments and jousts drank the tea to raise their spirits and make them fearless. It was once thought you could watch your entire family murdered without regret while under the influence of a strong dose of borage brew.

Gerard wrote, "The leaves and floures of Borrage put into wine make men and women glad and merry, driving away all sadnesse, dulnesse, and melancholy...". A conserve was made of the flowers in the form of a cordial and the leaves were chopped into salads to bring joy to those eating together. Flowers are a good addition to cold drinks. The beautiful star-like flowers will add grace and colour to your garden of serenity and the bees will adore it!

## *Dill*

The name dill may come from the Norse word, "dilla" which means to "lull". Dill water, also known as gripe water, has lulled many thousands of babies to sleep over the past 5,000 years. Part of the soothing quality of the herb is in its digestive property. It settles the stomach and so eases fretful babies into sleep.

It can be just as valuable for the many adults who suffer from indigestion, whether nervous or otherwise. The tea can be taken after meals, or the herb, known as dill weed, included in recipes. Tea from the bruised seed has a greater sedative effect and is a tranquillizer.

The seed heads should be cut before the seeds are fully ripe to be sure none are lost. Hang them upside-down over a clean sheet of material or paper and allow the seeds to fall as they are ready. This should be done in a quiet, clean corner of the house where they will not become damp or be blown away by sudden draughts. The dried seeds should be chewed a few at a time to quiet indigestion or a nervous stomach.

## *Garlic*

The pungent odour of garlic has proved a problem to some people. However the healthy properties of the herb should not be ignored. Garlic is a powerful medicinal plant which also enhances other flavours in cooking. Sharing the herb in food is certainly the most considerate way of taking it.

Garlic relaxes the blood vessels, helping to regulate any build-up of cholesterol. It is used to treat hypertension and arteriosclerosis and so forms an essential part of the

21st century herbal armoury against stress. You do not need to eat huge amounts of garlic to enjoy the relaxing effect. As with most herbs, a regular intake is better than a large dose every so often.

Perhaps it was an early belief in the efficacy of garlic against witches and evil which led to its being used to calm horses with nightmares. In the 17th century, Gervase Markham gave a compound of garlic, aniseed and liquorice to horses with this problem. I can find no records of garlic being administered for human nightmares, but, in the Anglo-Saxon Leechbooks there is the instruction to bind garlic with betony, lupins and incense onto a fawn's skin which was then laid on the sufferer for the problem.

## *Marigold*

The fresh or dried flowers were once commonly added to soups and drinks to comfort the spirits and the heart. Another way of administering marigolds was in a "Conserve made of the floures and sugar taken in the morning fasting". This, wrote Gerard, "cureth the trembling of the heart".

Gone are the days, however, when it was believed that eating marigold flowers would enable you to see fairies! The strengthening effect of marigolds on the heart and arteries was so common a belief that Arabs were said to feed their swift horses on the petals, so that they could be sure of winning races. For human consumption the petals of two flowers can safely be eaten each day as long as they are pot marigolds and not French or African!

A recipe from 1565 adds a touch of magic to the scene; if marigold "be gathered.....wrapped in the leafe of a Laurell, or baye tree, and a wolves tothe be added thereto, no man shall be able to have a word to speake agaynst the bearer thereof, but woordes of peace". A simple way of gaining tranquillity? Hardly, if you had to obtain a tooth from a wolf first! Perhaps there was a ready sale for such things at that time.

In the 21st century it may be more practical to enjoy the flowers in your garden and your diet, and utter words of peace yourself.

## *Mint*

Mint is so popular that it is even to be found in gardens where no other herbs are grown. Few people can resist savouring the smell of minted potatoes as they are cooking. The bruised leaves also give a wonderfully soothing fragrance as you pick the stems. This scent was once put to far greater use. In bygone ages watermint was strewn on the floors so that in walking about the house, the occupants were constantly breathing in that refreshing perfume which encouraged them to breathe deeply and feel contented.

The practice of strewing floors with mint certainly goes back to biblical times when temple floors were scented with the herb and tithes of mint were paid. In ancient Greece the effects were believed to be so powerful that an edict was made forbidding soldiers to include mint in their rations in times of war, as, "it did so much to incite venery, that it took away or at least abated their animosity or courage to fight".

In peacetime, centuries later, Gerard wrote that the fragrance, "rejoyceth the heart of man". Mint has properties quite apart from those appreciated in its perfume. Mint tea can act as a mild sedative and is particularly helpful to digestive problems in this role. Gain most from your soothing drink by enjoying the refreshing fragrance as you wait for it to cool. Alternate peppermint with other herb teas as it is powerful in action.

Harvest your mint for drying just before flowering as it will have the most essential oil at this point. If you have the space for a variety of mints then you can plan an area for them with the attraction of variegated leaves or golden colours amongst the green. They each have their individual scents to delight you. The most relaxing, heady scent is from eau-de-cologne mint which is perfect to grow alongside or even beneath a garden seat.

## *Sunflower*

It is fun to grow a few sunflowers to enjoy, whether you harvest the seeds, or find removing them from the hulls too much of a chore. If you do, you will have some fascinating birdwatching in store as the finches come to feast on the seedheads. The rapid growth of these remarkable plants never seems to fail in delighting children and at the end of the summer when other herbs are beginning to fade, you will have the full glory of the sunflowers to brighten the scene.

After the golden flowers, - which I have yet to catch following the sun across the sky, - will come the nutritious seeds. These contain the minerals so valued in combating stress. With a high proportion of calcium and some magnesium and zinc, sunflower seeds provide a tasty snack which is good for you. If you are struggling with the problem of giving up nibbling at junk food between meals, then toasted sunflower seeds are tempting enough to cure you of the habit. One word of warning however; they can be so deliciously addictive that you still put on weight through eating so many!

Sunflower seeds are tasty alone, but can also be sprinkled over salads and included in biscuits and cakes. (see Sunny apricot bars, page 92).

## Herb teas for inner quiet

THE full section on herb teas that follows will give you an idea of the great variety available from the herb garden. There are, of course, even more herbal teas and whole books have been written about them. **Always remember that taking three cups of herbal tea a day on a regular basis constitutes a medicinal dose. You should therefore expect to experience the medicinal effects of each particular herb. Do not take herbal teas in this way if already taking drugs for the problem.**

So far as calming, anti-stress herbs are concerned, lemon balm has a familiar, comforting lemon fragrance and flavour. It is just the herb to dispel the myth that herb teas are woody, or, as so many people seem to think, "an acquired taste". Thyme tea made from the fresh herb or dried flowering thyme, is another good flavour for "beginners". Very few people dislike it.

Chamomile has a stronger taste, which you either really love, or cannot bear. Try it quite weak at first. Leaving it to brew for too long can spoil chamomile. Mint teas tend to have a strong flavour, but with a very attractive, refreshing aroma which tempts the wariest of potential converts to try them. If you like peppermints, then you will love peppermint tea. Again, don't leave it to stand for more than a couple of minutes.

All the instructions for making herb teas are in the following pages. Bergamot milk is to be found in the details on the herbs which follow with other soothing tea herbs. Limeflower, otherwise known as linden tea is more usually bought, either by weight of dried herb, or as teabags. Limeflower has a delicious, honeyed flavour and may be used to sweeten another medicinal herb such as horsetail or nettle. Do not take limeflower tea if suffering from hot flushes, as it dilates the bloodvessels.

When making herb teas always remember to use a teapot of china, earthenware or glass. Never make herb tea in a metal teapot as this will ruin the flavour. I keep a separate teapot for herb teas only and a tea strainer with it, untainted by Indian or China tea. Warm the pot as usual and, unless otherwise stated in the recipe, add one teaspoon of dried herb per cup. Fresh herbs are more difficult to judge as the leaves vary so much in size; generally one or two sprigs will be sufficient for two cups. Wash the herbs briefly under the cold tap before chopping or tearing into the pot to release the flavour.

As you pour your first cup of herbal tea don't be disappointed by the lack of colour in the liquid. It doesn't have to be strongly coloured to have flavour and perfume. Appreciate these and you will gain contentment - for a time! See individual herb teas below, in the tea section in cookery (see page 95) and in Medicinal (see page 146) for more detail.

## Bergamot

This elegant herb will certainly add to the beauty of your serenity garden, both with its striking flowers on majestic stems and its soothing fragrance. The spectacular nature of the flowerheads is sure to gain attention from guests who will enjoy the red, purple, lavender or white blooms. Their fragrance is a sweet, fruity, orange or lemon scent.

The calming, sleep-inducing tea is made by infusing the fresh or dried leaves from the scarlet flowering bergamot. Both leaves and flowers can be added to pot-pourri or sleep pillows to set the mood for relaxation and restful sleep.

Bergamot tea has been known as Oswego tea. It was named after the Oswego Indians who lived on the shores of Lake Ontario and gathered wild bergamot. More recently it became popular on the Continent as a helpful nightcap to still active thoughts which run on and on, keeping sleep away.

To combine the relaxing properties of bergamot with milk, pour a cup of boiling milk over a teaspoon of dried herb, or two teaspoons of chopped fresh bergamot. Leave to infuse for a few minutes, covered, then strain and drink just as you are going to bed.

## Chamomile

A relatively small patch of chamomile will yield an abundant crop of flowers which you can harvest for weeks on end. Because chamomile will seed itself and spread readily it is a very valuable herb for regular teas, with a reassuring ability to provide more, and yet more, of the flowers you need.

There is a popular picture of Victorian ladies sitting sipping cups of chamomile tea. It is a relaxing habit we would do well to bring back into fashion. Already chamomile is available in teabags and many wholefood restaurants serve it. This is the tea to turn to after a long, tiring day, when your nerves feel decidedly frayed and you are heading for depression.

The herb has a long history of use in treating headaches, restlessness, neuralgia, painful periods, insomnia and infantile convulsions. It has a low toxicity and is mild enough to give to children as a bedtime drink. With toddlers, chamomile tea can be added to their bathwater. Check first for possible allergy by testing their hands only in water with chamomile added. If there is no reaction by the next day, use in a full bath. Chamomile has a happy association with lifting the spirits of fretful and distressed babies and children in a variety of treatments.

The tea is an acquired taste, yet not as powerful as many herbs. Chamomile is famous as a soothing tea to calm the nerves. It also helps digestion and has a lesser known use as a mouthwash after dental treatment. For sore gums, hold a mouthful of the tea over the sore place for as long as is comfortable, before swallowing.

Chamomile tea can be made from the fresh or dried flowers. Fresh give a superior flavour. Use one teaspoon of flowers per cup and do not leave it to stand for more than three to four minutes or it will be very strong. Bought dried flowers should have retained some of their white colour. Chamomile tea taken regularly should be from double flowers which do not contain the alkali liable to irritate the stomach lining.

## Lemon balm

If the claims for lemon balm have a true foundation, we should all be drinking lemon balm tea daily for its rejuvenating, soothing effect. As early as the 16th century Paracelsus, the alchemist, made an "elixir of life" containing lemon balm, called *primum eus melissae,* which he sold to royalty who believed it would keep them young. Paracelsus may have decided to use the herb knowing of the belief of the ancient Greeks in its rejuvenating effects. In Britain lemon balm was also appreciated as we read that Prince Llywellyn of Glamorgan drank lemon balm tea every day and was said to have lived to be 108 years of age. John Hussey of Sydenham, who was thought to have lived to be 116 years, was also reputed to have taken lemon balm tea for 50 years.

Again and again we find lemon balm quoted as lifting melancholy, sharpening the wits, treating nervous conditions and acting as a cordial to the heart. The tea will be found most helpful for nausea or tense headaches. It is mild and safe to use regularly as the legends tell us. Lemon balm slows breathing and pulse rate and moderates blood pressure. It is an excellent antidote to all kinds of anxiety, panic and hysteria, including nightmares. It is also regarded as an anti-depressant and was once infused in Canary wine to be drunk as a cordial to the heart

In more hopeful days lemon balm leaves were dried and worn as amulets wrapped in cloth to ensure the wearer might be happy and well loved.

Lemon balm tea is also known as Melissa tea, and carries with it a delicate taste and lemon fragrance, invoking the peace of a summer garden. Serve hot or iced. The herb does not dry particularly well and tea from the dried herb is not very appealing. It is much better to freeze the herb for winter use. For a greater lemon flavour lemon verbena can be added to the balm, or drunk alone. This is most refreshing in winter picked fresh from indoor plants.

Two sprigs of the top four to six leaves may be used per cup. Fresh growth is best. Tear the leaves first for greater flavour. The tea is delicious served iced, with a slice of lemon.

## Thyme

The very act of gathering sprigs of thyme from your serenity garden, or a container indoors, will release the fresh fragrance to ease tension. For centuries, thyme has been taken in the form of teas and syrups or added to bath infusions to calm the nervous system. In the 17th century there was even a soup made with thyme and beer to give new courage to shy individuals.

The tea has been taken for insomnia and especially to ward off nightmares. This seems a fanciful remedy, yet it is one which I have used successfully to cure a child of persistent frightening dreams.

Thyme was one of several cheering herbs planted on graves to give tranquil thoughts to the bereaved. In bath infusions thyme had a place in soothing the bather, but also in giving courage. Thyme therefore had a certain image as a masculine herb which Roman soldiers were happy to use in the belief that it gave them vigour. It was held by the Romans to cure melancholy and was an emblem of courage to the Greeks.

Enjoy the full flavour of thyme tea sweetened with honey as a soothing drink for coughs. Thyme tea taken daily will help to prevent infections, especially colds, sore throats and influenza.

To make the tea use two level teaspoons of dried herb for two cups, and leave to stand for five minutes. Or, bruise three or four sprigs of fresh thyme and tear in. The flowers are important for full flavour. Lemon thyme tea gives a very pleasant lemon undertone and may offer similar medicinal properties. For those new to herb teas, this is a popular, gentle introduction to a range of new flavours.

# Herbal baths to calm and refresh.

WHEN it comes to relaxing, there is nothing quite like a long soak in a warm bath to relieve tension. There are several ways of enhancing the effect by using the properties of tranquillizing and refreshing herbs. As with pot-pourri, the most pleasing base of herbs for any bath mixture will be lavender, rose or lemon verbena. An infusion can easily be made by pouring 900ml (1½ pints) of boiling water over 4 tablespoons of selected herbs in a large jug or bowl. Leave this infusion to stand for 10 to 15 minutes before straining it into your bathwater.

A blend of lavender, thyme and chamomile flowers will help to distance you from your cares and problems. For those who prefer a rose fragrance, sage and limeflower can balance the heady scent while adding soothing properties of their own. Lemon balm and pot marigold will quieten the stimulus of lemon verbena, leaving you simply refreshed.

Once you have found the blend you enjoy by making a herbal infusion, you can make up a ready supply of bath sachets for future use. These could be simple cheesecloth or muslin bags 10cm x 10cm, (4 x 4ins) which can then be stored in a dark coloured glass jar in the bathroom. Alternatively, a pretty lady's handkerchief in thin material could be filled with 7 tablespoons of herbs and tied into a "bag" with a long length of narrow ribbon which can then be looped to attach the bag so that it hangs beneath the hot tap.

The method which requires least effort to add the soothing powers of herbs to your bath, is, of course to add a few drops of essential oil to your bathwater. (Never more than eight). This is done after the water has been run and immediately before you step into the bath. Agitate the water to mix in the drops and remain in the bath for a good ten minutes for most benefit. Before using any essential oil in the bath put a drop of the oil into a bowl of water and soak one hand in this for a few minutes. Wait for several hours to be sure your skin does not react to the oil before stepping into a full bath with the oil added. You do need to know and follow the correct dosage for the oil you are using. Essential oils vary in strength and it is not safe to assume that because six drops of one is pleasing, the same amount of another should be added. For oils which should not be used in the bath when pregnant (see Medicinal page 161).

Before experimenting with the following recipes please note that anyone with a sensitive skin, likely to suffer from allergies, should test their hands and arms for reactions before stepping into a full herbal bath. Remember to test children as well. Asthma sufferers should seek medical advice.

Once you have tried the recipes below, you will be ready to make up your own personal combinations of herbs. If you are not certain of a new blend - or one of mine - make up a smaller amount first.

## *Herbal bath infusions*
All measurements given are for the dried herb
*Lavender*
2 tablespoons lavender
1 tablespoon lemon thyme
1 tablespoon chamomile flowers

*Fragrant mint*
2 tablespoons eau-de-cologne mint
1 tablespoon lavender
1 tablespoon marjoram

*Bath sachets*
Note. Sufficient to fill a large lady's handkerchief or two
10cm x 10cm (4in x 4in) bags.

*Rose sachet*
4 tablespoons fragrant rose petals
1 tablespoon marjoram
2 tablespoons limeflowers

*Lavender sachet*
4 tablespoons lavender
1 tablespoon pot marigold petals
2 tablespoons chamomile flowers

*Lemon sachet*
2 tablespoons lemon verbena
4 tablespoons lemon balm
1 tablespoon lemon mint or thyme

## Essential oils

These oils can be blended with others but this must be done to a recipe. You can, if you wish, drop the essential oil into a teaspoon of carrier oil, such as sweet almond, and add this to the bath. You could also drop them into a spoon of milk before adding. Either method means you are less likely to add too many drops accidentally. It also gives you a greasier bath to clean! The oils below are individual suggestions. Always add essential oils one drop at a time, do not shake the bottle to help the oil out. Some emerge much faster than others.

| | |
|---|---|
| *BERGAMOT* | 5 drops, to relax you and lift depression. |
| *CLARY SAGE* | 4 drops to lift your mood. |
| *GERANIUM* | 4 drops, to calm and balance your emotions. |
| *NEROLI* | 3 drops, to relieve stress. |
| *LAVENDER* | 5 drops, to relax and soothe. |
| *FRANKINCENSE* | 4 drops to feel pampered and care for your skin. |

3 drops Lavender and 3 of geranium are helpful to ease pain.
*Note:* Bergamot oil will increase your skin sensitivity to the sun. Do not use this oil immediately before sunbathing.

## Marjoram and Oregano

The wild marjoram, oregano, is also known as "Joy of the Mountain", a name which reveals the love the herb has attracted in the past. With such long-lasting, pretty flowers, it is as much of a joy cultivated in the garden as it is when discovered growing wild.

In the past marjoram has been grown on graves to wish a happy peace to the departed, and to comfort those left behind. It is antispasmodic, and oregano has been applied to treating headaches, due to an antineuralgic action. Marjoram tea was once drunk by those who were feeling melancholy, to lift their spirits. Also as a hopeful remedy for nightmares.

Since there are so many marjorams, - with sweet, pot, crinkle-leaf, winter, golden, variegated and oregano - the choice of which to grow in your serenity garden is wide. Why not grow several as I do, some for their cheering appearance and fragrances in the garden and others perhaps for their perfume when dried? The latter could then be included in bath sachets, pillows or pot-pourri. (see recipes pages 118-120).

Marjoram oil has many applications in aromatherapy treatments. One of these is in treating anxiety. Just drinking in the fragrance from the herb, especially when it is in flower, will also help to lift depression and restore confidence in the world.

## *Sage*

In some parts of southern England it has been the custom to plant sage on the grave of a relative or friend. If the sage grew and flourished, then it confirmed the belief that the departed was at peace. Sage has also been associated with easing grief. It was given to the bereaved in posies and taken as a tea or in wine.

Sage in soothing bath sachets, herb pillows and pot-pourri adds a special quality to the blend. While remaining as an undertone, it softens and deepens the high notes which might otherwise be dominant. Any of the three sages can be used in this way. Spanish sage, with thinner, pointed leaves, has a slightly different fragrance, more reminiscent of lavender. Clary sage is another member of the *Salvia* family. The biennial herb is both dramatic in appearance, as the tall flower spikes unfurl, concertina-like from tightly packed buds, and breathtaking in its perfume. A small spray in a flower arrangement in the house will help to lighten your mood. Clary sage is the perfect herb to include in displays for parties or an occasion when a guest might feel shy or nervous. It is also credited with aphrodisiac properties.

Anyone who has inadvertently filled a vase with clary sage in a small room will be aware that while a little is soothing, clary sage can soon become overpowering. The herb was once included in alcoholic drinks to make them more potent and breathing in a large dose of clary sage will give the unpleasant feeling of a hang-over. Four drops of the essential oil of clary sage in your bath will be uplifting, but never be tempted to increase the dose as this can result in a nasty headache.

Clary sage oil is now used in treatments in preference to essential oil of sage after reports of disturbing side effects from the common sage.

## *Lavender*

The sedative properties of lavender are well known. Perhaps this partly explains the strong connection in most people's minds between lavender and old ladies, who are inclined to be nervous and find difficulty in sleeping. Even though there is a distinctly Victorian air about lavender, it has never lost popularity, for its effects are far too valuable.

The simple lavender bags of bygone years still appear every summer at fetes, herb stalls and in superior packaging in expensive stores. The perfume of lavender seems to last better than almost any other herb and few dislike it.

Lavender-based pillows not only encourage sleep, but, as you will see in the recipes, blended with other soothing herbs can quieten the nervous system when panic is imminent. We all have some situation which unnerves us in our lives, it may be travelling by air, or by car with a particular driver, going to the dentist, or attending an interview. A small, inconspicuous panic pillow can be held at the ready to prepare you for the ordeal.

Lavender is the main ingredient because it is a relaxing herb which suits almost everyone. By balancing the emotional state in a gentle, effective action, lavender can, used regularly, help you through even prolonged stress. It is one of the least toxic of herbs; one of only two which have an essential oil safe to be applied directly to the skin. This essential oil calms the nervous system, having analgesic and antispasmodic properties which will ease physical symptoms of distress, such as nervous headaches.

In earlier times hats were made which could be padded with lavender in the lining to help those suffering from chronic headaches. We are unlikely to need such drastic measures now, but a lavender pillow remains a welcome, calming influence.


# Herb pillows, sachets and pot-pourri

THE comfort of a herb pillow is often appreciated most when we are in a stressful situation. A sleep pillow can help us to settle our thoughts and body, ready for a restful night. The fragrance of the essential oils eases tension and sometimes slows our breathing rate. A herb pillow slowly releases what becomes a familiar perfume, associated with sleep and calm. The effects should last for at least six months at full strength and then slowly reduce over the following six months, at which time a fresh blend of herbs can be exchanged for the old one. The discarded herb filling need not be thrown away however; it can be pounded a little in a mortar and, with a drop or two of oil added, re-used in small sachets for drawers or to tuck into sofa cushions.

The particular blends of herbs used in pillows and sachets can be brought together to suit individual needs. The joy of making your own is that you can quickly discover which herbs are right for you.

For those who find it difficult to sleep in a strange bed while away from home, especially when in hospital for instance, taking that "aura" of your own bedroom with you, in the form of a small pillow, can make all the difference. Sleeping while travelling long distances on trains or in planes can also be a problem. As a nervous air passenger myself, I understand the fears many endure on long flights. I therefore began making a "panic" pillow to take along to soothe frayed nerves in such times of stress. The panic pillow is smaller, so that it can be tucked into a handbag or pocket and slipped easily over your shoulder held by a seatbelt if necessary. Clutching it, will of course release even more fragrance. After a few moments you should have relaxed sufficiently to use the pillow a little less conspicuously. Alternatively this can be made up as an attractive and handy neck pillow for travelling.

Again the blend of herbs given below is one I find best for me and which also has a wide appeal to others. Changes in the ingredients can be made as long as the lavender content remains the same and the essential oil is used. Your pillow can then travel with you to far-off places, or a hospital waiting-room, the dentist, examinations - wherever you feel in need of a little support.

Pot-pourri in a room can also offer a quiet atmosphere of welcoming serenity. You may wish to place this in a bedroom, sitting-room or study. The herbs in the recipes below have been thoughtfully chosen with these rooms and their individual needs in mind.

### Sleep pillow

| | |
|---|---|
| 2½ cups lavender | 1 cup angelica leaves |
| 1 cup chamomile flowers | ½ cup thyme |
| ½ tablespoon pounded dill seeds | ½ tablespoon orris root |
| 1 cup rosemary (dried flowering if possible) | |

4 drops essential oil of neroli, or 5 drops essential oil of lavender and 3 drops geranium. Mix together the flowers and green herbs. Add the pounded dill seed and powdered orris root. When the herbs are well blended, add the drops of essential oil carefully, one at a time. This blend can be used straight away to fill a muslin sachet, 23cm x 23cm, (9in x 9in). Enclose this in a cotton case.

**Panic neck pillow**

| | |
|---|---|
| 2¹/₂ cups lavender | 1 cup chamomile flowers |
| 1 tablespoon marjoram | 1 heaped tablespoon sage |
| ¹/₂ tablespoon aniseed | ¹/₂ tablespoon orris root |

¹/₂ cup limeflowers and bracts (stalks removed)
3 drops essential oil of clary sage
2 drops essential oil of geranium

Mix together dried herbs and flowers, being careful to see there are no sharp stalks left in. Pound the aniseed and orris root and add to the blend. Lastly add the oils, one drop at a time. The blend can be put straight away into a muslin case for a neck pillow, or into smaller sachets. **Please note** these recipes may be unsuitable for asthma and heart patients.

## *Fragrant car cushion*

Although this scented blend is one to help you keep wide awake and alert while driving your car in stressful conditions, it is not a substitute for taking a break from driving. Frequent stops on long journeys are always advisable. When feeling tired and stuck in traffic, however, this cushion could make life that much easier.

| | |
|---|---|
| 2¹/₂ cups lemon verbena | 1¹/₂ cups lemon balm |
| 1 cup rosemary | 1 cup thyme |
| ¹/₂ cup lemon geranium leaves | 2 teaspooons aniseed |

1 heaped teaspoon cloves
¹/₂ tablespoon pounded, dried lemon rind
1 level tablespoon orris root
4 drops essential oil of lemon
3 drops essential oil of cinnamon
2 drops essential oil of peppermint

Blend all the dried herbs together, taking care to pound the rosemary first to release the fragrance. Next add the pounded aniseed and lemon rind, followed by the powdered orris root. Lastly add the essential oils one drop at a time, being especially careful with the oil of cinnamon. Stir the mix again before putting it into a 23cm x 23cm, (9in x 9in) muslin bag and enclosing this in an outer, cotton case. The cushion is ready for use immediately.

## *Pet comforter*

This cushion is one I have been asked to make for dogs suffering from arthritis or stress. It contains herbs to relax the animal, so easing pain, and oils which are helpful in having a warming effect. The cushion should not be considered a treatment in itself, merely an aid to recovery. The dog may take a day or two to become accustomed to such strong odours in its bed. Try placing the inner sachet of herbs inside the dog's familiar cushion with the bulk of the cushion above the herbs at first. When the dog accepts this then turn the cushion over to bring the herbs closer to the surface.

| | |
|---|---|
| 3 cups lavender | 1¹/₂ cups rosemary |
| 1 cup marjoram | 1 cup sage |
| 1 cup chamomile flowers | 2 tablespoons fennel seed |

³/₄ tablespoon orris root
3 drops essential oil of rosemary
1 drop essential oil of eucalyptus

1 drop essential oil of ginger
2 drops essential oil of fennel.
Blend the dried herbs together. Pound the rosemary before adding. Pound the fennel seed and powdered orris root together and add. Lastly drip in the essential oils, one drop at a time. Fill an inner muslin sachet to place in the dog's cushion and sew tightly to enclose in the outer material.

**Please note** you should not use this cushion for a dog with breathing problems or allergies.

## *Relaxing rose pot-pourri*

6 tablespoons heavily scented rosebuds or petals,
1 tablespoon bergamot leaves and flowers,
1 tablespoon rose geranium leaves
2 tablespoons marjoram
$^1/_2$ tablespoon powdered orris root
2 drops essential oil of geranium
4 drops essential oil of bergamot

This blend is lovely for a bedroom or quiet sitting-room. If you wish to make a larger amount then multiply the herb quantities by two and add 2 additional drops of essential oil of rose geranium or bergamot.

Mix the dried flowers and herbs, adding the orris root, then the essential oil, one drop at a time. Put all the ingredients into a screw-top jar and set this into the airing cupboard for six weeks to cure. Shake it each day as you go to the cupboard. Then place in a bowl to be left open for only half an hour when needed. Cover the container when you are not using the room.

## *Sweet citrus serene pot-pourri*

8 tablespoons lemon verbena
4 tablespoons bergamot leaves and flowers
2 tablespoons pineapplemint
2 heaped tablespoons crumbled lemon balm
$^1/_2$ level tablespoon orris root
3 drops essential oil of bergamot
3 drops essential oil of lemon

This blend, while it is relaxing, also has the refreshing qualities of the citrus herbs. It will therefore help those who need to work calmly with a difficult task. Mix the dried herbs as before, adding the orris root to fix the fragrances and the drops of essential oil, last. Put the mixture into a screw top jar as before and place this in the airing cupboard for six weeks, shaking it as you go to the cupboard. Then fill a suitable bowl or jar with a lid with the pot-pourri. Keep it closed when not using the room and open for 30-60 minutes at a time to extend the life of the pot-pourri.

# Fragrance and Flowers

THE full, rich harmony of a summer's garden never fails to evoke the desire to capture its beauty, holding it through the winter months. A pot-pourri of herbs, flowers, spices, roots and oils can be a magical mystery tour, arousing such precious memories.

Familiar friends will be found amongst the ingredients: roses and lavender, rosemary and cloves, exotic spices, star anise and cardamom, the seeds of coriander, anise and lovage, calamus root, tonka beans, gum benzoin and oil of neroli.

Your horizons may be widened in joyous discovery, where gum benzoin and calamus come from, how tonka beans are cured and the best methods of harvesting, storing and preparing home-grown ingredients - all are revealed with detailed explanations.

A variety of recipes are designed to meet the very individual requirements when adding the right "atmosphere" in different rooms in your home. These may guide your first practical experiences in making pot-pourri. Once the joy of blending the herbs has been explored, the background notes will provide a useful reference as new experiments are made.

The perfect forms of flowers such as bergamot, honeysuckle and clove pinks can be preserved in silica gel crystals or borax. Decorating a glass bowl of pot-pourri, these add a natural beauty straight from your garden to the sweet fragrance.

Exploring the fragrances and flowers of a summer garden is an idyllic experience; one likely to convert anyone who knows little about them into an ardent enthusiast. Tastes vary, but there is always sufficient choice to delight those who take the time to "follow their nose" amongst the flower beds.

Flowers have a magic of their own in creating atmosphere in a garden. The blue stars of borage drooping in elegant, demure beauty are contrasted by the homely, colourful character of bright orange pot marigolds. The striking brilliance of bergamot, bearing intricate crowns of jagged petals in bright red or purple, is as extrovert; as the low clusters of soft pastel blue and pinks, clustered together in forget-me-nots are introvert; huddling beneath the lilacs.

The friendly, daisy-like flower heads of chamomile in yellow and white seem to invite you to pick them with a reassuring promise of more and yet more blooms to come. Amongst the soft, feathery foliage of the chamomile, heartsease of the *Viola* family, is another willing nurse for tired spirits. The tiny, tricolor flowers evoke memories of a meadow I once walked in, starred with the purple, yellow and creamy richness of their petals, on an island surrounded by the River Tees, in northern England.

Bright nasturtiums, eager to join in even where they may not be wanted; heavenly honeysuckle, best appreciated when arching overhead; an early spike or two of lavender and the first yellow stars of St John's wort - all grace a June herb garden. One of the beauties not to miss is the deep blue and lilac spikes of hyssop coming into flower as June ends, so perfect for posies.

On a gentler note, the tiny yellow flowers of agrimony delight with a quiet sense of loveliness. The special delicacy of a waving sea of blue flax flowers must be enjoyed early in the day, for they are closed long before evening. Their stems seem so fragile, it is hard to credit they can support so many blooms. One might imagine that, instead of flowers, the herb is visited by a mass of soft, blue butterflies, all with their wings opened to the sun.

Old roses with their heady fragrance on still, summer afternoons are the jewel in the crown of the herb garden. The *Gallicas,* which include the rich, red "apothecary's rose", the prolific *alba,* white, with the hint of a blush at inevitable compliments; the "York and Lancaster" with red and white mixed in soft pink; and the favourite of many, pink and white striped *Rosa mundi;* all have their own characters and place. Damask roses are welcomed for their strong perfume, "sweetbriar" and "dog roses", or *Rosa rugosa i*n hedging, and *Rosa moschata,* or, closer to our own time in history, "Albertine", are the finest climbers to cover a pergola or arbour.

Old pinks and carnations offer the greatest variety of flowers of all the herbs: from "sops-in-wine", shaggy white with maroon markings and a powerful clove perfume, reminiscent of Elizabethan recipes, to "Queen of Sheba", petite by comparison, with magenta patches on each of the creamy petals in perfect form. The "dark red", jagged-edged pink of even earlier, medieval times, contrasts with the white of "Mrs. Sinkins", a late arrival in gardens in the last century. Both have a rich, aromatic quality. The brilliance of "allspice" or "Fenbows nutmeg clove" carnations stand out amongst the white, "old fringed" and "old Dutch". The names of the pinks are sufficient to set the imagination racing, painting wonderful pictures of their flowers: "laced hero, Sweetheart Abbey, painted lady, Madonna" and "old velvet".

Best of all, the bright red spicy flowers of *Dianthus caryophyllu*s brighten the garden in July, later than many pinks. These are treasured for their harvest for liqueur and syrup.

Humbler flowers which add colour almost all through the season are borne on the little-appreciated yarrow, wild or cultivated. From white or yellow to pink and cerise, the yarrow is ever circulating in the garden, popping up here and there, often uninvited, but not necessarily unwelcome. Cotton lavender and germander are left to flower in places for posies. Given welcome release from being "clipped to attention" as low hedges, they revel in this freedom, running riot amongst the other herbs. Thymes flower on the scented bank, sending bees drunk with nectar. Caraway and basil-scented, *alba,* the purple flowered *Thymus serpyllym,* wild lemon, "silver posy" and "Doone Valley" giving a variety of colour, form and aroma to please every taste. Although their scent will not be noticeable in the day, the cool of evening coaxes the lemon-yellow evening primrose flowers to fill the air with romance.

With the sudden glory of the peonies over, valerian heads fading and the ivory-like wonder of elderflowers almost gone for another year, the overwhelming musky perfume of biennial clary sage proclaims its magnificence to all. The fairytale spire of elaborate blue and white flowers, backed by perfect shades of lilac, open from concertina-like buds in a magical fashion.

We must not think of fragrance as coming only from the flowers of the herbs however. Their foliage can sometimes be both their most impressive visual attraction and carry the intensity of the essential oil of the plant. The mints give of their best just before their flowers open. They seem to "lay in wait" to surprise you with bursts of perfume as you brush against them. The dark, rounded, sometimes purplish leaves of eau-de-cologne mint make the perfect ground cover beneath the seat in the serenity garden. Bruised by the feet of all who sit there, they perfume the air beautifully.

The woolly leaves of variegated pineapplemint are less shy in seeking the attention of all who pass by, inviting enquiring fingers to touch their cream and green leaves, releasing the scent of pineapple which intensifies as the plant is dried. Gingermint, with gold and green regimented into more orderly variegations, calls you to bruise rather than stroke the pointed leaves with their spicy ginger flavour and fragrance. Peppermint is equally strident, whether dark- or light-stemmed, and gives a pretty harvest of purple flowers if allowed, to boost the aroma of dried posies.

Fennel, angelica and lovage offer such powerful fragrances in the still, warm air as they tower above the other herbs, that they tend to overwhelm lighter scents, discovered only on contact. Rose, lemon and orange-scented geraniums and tangy lemon verbena bask in the sunshine, released briefly from their winter pots and life indoors. The bitter aromas of silvery leafed *artemisias*, southernwood, wormwood, "silver queen" and "silver warrior" release their challenge to the softer quality of lemon balm, humble and cordial.

Rue waves blue foliage in the breeze, once a protector with its sour, coconut aroma, green tansy towers above, pungent and yet with a scoured clean smell which describes its role perfectly. Feverfew and savory add their notes to the bitter tones, while the sages, protectors still, give a fullness and depth to nature's pot-pourri.

Before autumn the giant sunflower heads will turn their massed petals to the sun, high above the layers of perfumed flowers and foliage of shorter herbs. Their smaller "look-alikes", the elecampane, will open out their fascinating clusters of buds into golden discs, inviting butterflies to pause and taste of their goodness.

The deep lilac heads of oregano and peppermint will give a plentiful harvest for drying before the waving clusters of yellow tansy "buttons" dance above them. Then the muted pink of shy marshmallow flowers will peep from their tall, grey foliage while the cheery white daisies of feverfew flower on and on below.

The abundance of flowers and perfumes in June and July will surely kindle the desire to capture such a sweet atmosphere in a pot-pourri for dark, wintry days. As we leave the garden and the house, a parting blessing is given by the thriving bush of rosemary beside the door. It is a welcome evergreen reminder of friendship, protection and its own special gift of rejuvenation. May your pot-pourri bring the spirit of the herb garden to life for you.

# Pot-pourri ingredients

**Flowers**
bergamot
borage
chamomile
clove pinks
cotton lavender
forget-me-not
golden rod
helichrysum
honeysuckle
hyssop
jasmine
lavender
lilac
pot marigold
nasturtium
peony
primrose
rose
tansy
violas
wallflower
yarrow

**Herbs**
angelica
basil
bay
bergamot
cotton lavender
hyssop
lemon balm
lemon verbena
lovage
marjoram
mints
myrtle
patchouli
pennyroyal
rosemary
sage
savory
scented geraniums
southernwood
sweet cicely
tansy
thymes

**Spices**
allspice
cardamom
cinnamon
cloves
galingale
mace
nutmeg
star anise

**Seeds**
angelica
anise
caraway
coriander
dill
fennel
lovage
sweet-cicely

**Fixatives**
angelica root
avens root
calamus root
elecampane root
gum benzoin
lovage root
orris root
sweet cicely root
sweet woodruff
tonka beans
vanilla pod

**Oils**
basil
bergamot
cinnamon
clary sage
frankincense
geranium
lavender
lemon
lemongrass
neroli
orange
patchouli
peppermint
pine
rose
rose geranium
rosemary
thyme

**Peels**
grapefruit
lemon
orange

**Pot-Pourri Ingredients**
(Right to left) *A glass bowl of green herb holds lemon verbena and flowering thyme. On the wooden platter are the herb flowers – lavender, scented geranium, bergamot, curry plant, violets, chamomile, primroses, pot marigold and rose petals. In the glass dish lay root slices of angelica, elecampane, and sweet cicely, all effective fixatives along with the more usual powdered orris root. Seeds and spices in the glasses and foreground include dill, fennel, aniseed, cardamom, sweet cicely, star anise, allspice, nutmegs and cinnamon stick.*

# Fragrance and flowers

*Herbs hang dry in a dark airy place – here under thatch.*

*One summers days harvest for drying.*

## Preparing the ingredients.

FLOWERS and herbs for pot-pourri should be gathered on a dry day, generally before lunch. They must be picked in perfect condition, preferably for flowers as they are first opening. Herb leaves will contain most essential oil just before the plant flowers.

Herb leaves and the less delicate flowers can be dried laid one layer deep on fine net or muslin stretched over a frame in the airing cupboard. Strip the leaves from the stems when they are crisp to touch and store each herb separately in a dark, glass screw top jar. Alternatively green and flowering herbs can be dried on short stems, hung upside down in the airing cupboard or from a line in a well- ventilated room. In this case keep them away from direct sunlight. Rosebuds should be tightly closed when picked as they will open slightly as they dry. Or the petals can be pulled from opening roses and dried on muslin.

Delicate whole flowers, such as white lilac, wallflowers, borage and heartsease, are best dried in silica gel (available from florists) or borax. Fill a small cardboard box with alternate layers of the crystals and flowers, covering the final layer of flowers completely. Most take between two days and a week to dry. Do not leave them in the crystals too long or they will become brittle. With borax, which is a cheaper medium, it is more difficult to replace flowers removed to test for dryness and it may not give such good results. Some of these carefully preserved whole flowers can be reserved to add as a final decorative layer when the pot-pourri has been cured and is set out in its container.

Flowers with many petals, such as pot marigolds *(Calendula)*, are easier to cope with if taken apart and the individual petals spread one layer deep on a large, flat dish in the oven with the door ajar. Dry them on the lowest setting, below 50°C (120°F) for about two to three hours, until crisp. In this way they will keep their colour and properties.

Always dry one herb at a time to avoid problems in identification and a blend of perfumes before you even begin. A further drying method is the microwave. Not all microwaves are suitable. Check instruction leaflet. Large-leaved herbs, such as lovage and sage, are easier to dry in this way than the delicately formed savory. It really requires a little experiment and practice to discover the time needed for an individual herb in your particular microwave. As a general rule, unless otherwise instructed in the accompanying manual, dry the herbs between sheets of paper kitchen-towel, on full power. After one minute check for progress. It will speed the drying to flip the herbs over at each check, setting the drier top paper underneath and replacing the wet sheet from beneath the herbs. Further checks at one-minute or half-minute intervals will give you times needed for succeeding batches.

Herb seeds can be gathered when mature and dry, and stored in airtight containers to pound into mixtures as spicy additions. Lovage, dill, fennel, coriander, caraway, angelica, anise and sweet cicely are all suitable.

Some herb roots can be dug in spring or autumn and dried to use as fixatives. These are generally gathered in the plant's second year. Sweet cicely and angelica roots mixed together in equal proportions can have a similar effect to orris root in fixing the perfumes, but will add their own musky quality. The root of avens has been credited with giving a spicy clove-like fragrance. Elecampane root is surprisingly subtle, considering its strong flavour. Lovage root is very powerful as it is drying.

It is only practical to grow your own orris root if you are looking to results in the long term. As with the other herbs, the root is taken from a plant at least two years old, dried and then matured for a full year before use. The best harvest time for roots is in the early autumn. Clean the root as soon as it has been dug, removing small tendrils, and slice. The scrubbed, sliced root, (no more than 3.75cm (1½in) thick) is laid on a dish and set in the oven to dry as for pot marigolds. Remember that the thinner the slices, the easier it is to be sure the root is dried right through. Keep the temperature at no more than 50°C (120°F) and have patience. It will take several hours.

When dry, the root slices should be quite hard to touch. It is safest to leave the root in a dry atmosphere, such as the still-warm oven overnight. Store in dark glass jars as before, checking daily for a week to be certain no moisture has been left in the root. If it should begin to soften, return to a warm oven until completely dry. Grind to a powder only when you are ready to use it and the root can retain its pungency for several years.

When buying fixatives look for orris root as a powder. Store it in an airtight jar once the packet has been opened. Sandalwood from the heart of the evergreen sandalwood tree, grown mainly in India and Indonesia *Santalum album;* is no longer recommended as the trade may endanger the trees. Many suppliers have stopped selling it for this reason. The red sandalwood which remains on sale is from the *Pterocarpus santalinus L.* and is sometimes labelled sanderswood. This is a good colouring agent but has no perfume. Tonka beans are either Angostura or small Para beans. They come from tall trees in the forests of South America. These seeds have a fascinating preparation before they reach us. They are first dried in the hot sun and then immersed in rum which cures them, leaving tiny crystals of coumarin on the now-black beans. The coumarin adds a scent reminiscent of sweet woodruff or new-mown hay. Pound them in a mortar before use. Dried sprigs of sweet woodruff herb may be used in their place. Patchouli, *Pogostemon heyneanus* can be grown as an indoor plant and the dried brown leaves crumbled into pot-pourri to help fix the perfume. Star anise, *Illicium verum* can also be a lovely house or greenhouse plant with fragrant dried leaves and creamy star flowers.

Several gums have a long history of use in pot-pourri. Since part of the attraction of making your own specialities is exploring different ingredients, these are fun to try. Gum benzoin was once very popular and can still be obtained from some specialist shops. Once known as Gum Benjamin, it oozes as a sticky resin from wounds made in large *Styrax* trees. The best is from Siam and Sumatra. It comes in very hard rock-like lumps, guaranteed to destroy the plastic goblet of your electric grinder. Amazingly it is quite easy to pound in a mortar. Calamus powder comes from the dried rhizomes of the sweet sedge, *Acorus calamus,* which grows in marshy ground and around lakes. Small pieces of dried root gathered in autumn, or the powder which is commercially available, are useful fixatives.

Spices should always be bought whole and ground either with a pestle in a mortar or in an electric grinder - if your grinder goblet is strong enough to take the wear! Prepare them as you are mixing the herbs together for real freshness. Cinnamon sticks can be flaked over the blend. Star anise are often added whole or broken in halves to give decoration as well as spice. Cloves may be ground or pounded according to the recipe. Small amounts of nutmeg are readily grated. Remember to pound spicy seeds to release their oil before stirring in.

Orange, lemon or grapefruit peel offer a fresh vibrance to the mixture. They can be pared thinly with a vegetable peeler, discarding any pith. Roll the strips in orris root powder or ground sweet cicely root and dry until crisp on a rack in a warm oven. For a spicier effect, stick cloves through the peel at intervals before rolling in the root powder. Store in an airtight jar.

In the ingredients list I have recommended those essential oils which I have found cover a wide variety of blends for almost every occasion. Some, such as the cinnamon and orange, are mostly of value in Christmas recipes. (Mandarin can also be used instead of orange at this time.) Since essential oils vary greatly in price - rose and neroli being the two most expensive on the list given - it is a good idea to think carefully and consult likely recipes before deciding on how to stock your cupboard. Remember that you will be using only a few drops of oil at a time. Patchouli oil actually improves with age, but this is an exception.

Most essential oils are distilled from large quantities of the flowers or herb. For instance, the stills at Norfolk Lavender in England take ¼ ton of flowering herb at a time and produce about 600ml (1 pint) of oil from this quantity. The oil, which has some 50 chemical ingredients, is then matured for a year before it is blended to produce the typical lavender odour we expect. Citrus oils are expressed from the peel of the fruits. These include bergamot which comes from *Citrus aurantium,* not the familiar garden herb, *Monarda didyma.* Delicate flower oils, such as rose and jasmine, need to be macerated in a solvent before the mixture is centrifuged and finally distilled in a vacuum at a low temperature. This is why they are so expensive. Alternatively, enfleurage may be used with successive layers of flowers giving their perfume to fats.

A selection of four oils will give you plenty of choice in the recipes. I like to keep bergamot, geranium, lemon and either rose or lavender as the basis of my own collection. The oil in a recipe usually brings out the perfume of the main flower or herb ingredient. If you are making blends for a man's study and wish to give the pot-pourri a masculine touch, cinnamon or thyme will do just that.

Smelling rows of tester bottles in a shop is not recommended as this could result in a bad headache. It is better to go with certain oils in mind. When you do come to use them, most bottles have a dropper in the top. If they do not, and you are loathe to buy a dropper for each oil, a straw can be used as a pipette. Dip the straw into the bottle of oil and place your forefinger over the top before lifting the straw out of the bottle and over the mix. Remove your forefinger and a drop or two of oil will drip out at the bottom of the straw. Particular care should be taken however, as one, two or even three drops may have been sucked in. Do not "help" the oils out of the bottle with your finger (rose is particularly thick and slow to emerge), as only lavender and Ti-tree oils are safe to use neat on the skin. Others can cause allergic reactions as they are very powerful substances. **Always add oils carefully one drop at a time.**

The essential oil carries within it the concentrated "spirit" of the herb, together with some of its properties. One drop too many can spoil the whole blend. When doubling the quantities of herbs in a successful recipe it can be better to add a little more of the original oil with one or two drops of another, complimentary oil. Do not be tempted to double the original quantity of a single oil as this will not necessarily give the same effect on a larger scale. Experiment and careful notes are the keys to success.

For maximum shelf-life always keep essential oils in a cool, dark place and replace the tops immediately after use. **Keep essential oils out of the reach of children,** safely locked in a cupboard to avoid accidents. Before choosing from the following recipes for your first experience with making pot-pourri, *please note the fragrances of some pot-pourri can have unpleasant side-effects for asthma and heart patients. If you suffer from either problem your appreciation of herbs can be better served in other parts of this book. Anyone with persistent skin allergies should take care not to mix the dried herbs and oils with their bare hands. Stripping dried herbs from their stems can also provoke allergic reactions and is best done outdoors, wearing gloves if necessary.*

# Making Pot-Pourri

POT-POURRI is an aromatic blend, usually of flowers, herbs, spices, a fixative and a few drops of essential oil. At first glance the whole may seem to be a random selection of ingredients, chosen for colour, contrast or simple fragrance. However, certain basic rules need to be understood before you can successfully create a whole pot-pourri which is truly greater than the sum of its various ingredients.

Powerful fragrances need to be balanced by other herbs which add tone and depth to the mixture. "Top notes" of fragrance, which are sweet yet fleeting, need "base notes" in those with a slower release for the pot-pourri to be appreciated. Some pot-pourri can be pungent rather than enjoyable. Other blends can offer a subtle undertone with highlights of freshness. If care is not taken as the last ingredient is added, one drop of oil too many can ruin the effect completely.

Making several of the recipes given before you begin creating your own personal fragrances will help you to gain experience with different herbs. Add each ingredient separately, smelling the mix between additions to identify the precise effect of one herb upon another. Record your observations in a notebook kept for pot-pourri recipes, as no matter how certain you are that you will remember whether a particular herb heightened the effect, sweetened it, or added a bitter tang, you will find detailed information difficult to hold in your mind.

Rose, lavender, or a lemon herb are the most popular base materials for a pot-pourri. Each can be powerful and needs another herb to complement the fragrance. Lavender can be balanced by adding an equal quantity of rosemary. The two herbs have been described as the "soul" and "spirit" of the herb garden and will always partner well. Mint, and a touch of spice - either cloves or cinnamon - have been used for centuries to lighten the heady richness of rose pot-pourri. Care must be taken with mints, however, as they can easily become the dominant aroma. Even a pinch makes a difference. Mint and lemon combine well, especially peppermint, but again, add the mint with caution. A lemon mint is nature's own combination. Lemon verbena or lemon thyme should always have the addition of the softer tones of lemon balm, which is not sufficient to carry a lemon freshness alone. Lemon geranium is particularly powerful with a richness of tone not present in other herbs.

Common thyme is a useful herb to give fullness to a recipe, but it has a strong, sharp undertone and needs a subtle base such as marjoram to sweeten the tangy effect. As you add herbs remember the full impact of blending the ingredients is yet to be brought out by the curing process. Depth and tone increases during the six weeks every pot-pourri mixture spends in a warm, dry place, sealed in a screw top jar. The airing cupboard is a good choice as each time you go to it you will be reminded to shake the jar of pot-pourri, ensuring an even blend. At the end of this time the pot-pourri can be poured into a suitable dish.

With practice you will be able to stir two or three herbs together, breathe in the fragrance and know instantly whether it needs to be sweetened, given body with subtle undertones, or have one particular aspect heightened. In time you will also learn which combinations give the effect you are seeking. There is no substitute for careful observation and experiment - which is not to say it is an art to be taken too seriously! The whole point of the exercise is to re-create a balance of fragrances which revived or relaxed you in the garden; to capture the sheer pleasure of it. Your enjoyment of the experience can live on in the harvesting, drying and mixing of the herbs. A pot-pourri made with thought and love will always lend a quality to the atmosphere of a room which cannot be bought.

To appreciate the results for the longest period do not leave your pot-pourri in an open bowl or basket. A pretty glass or china dish with a lid will enable you to cover the herbs during the hours when they are not needed. Removing the lid for an hour before a room is used, particularly when it is set in a place where warm air rises, will become part of the personal care you give to your home. It may even encourage you to add other thoughtful touches when preparing for guests and remind you that you deserve a soothing atmosphere too.

## Spicy Lavender and Marigold Pot-Pourri

| | |
|---|---|
| 2½ cups lavender | 1 cup pot marigold petals |
| ½ cup eau-de-cologne mint | 1 tablespoon thyme |
| 2 tablespoons basil | 3 torn bay leaves |
| I vanilla pod, sliced | 1 stick of cinnamon |
| 1 tablespoon star anise | 1 teaspoon cloves |
| ½ tablespoon sweet cicely root | ½ tablespoon orris root |
| 4 drops essential oil of lavender | 3 drops essential oil of frankincense |
| 3 drops of essential oil of cinnamon | or thyme |

Begin by mixing the flowers and leaves in a large bowl. Tear the cinnamon stick into lengths of about 1.25-2.5cm (½-1in) and add. Tear in the bay leaves. Pound the cloves and some of the star anise before adding. A few star anise whole will be decorative for the finished pot-pourri. Slice the vanilla pod into several pieces before adding, if it is a large one you may only need half. Grind the sweet cicely root and add with the powdered orris root. Lastly, when all is stirred well together, add the oils carefully, one drop at a time. Pour the blend into a large screw top jar and place in the airing cupboard for six weeks to cure, shaking often.

This pot-pourri would be equally suited to a hallway, study, or man's bedroom. In smaller amounts it could be used to fill sachets or a cushion for his car.

## Sharp and Sweet Lemon Rose

3 cups lemon verbena
2 cups heavily scented rosebuds or petals
½ cup rose or lemon geranium leaves
1 tablespoon dried orange or lemon peel
1 tablespoon marjoram
½ tablespoon orris root (or 3 Tonka beans, pounded)
4 drops essential oil of geranium
2 drops essential oil of lemon.

Crumble the lemon verbena and geranium leaves a little as you mix them with the rosebuds. Stir in the marjoram and dried grated peel. Mix well before adding the orris root to fix the perfume. Lastly add the oils, one drop at a time. Seal in a screw top jar and cure for six weeks in the airing cupboard.

I like to place this pot-pourri in a bathroom or kitchen as it is both fresh and sweet. It leaves the air feeling clean.

### *Fruity Flower Pot-Pourri*

1 cup rosemary

2 cups lavender

¹/₂ cup pot marigold petals

¹/₂ cup pineapplemint

¹/₂ cup chamomile flowers

1 tablespoon orris root

¹/₂ tablespoon dill seed

1 tablespoon dried

3 drops essential oil of lavender

2 drops essential oil of rosemary

Pound the rosemary a little before mixing it with the other flowers and herbs. If the rosemary has been dried while flowering this will be even better. Pound the dill seed and add, stirring in the orris root. Lastly add the essential oils one drop at a time. Seal in a screw top jar and place in a warm, dry place out of sunlight for six weeks to cure, shaking occasionally.

This pot-pourri could be placed in a sitting room, bedroom or on a landing; wherever you like the sweet fragrance.


### *Fly Repellent Pot-Pourri*

1 cup basil

1 tablespoon peppermint, preferably with

1 cup lemon verbena

flowers

1 cup tansy leaves and flowers

1 tablespoon southernwood

¹/₂ tablespoon ground orris root or angelica root

3 drops essential oil of lemongrass     2 drops essential oil basil or thyme

Mix the flowers and herbs together. Add the pounded root fixative and lastly the oils - with great care. This pot-pourri will need to be cured as before for six weeks in a screw top jar in the dark to fix the powerful perfume. It makes a particularly pretty pot-pourri if you use peppermint flowers as well as the leaves, but will be just as effective with leaves only in repelling flies.

This blend can be moved around the house to wherever it is needed. You can also make up sprays of the herbs and add a drop or two of lemongrass to the stems and hang these in the windows in summer. Oil of peppermint could be used instead of lemongrass, in which case use only two drops, not three.


### *Sachets and Aromatic filling*

Herb sachets have always remained popular, despite the many synthetic alternatives; in fact, they are once again growing in popularity. Whether they are to be laid between clothing in drawers, hung in wardrobes, slipped into shoes or boots overnight, hung in the car, or popped into boxes of writing paper or birthday cards - they are fun and simple to make.

The wide range of needs which are to be met by the herbs in repelling moths, combating unwelcome odours from sweaty feet, pets, smoking, cooking and so on, provides a series of challenges provoking a new recipe for every occasion.

The number of combinations of ingredients is endless. Try the sachet recipes below to gain experience and then experiment from there on. If you tire of filling simple sachets, remember the many opportunities to add fragrance in fillings and stuffings: aromatic tea cosies, padded coat hangers, nightdress cases, soft toys stuffed with herbs, mobiles filled with chamomile and dill for babies, padded boxes, pin cushions, needlecases, catmint mice for your cat, basket linings with fennel seed in the filling to keep your dog free from fleas. The list is only limited by your imagination.

## Sachet against Moths

2 heaped tablespoons southernwood
3 tablespoons tansy leaves
3 tablespoons cotton lavender
1 tablespoon lavender
2 heaped tablespoons rosemary
1 tablespoon thyme
2 teaspoons ground cloves
1 tablespoon orris root
5 drops essential oil of rosemary.

Mix the herbs, pounding the rosemary a little first. Pound the cloves and add with the orris root. Lastly stir in the drops of essential oil of rosemary.

Sachet fillings do not need to be cured as they will be enclosed straight away. This recipe makes sufficient to fill 2 sachets, 13cm x 13cm (5in x 5in). Almost fill muslin squares and stitch closed. Push these into a small outer case of cotton material. Whether it is your husband's favourite tweed jacket he hardly ever wears, or an expensive wool jumper of your own, this recipe is just as suitable and you won't go round smelling of mothballs!


## Car Refresher

2 cups heavily scented rosebuds or petals
1 cup lavender
$\frac{1}{2}$ cup rose geranium leaves
1 tablespoon marjoram
1 tablespoon rosemary
1 teaspoon ground cloves
1 tablespoon orris or sweet cicely root, (or 3 Tonka beans, pounded)
3 drops essential oil of geranium
1 drop essential oil of neroli

Mix the flowers and herbs as before, grinding the cloves and pounding the rosemary and fixative root before adding. Lastly add the essential oils, one drop at a time. The recipe is even better with 1 drop of essential oil of rose, but this is luxury indeed. Small sachets of this mixture can be hung in your car, or the whole used to fill a small cushion to be left on the seat, releasing perfume.


## Rich Rose

$1\frac{1}{2}$ cups rosebuds or petals, heavily scented
$\frac{1}{2}$ cup bergamot leaves and flowers
1 tablespoon eau-de-cologne mint
$\frac{1}{2}$ cinnamon stick, flaked
1 teaspoon allspice, ground.

Mix the flowers and herbs, flake the cinnamon stick over the blend and grind the whole allspice in a blender or mortar with a pestle. Stir all well together and fill sachets to set with writing paper, slip into cushion covers or pad coat hangers.

## Small Cushion

2 handfuls lavender
1 handful lemon verbena
4 sprigs sweet woodruff
1 teaspoon ground frankincense
$1/2$ tablespoon ground orris
4 drops essential oil of bergamot

2 handfuls rose
1 handful thyme (dried flowering)
1 tablespoon eau-de-cologne mint
$1/2$ teaspoon ground clove
2 drops essential oil of rose geranium
2 drops essential oil benzoin res.

This is a particularly lovely and long lasting filling if it is used for a small cushion with a velvet back and needlepoint front. This should be 12.5cm x 12.5cm (5in x 5in).

Mix the dried flowers and herbs. Add the frankincense and crumbled sweet woodruff. Grind the cloves and orris root before adding. Lastly add the essential oils. The benzoin res. is unusual but is necessary for a really long-lasting perfume. I have known this to last for 10 years.

# Medicinal Herbs

**H**ERBS have been used medicinally for many thousands of years. Some are extremely powerful and must only be taken on prescription, while others have proved safe to be used in home-remedies. The historical introduction to this section gives a valuable background to understanding changing forms of treatment. The births of modern pharmacology, homoeopathy and aromatherapy are all connected with herbal medicine.

The individual herbs listed are divided into two sections: those that are grown for use in home-remedies and those that will add grace and interest to a collection of medicinal plants.

Recipes for remedies have been chosen for their effectiveness in the experience of the author. Correct diagnosis, preparation and dosage are important for home-treatment, and medical advice should always be sought if there is any doubt. **If a remedy is tried and there is no improvement in 48 hours, or the symptoms worsen, stop the treatment and seek advice. Do not continue taking a tea or other treatment if it does not appear to suit you.** A list of herbs and essential oils not to be taken or used when pregnant and a list of irritant and poisonous herbs are essential reading.

Instructions on how and when to harvest herbs, so vital in tapping their natural healing properties, is given. Herbs when handled with respect, have much to offer in healing.

## A Historical Perspective

Since the earliest times mankind has gathered herbs for medicinal use. Watching animal behaviour may have played a part in some discoveries. Many plants were gathered as foods and flavourings and the medicinal effects on those who ate the subsequent meal would soon have been noticed. If the addition of particular herb leaves to a stew consistently helped a sick member of the group, then the same plant would be searched for when someone else had a similar problem. Nettles, which are such a valuable food in spring, have diuretic effects when the young growth is picked and cooked. Later in the year, however, the older growth will have laxative properties. On days when there was little meat available, the herb broth may have been powerfully medicinal.

Styptic and healing properties of herbs such as yarrow, self-heal and shepherd's purse are likely to have been discovered initially by simply packing a wound with whatever was close at hand. All three herbs, but especially yarrow is often to be found in a fistful of grasses plucked at random. One very old recipe for chronic chest complaints was to take coltsfoot leaves and burn these on the fire. The patient sucked the smoke into their lungs through a reed. Since the white down on the back of the coltsfoot leaves is good for lighting fires and has had that traditional use, the discovery of this remedy may have been through a chance blowing into the fire with extra coltsfoot thrown on when it had lit.

All manner of scenarios may be imagined, with dye from plants catching people's attention as it stained their hands, or the later observation that herbs with yellow flowers often do have properties linked to kidney or liver complaints. Of course, not all experiments will have come to a good end, working out the correct dosage has always required test patients. No doubt, over many centuries, trial and error played its part, disclosing herbs were potentially poisonous; some in large or continued doses, others when only a little was taken. A few will have brought relief quickly, others might need to be taken for a long time.

Evidence from the grave of a Neanderthal man in Iraq has revealed the identities of the herbs which had been heaped around his body. Seven of the eight species still growing in the region, some 60,000 years later, remain in use as medicinal herbs. Two of these herbs from ancient times, marshmallow and yarrow, grow in my physic garden. Marshmallow is soft and gentle, both in its appearance and nature. It provides leaves and roots rich in soothing mucilage to treat ulcers, gastritis, coughs, bronchial problems and cystitis. Yarrow has been a healer of injured soldiers, certainly from the period of the Trojan Wars and probably in far earlier times, through to the First World War. The herb checks haemorrhaging and encourages the growth of scar tissue. It is still used in herbal medicines to treat a variety of conditions.

It is fascinating to trace the history of medicinal herbs, though there is only space for brief comments here. The Chinese Red Emperor, Shen-Nung, wrote the Pen Ts'ao Ching some 4,000 years ago. This work lists 366 plant drugs then in use. Clearly such a treasure-house of knowledge had been brought together over a vast period of time even then.

In the eighteenth century B.C. King Hammurabi of Babylon ordered valuable information to be carved on stone tablets and kept as official records. Part of this was medicinal knowledge and two more herbs in my garden were included; liquorice and mint, *(Mentha viridis)*. Dark red liquorice root is yellow in the centre and largely grown for medicinal use. The main sweet ingredient, glycyrrhizin, (50 times sweeter than sugar) is anti-inflammatory and useful both for soothing coughs and acting as an expectorant. Peppermint, a hybrid between the *Mentha aquatica* of early times and *Mentha spicata*, is valued in herbal teas. The essential oil combats indigestion and colic. A flavouring for medicines and other products, it also has other properties of its own.

Trade in herbal drugs was already well established by 1500 B.C. In Mesopotamia, India and Egypt the same herbs were being used and clearly medical knowledge was exchanged. More of our familiar herbs emerge in physician's prescriptions. The seeds of linseed *(Linum usitatissimum)* were already harvested for a soothing oil to mix in cough medicines and poultices; the mucilage, together with the glycerides of linoleic and linolenic acids, acting internally to relieve bronchial problems and externally in poultices to relieve burns and scalds. Flax is obtained from the stem of the plant which has pretty, pale blue flowers, a delicate delight in any physic garden. Fennel, which in clay soil will tower above the other herbs with its intense aniseed perfume, was also appreciated medicinally, as well as in the kitchen. Soothing inflammation in eyes and the digestive system alike, fennel also increases the milk in nursing mothers.

"Herbals" as we know them, with lists of herbs and information on their healing properties, began around 400 B.C. in ancient Greece. Three hundred years later, Crataeus, physician to Mithridates VI Eupator, King of Pontus, wrote a herbal illustrated with paintings of the plants; a wonderful step forward in ensuring correct identification.

Agrimony *(Agrimonia eupatoria)* is thought to have been named in honour of Mithridates Eupator, as the king was certainly deeply interested in herbs. Agrimony has been taken inwardly for liver problems and applied outwardly to treat wounds and sores. It continues to be used in herbal treatments for liver complaints and for diarrhoea and inflammations. It is one of the prettiest of the physic herbs with a tall spire of tiny yellow flowers reaching up into the summer sunshine.

More herbals were written, some far less accurate than others, until an army surgeon with the Roman Legions in the first century A.D. Dioscorides, decided to write an authoritative and complete herbal. With his practical knowledge as a surgeon and physician, the range of healing herbs he had encountered in travelling from one country to another across Europe, and thorough training; Dioscorides was perhaps in the perfect position to write a truly great work. The Roman army carried herbal stocks which included not only the dried plants, but also seeds and plants to ensure future supplies. Their foresight in doing this meant they brought many Mediterranean herbs to northern Europe and Britain with them. Sage and thyme, both so important to us over the centuries and still a must in every herb garden, came with the Romans. Both of course, are antiseptic and antibacterial, making them valuable in fighting infections.

It should not be imagined that Britons had no medicine of their own at this period. The Celts were skilled in healing with herbs and the Druid knowledge was considerable. For 500 years before the Romans invaded, medicine was protected by law and contact with Greek herbal practices had been made through trade with the Phoenicians. Druids appear to have made wide use of vervain, amongst other herbs; a plant which is magically graceful and fragile in form, in keeping with its associations with sorcery. Vervain is in fact a nervine and sedative still given to treat asthma, whooping cough, and a range of complaints including metabolic disorders.

What remained of "Roman" knowledge and plant introductions survived through the Dark Ages together with native healing remedies. The Anglo-Saxon Leechbooks reveal fascinating glimpses of sometimes complex recipes, occasionally ingeniously using repetitive chants or prayers as a method of timing while heating or stirring herbs. The recipes are from several sources, some appearing to be downright fanciful but others showing use of herbs such as white horehound and elecampane for coughs, which would have been effective. Thought was also given to diet in disease.

Betony was a great favourite at this period, treating serious agues and fevers. In addition, it was popular for all manner of problems with the head, including ears and eyes and for treating head injuries. For this reason I grow it in my physic beds, allowing its mauve, trumpet-like flowers to proclaim a herb still worthy of notice. It continues to be used particularly as a sedative and expectorant. Some disease in the eighth to eleventh centuries was believed to be brought about by flying venoms (applied to sudden infections – a picturesque description of bacteria with less than accurate biological origins) or less credibly from the arrows of wicked elves. The patient having been "elf-shot". However, many of the recipes, stripped of their magical language, show real herbal knowledge which must have been effective.

Herbal medicine in Britain had changed only slowly as monasteries were built and their physic gardens stocked. They became the repositories of written healing knowledge, and of medicinal plants brought from other countries. While monks and nuns cared for the sick, they were not allowed to shed blood and so when surgery was necessary they called in a lay medic. However, development of medicine was hampered by the definite teaching of the Church that healing should be obtained through prayer and not by resorting to medicine. The role of the village "herb woman" in offering her services just the same, takes on the later familiar links with witchcraft in the common mind from here on. The lady of the manor also held a role in caring for the welfare of her household and other workers. She too made home remedies.

One man who was to have far-reaching effects on the future of medicine in general was Paracelsus. Born in 1493, the son of a physician interested in alchemy, Paracelsus spent part of his childhood in a mining town in Germany. This allowed him to observe the symptoms of poisoning from the minerals which were mined there. Interested in the causes of disease and with a great belief that herbs grew where they were needed, and did not have to be imported at great price; he challenged the authorities of the time. Following his father as a physician and alchemist, Paracelsus used alchemy to research the healing properties and actions of herbs, for which he has been regarded as the founder of chemical pharmacology. He also gave tiny doses of poisonous minerals to antidote the effects of other poisons, a practice later to be used again in homoeopathy.

Meanwhile the Elizabethan housewife in Britain, using recipes and practical knowledge handed down for many generations, stocked her own herb garden and filled her cupboards each summer with cough syrups, liniments, ointments and herbal leaves, roots, flowers and bark. If the household was rich enough she would have her own stillroom where she could make perfumed and medicinal waters.

So many herbs were popular at this time for a variety of reasons, that it is difficult to pick one out. Rosemary comes to mind first, because it was present at almost every Elizabethan celebration as well as times of sickness and bereavement. Always a protective herb, it acted both as a stimulant and calming agent and it was believed could ward off all manner of evil. Rosemary helped cold diseases, loss of speech, toothache, a weak memory, dim eyes, jaundice and so on. Culpeper writes that it was as much used as any other herb.

Many theories as to the causes of disease were explored during the next 200 years, mainly at the expense of the suffering. Medicine developed and again a figure came forward in Germany to challenge accepted practices.

A professor at Leipzig University, Hahnemann (1755-1843) studied the theory that like cures like. He concluded that certain herbs were effective because they produced a similar illness in the patient's body, stimulating their own body defences to overcome both. By taking cinchona when healthy and producing symptoms in his own body resembling those of his malarial patients who responded to quinine, Hahnemann proved his theory. He was then ready to make further experiments on himself with equally meaningful results. Later, his students also "proved" more herbs in the same way. Finally he began testing these proved remedies on patients, finding the more he diluted them the greater their effectiveness as a cure. We now know this method of treatment as homoeopathy. Herbs are included in the remedies together with minerals and poisonous substances such as snakes' venom.

In the last century homoeopathy came close to becoming the accepted form of medicine in Britain. It is again growing in popularity and a "new" therapy to the scene, aromatherapy, is also being applied on a small scale in clinics and hospitals as an alternative therapy.

Aromatherapy, along with herbal medicine, is in fact thousands of years old. We find references to burning aromatic herbs, enclosing the patient in a cloud of therapeutic aroma from the earliest times. Anointing with aromatics appears many times in the Old Testament of the Bible and the Greeks were aware of both sedative and stimulating perfumes in medicine. Aromatherapy, as we understand it, using therapeutic essential oils in massage, in infusers, even in ventilators in intensive-care units and in air-conditioning systems, began with research at the end of the last century.

This research revealed the antiseptic properties of many essential oils. Rene-Maurice Gattefosse was not originally interested in their medicinal possibilities, but was a chemist working in the perfume industry. A chance near-tragedy when an explosion badly burned his hand, led him to discover the healing power of the essential oil of lavender which he used to kill the pain. When a colleague set up an aromatherapy clinic in America Gattefosse was eager to give it publicity. His first book, *"Aromatherapie"* was published in 1928.

Since then aromatherapy has grown considerably in popularity and the essential oils are becoming widely available. In the pages which follow I have detailed the uses of the herbs in herbal medicine, and homoeopathy and aromatherapy where applicable.

# Herbal Medicine

THE whole philosophy of herbal medicine differs from the allopathic view which most Westerners are accustomed to taking. The notion of using herbs to thwart the "wicked elves" which caused disease was popular in the Anglo-Saxon period and many medicinal herbs were credited with protective powers. This is the closest herbal medicine has come to the modern treatments which seek to kill the cause of the disease, or sometimes merely to stop the symptoms. Herbal treatment seeks instead to support the patients own powers of recovery, looking upon their body, mind and spirit as a whole. Symptoms of the workings of the body's own protection mechanisms, fighting the disease, may be viewed as constructive if controlled and assisted.

The herbalist responds with quite different treatments for fever or some inflammatory conditions. Herbs may be used by a skilled herbalist to support the body temperature in a fever. In this way the optimum conditions can be met for the body to destroy the infection. Sometimes a counter-irritant herb may be deliberately used in order to promote a better blood supply to an inflamed part, so speeding the removal of dead cells and waste products to aid natural repair. Dosage in treatments is calculated with deference to old age as well as to extreme youth . When babies are breast-fed, the mother may be given the remedy which is then passed through her body to the infant.

People tend to think that while drugs are dangerous, medicinal herbs are safe. This is a concept which needs to be examined carefully. Herbal medicine, administered by a qualified herbalist who has undergone a long and thorough training are possibly safer than drugs. This is because drugs administer an active ingredient aimed at action on one particular part of the body or body function. When altered rapidly, this may produce strong reactions elsewhere. If, on the other hand, the whole herb is given in some form, the patient is being treated by the active principles, together with the other substances which nature has included in the structure of the plant. Even an essential oil can be made up of over 50 ingredients which balance each other. The resulting effect of herbal medicine is likely to prove less dramatic with fewer side effects. Occasionally a plant contains a substance which directly inhibits a predictable side reaction.

Certain herbs are, however, very powerful and toxic. Refer to the lists at the end of this section which indicate herbs not to be used in pregnancy and irritants and poisons.

Naturally some herbs will have unpleasant side-effects on a few people and for this reason it is wise always to test a small amount of a herbal application before undertaking a full treatment. Allergies appear to be much more common than previously. Where herbs are likely to cause a skin rash or other problems through handling I have mentioned this in the notes on the individual herbs. Anyone suffering from asthma or a heart condition should avoid using inhalations or being in close contact with powerfully fragrant herbs. Stripping dried herbs from the stems can cause allergic reactions in sensitive people. This may be avoided by doing it out of doors.

Although the more powerful healing plants are discussed in this section, the recipes are restricted to safe remedies which my family, friends and I have used over a number of years and found helpful. They are not intended to be applied to serious conditions, or those which persist. These should be properly diagnosed and treated by a medical practitioner or qualified therapist. However, I would point out that the dosage and frequency of dose should be followed with care. Please remember that more than one cold remedy taken alongside each other whether one is from a pharmacy or not is potentially dangerous. Pregnancy is a particularly vulnerable time when special care should be taken. Where possible avoid taking all but herbs or drugs known to be safe during the first three months. Some herbs have been used over the centuries to cause abortions or may produce unwanted side effects. The most powerful are listed on page 161, together with emmenagogues which increase menstrual flow. On the advice of a trained aromatherapist I have also listed those essential oils to be avoided during this time. Always check with a professional therapist or medical herbalist when wishing to use treatments during pregnancy.

I have tried in the details on individual herbs to restrict technical information to that frequently requested. While not giving details of the entire composition of the herb, I have simply related the more important known active ingredients and their action within the body. In some cases this has been more thoroughly researched than others. My sources in this have been *Potter's New Cyclopaedia of Botanical Drugs and Preparations* by R. C. Wren, F.L.S. (revised edition 1988), *The Macdonald Encyclopedia of Medicinal Plants* by Roberto Chiej (English translation 1984) *Out of the Earth* by Simon Mills, 1991 and, for this second edition, *The Physician's Desk Reference for Herbal Medicine 1999*.

Here and there you will find mention of alkaloids, glycosides, tannins, acids, essential oils and mucilage. For those who wish to understand these substances and their actions a little better, I will briefly describe them here.

Alkaloids are very powerful and potentially toxic substances. However, only some of the many herbs which contain them are poisonous. These generally give rise to very clear warning symptoms, such as convulsions, vomiting or diarrhoea. The level of alkaloids in growing plants varies according to the season, weather, time of day and phase of the moon. Plants which are poisonous due to alkaloids in foliage are usually more so after a long, hot spell than at the end of winter, for instance. In remedies the alkaloid is less soluble in water than in alcohol. The best known are morphine, the chief constituent of opium, atropine in deadly nightshade, and nicotine in tobacco.

In the *Boraginacae* family alkaloids are present in varying degrees. Houndstongue is regarded as a poisonous plant, due to its alkaloid content, and comfrey as potentially toxic in large amounts as the alkaloids can cause liver damage. Borage contains the same pyrrolizidine alkaloids and recent research has led to advice not to eat the leaves in any quantity. The flowers are perfectly safe.

Another especially potent and more common active substance in plants are glycosides. All glycosides will separate into a sugar and a non-sugar in water. The digitalin in foxgloves is a cardioactive glycoside, acting directly on the heart and being, as a result, potentially dangerous. Cyanogenic glycosides are found in elder, and other berries. These are only toxic in large doses. In elderberries they are rendered harmless by cooking.

Tannin is well known to us in "tea", it is in fact contained in varying amounts in all green leaves. Some people are allergic to tannin and can only drink such herbal teas as chamomile and rosehip. Tannin has a healing action due to its ability to bind albumen in the mucous membranes or the skin, which acts as a protective barrier against bacteria. The effect is also that of a local antiseptic and tannins are particularly helpful for burns and reducing bleeding. Tannin can also affect the way in which other substances in the herb act.

Mucilage is contained in many plants but only a few offer enough to be of medicinal use. Mucilage forms a protective and soothing layer over inflamed mucous membranes. This enables it to relieve vomiting, colic and diarrhoea for instance by soothing the digestive tract. Mucilage can only help where it comes into direct contact with the problem area, except where a reflex action is concerned, as from the digestive tract to the bronchial tubes. The nerve connection retained from the developing embryo into the adult body, is why marshmallow is so good for coughs. In addition, mucilage can aid the effects of other substances in the herb.

A variety of acids are present in plants and their fruits. These are generally astringent and have other individual qualities. Bitters, which give many herbs their familiar bitter flavour are also important, acting mainly on the efficiency of the digestive system, including the liver and pancreas.

The essential oil of a herb may come from the flowers, leaves, root, bark, seeds or peel. The content varies during the day, as the oil is drawn out of the leaves or flowers by the sun. This is why herbs are gathered for drying before the sun has been on them for any length of time. The essential oil may be extracted by distillation at high pressures and temperatures; or, in the case of citrus oils, such as bergamot, it is expressed from the peel of the fruit. Extraction from delicate flowers such as jasmine and rose is more complicated. Since the fragrances would be damaged at high temperature, they are first macerated in a solvent, and the flower mixture is then centrifuged, separating the oils and waxes. Lastly these are distilled at a low temperature in a vacuum.

Enfleurage – laying freshly gathered flowers on cold, purified fat spread over a glass frame – is another method widely used with flowers, such as jasmine. After some 70 days when the fat is saturated with perfume from a daily replenished harvest of flowers, the resulting pomade is washed with alcohol. The alcohol can then be evaporated to give the pure essential oil.

Essential oils are made up of many different substances. They may be thought of as expressing the "personality" of the herb in a highly concentrated form. Pure essential oils vary in their toxicity and are powerful therapeutic agents. They should not be used without knowledge of the correct dosage and restrictions, for instance not using certain essential oils when pregnant (see page 161). Some, such as rue, are not safe to be used at all in the home.

The medicinal effect of numerous essential oils is very valuable. A great number of essential oils are antiseptic, and others, in keeping with the nature and properties of the individual herb, may be diuretic, tonic, antispasmodic, expectorant, or anti-inflammatory in their action.

Other plant oils expressed from the seeds, or fruits, which have not been distilled and are therefore less concentrated, are also famous for their medicinal actions. Castor oil, and linseed oil from flax have had a long medicinal use. More recently evening primrose and borage (starflower) oils have been more widely appreciated. Such oils can also serve as base oil carriers for essential oil treatments.

Plants also contain sugars and starches. A substance related to starch, which has a valuable medicinal use is inulin. This is found in the tuberous roots of elecampane in large amounts.

In order to take advantage of any or several of these substances medicinally, it is necessary to harvest the correct part of the plant at the time when that particular substance is most available. Season, weather conditions and the health and maturity of the herb in question all need to be considered to give the best results. The leaves of herbs are best collected in mid-morning, after the dew has dried, but before the sun's draws out the essential oil. Most herbs contain the greatest amount of essential oil just before they flower. Mints for instance, should be harvested as the flowers begin to make an appearance in buds. Only leaves in perfect condition should be gathered, discarding any with insect damage or of poor quality. With thyme and rosemary, I prefer to gather them just as the first flowers open, as this makes a difference to the flavour and will help the remedy to be acceptable. It must be as they first flower however, and not when some of the flowers are already dying. Marshmallow is also an exception; the leaves should be gathered when the flowers are open.

Flowers can be gathered slightly later in the day, but should be newly opened and in perfect condition. Buds are harvested as they are beginning to swell and before they show real signs of opening. These will always open a little more as they dry.

Seedheads are best cut just before they reach maturity and left to ripen completely hanging upside down inside a large paper bag, or over a cloth to catch the falling seeds. The sunflower heads should be cut when the back of the flowerhead turns yellow. Leave to stand in a warm, dry place with a length of stalk to keep the head off the floor, again over a piece of cloth. When the head is completely dry and the seeds ready, they can be shaken out.

Roots of perennial herbs are usually dug in the autumn of their second or subsequent years growth. Elecampane and marshmallow are best harvested in mid-autumn. The root is washed carefully, small rootlets removed and the main root cut into slices, 1-2cm ($\frac{1}{2}$ to $\frac{3}{4}$in) thick, and set to dry. Place them on a dish in the oven with a temperature of no more than 60°C (140°F) and the door ajar. They will take several hours to dry thoroughly. Before storing them with the lid screwed on tightly, check daily for the first few days to be sure they are completely dried. The roots of annual herbs are gathered just before the plant flowers.

Harvested herbs should be carefully kept in sealed dark glass jars and labelled with the name of the herb and the date it was harvested. Most will keep for one year only.

# HERBS FOR HEALTH

OILS - St. John's wort, Mullein (flowers), Comfrey, Yarrow, Calendula

OINTMENTS – Chickweed, Yarrow and Comfrey, Calendula, Elderflower, Cowslip

HERBS IN HONEY - Rose, Thyme, or Thyme and Sage, White Horehound, Rosemary

BATHS & FOOTBATHS - Calendula, Lavender, Rose, Lemon balm, Eau-de-cologne mint, Peppermint, Comfrey, Chamomile

MASSAGE - Rose, Biennial clary sage, Lavender, Peppermint, Rose geranium

SYRUPS - Elderflower, Elderberry, Cowslip, Clove pink, Rose, Lavender, Peppermint, Angelica, Nettle, Elecampane, Violet, Marshmallow

LIQUEURS - Rosemary, Lemon balm, Thyme, Sage, White Horehound, Peppermint, Hyssop, Fennel, Dill, Angelica, Lovage, Rose, Clove pink, Elecampane
(see Herbcraft Naturally for recipes)

# Medicinal

*Bed of Physic herbs.*

*St. John's wort oil in the making.*

# Medicinal

(Top left) *Lavender*                    *Dill*

(Left) *Feverfew*

(Below left)
*Chamomile*                              *Fennel*

# Recipe guide

Sore eyes, conjunctivitis. . . . . . . . . . . . . . . . . . . . . . . . . . . . . . . . . . . . . . fennel tea

Sore throat . . . . . . . . . . . . . . . . . . . . . . . . . . . . . sage gargle, garlic and honey
horehound honey, thyme tea

Cough . . . . . . . . . . . . . . . . . . . . . . . . . . . . . . . . . . . . . . thyme tea with honey
marshmallow syrup

Cold with catarrh . . . . . . . . . . . . . . . . . . . . . . . . . . . . . . . . . . . . . . . . inhalant

Feverish cold . . . . . . . . . . . . . . . . . . . . . . yarrow sage and peppermint footbath

Headaches . . . . . . . . . . . . . . . . . . . . . . lemon balm or chamomile tea, or dab
with essential oil of lavender

Period pains . . . . . . . . . . . . . . . . . . . . . . . . . lemon balm or raspberry leaf tea

Nausea . . . . . . . . . . . . . . . . . . . . . . . . . . . . . . . . . . . . . . . . . peppermint tea

Mouth ulcers . . . . . . . . . . . . . . . . . . . . . . . . . . mouthwash of sage gargle

Map tongue . . . . . . . . . . . . . . . . . . . . . . . . . . . . . . . . . . . . . . . . . as above

Insomnia . . . . . . . . . . . . . . . . . . . . . . bergamot tea or milk, limeflower tea
chamomile tea

Nightmares . . . . . . . . . . . . . . . . . . . . . . . . . . . . . thyme tea before retiring

Sprains . . . . . . . . . . . . . . . . . . . . . . . . . . . . . . . poultice pot marigold leaves
or comfrey leaves

Sore feet . . . . . . . . . . . . . . . . . . . . . . . . comfrey & pot marigold footbath

Deep bruises . . . . . . . . . . . . . . . . . . . . . . . . . . . . . . . . St John's wort oil

Minor burns and scalds . . . . . . . . . . . . . . . . . . . . . essential oil of lavender, then
St John's wort oil

Insect stings . . . . . . . . . . . . . . . . . . . . . . . . . . . essential oil of lavender

Indigestion . . . . . . . . . . . . . . . . . . . . . . . . . . . . . chew leaf or seeds of dill

Sunburn . . . . . . . . . . . . . . . . . . . . . . . . . . . . . . . . . . . . . . . . calendula oil

Chapped skin, grazes . . . . . . . . . . . . . . . . . . . . . . . . . . . . see ointments

# Recipes

*P*lease note the date of expiry given on the original bottle of olive oil when following the herbal oil recipes. This will guide you on replacing your oils. Hypericum, St. John's wort oil is the exception as the hypericin acts as a preservative. Test individual herbs oils or ointments for allergic reactions before using by smearing a small amount on the arm. Leave for 1 hour. Check for any inflammation. **Please also note that herbal inhalants should not be used by anyone suffering from asthma, heart conditions or high blood pressure without medical advice.**

## Hypericum Oil

This is made from the flowers of perforate St. John's wort. If these are examined closely you may see tiny red dots at the edges of the petals which mark the presence of the oil glands. The leaves are also perforated with tiny holes. The flowers should be picked when the dew has dried, generally at mid-morning. Choose perfect, newly opened flowers, insect free and drop them straight into extra virgin or pharmaceutical quality olive oil in a glass bottle. A little of the oil needs to be poured out of each bottle into another container first, to make extra space for the herb. Fill each bottle with the flowering tops including as little stem and leaf as possible. Keep pushing the flowers down into the oil with a stem from the same plant; it is amazing how many flowers even a small bottle of oil will take.

When the bottle is completely full, pour a little oil back over the flowers if necessary to ensure they are all beneath the surface. Replace the top and tilt the bottle before placing it on a sunny windowsill. For the next two to three weeks simply tilt the bottle each day as you pass, noting the changing colour of the oil. Bottles can also be stood out of doors during the day. Be aware if you do so that standing a glass bottle in strong sunlight can result in the oil expanding with the heat. If the top is screwed right down this can cause the bottle to explode. When the oil has turned a deep red, strain out the flowers through a coffee filter paper and thoroughly cleanse the bottle with hot soapy water with a final rinse of boiling water, before re-filling with the strained oil. Label and store in a cool, dark cupboard for use on burns, scalds, deep bruising, nerve damage, to relieve the pain from shingles, skin problems and grazes. The oil can also reduce scarring on older wounds and can be applied after the initial healing of an operation scar. Please note that this is not a suntan oil. Do not apply the oil immediately before exposure to hot sun as St John's wort can increase sensitivity to sunlight.

## Calendula oil

Buy one or two bottles of olive oil of pharmaceutical quality, or cold pressed, and pour off a little of the oil as above. Pick about 15-18 heads of pot marigolds to a 200ml (7 fl oz) bottle of olive oil. Dip the flowerheads briefly in cold water to remove any insects. Pat dry between layers of kitchen paper-towels. Remove the petals from the flowerheads and push them down into the oil until it is full of petals. As before, check the last petals are covered in oil, adding a little from that poured out at the beginning if necessary. Give the bottle a shake and place on a sunny windowsill for about 14 days. Alternatively, heat the bottle of petal-filled oil in a waterbath on the stove for about one hour.

At the end of this time the oil will have deepened slightly in colour. Strain out the petals through a coffee filter paper and thoroughly clean the bottle as above. Label. Keep the bottles in a cool, dark place for use on sunburn, chapped hands, nappy rash, sore nipples and superficial wounds.

Comfrey, mullein flower and yarrow oils are made in a similar way. Make the comfrey on the stove in a waterbath, rather than on the windowsill. Comfrey is especially soothing for sprains and joint pains. Mullein flower is helpful to dry skin conditions and mild ear discomfort, one drop in the affected ear twice a day. If the earache or mild deafness continues, longer than 24 hours consult a medical practitioner.

**BEESWAX OINTMENTS**     600ml (1 pint) sweet almond or olive oil
Herb 50g (2oz) beeswax

Although other base oils can be used, sweet almond oil is gentle and enriching for the skin and gives good results.There are several really useful herbal ointments.

*Calendula* has the benefit of being both antiseptic and soothing. The flowers can be picked throughout the summer and early autumn. The base oil is best made as above. To make the ointment, set the jar of oil in a deep bowl or jug of very hot water to heat it gradually through. Cut the beeswax into cubes or pieces and melt in a pyrex bowl over a pan of boiling water. The oil and wax should ideally be of a similar temperature when you mix them. Add the beeswax gradually to the oil, stirring all the time. With the two combined, pour the liquid ointment into clean, sterilized jars or pots with screwtops. Seal and label. Use as required for grazes, nappy rash, sore nipples and mild skin irritations.

*Chickweed* so unpopular with gardeners, makes a soothing ointment which is particularly recommended for irritating chronic skin conditions - from skin rashes and sores to mild eczema and psoriasis. It is certainly valuable enough to warrant a place of its own in a herb garden. Make the ointment as for calendula, adding as much leaf, stem and flower of chickweed to the oil as you can for a deep green colour.

*Comfrey* ointment can be made from the leaves and will be excellent for healing cuts and grazes, so long as they are clean. Comfrey can heal so quickly at the surface level that it may seal grit or other problems inside, which will then make difficulties later. Ointment from the root has generally been used for varicose ulcers and long standing skin problems, this contains more of the pyrrolizidine alkaloids which have seen it removed from sale in some countries. Comfrey is judged perfectly safe to apply outwardly. It will also help aching joints and sprains, swellings, torn ligaments and broken bones.

In this case make comfrey oil using the waterbath method. Then follow the beeswax ointment recipe as for calendula. Add 3 drops essential oil of lavender or tea tree immediately before pouring into the jars. The root gives a better extract with a water decoction added into a cream.

*Elderflower* is a lovely, fragrant ointment to make and one which will come in handy if you gain numerous scratches on your hands when picking gooseberries and other fruit. I have also found it useful for itchy dry skin with mild eczema conditions.

Pick the elderflowers on a dry, sunny day in late morning, choosing only those which smell sweet and are in perfect condition - having newly opened.

Pour 250-500ml of sweet almond oil into a glass, pyrex or enamel pan. Remove the

143

thick stems from the umbels and push as many flowers as you can under the surface of the oil. Leave the pan over a very low heat (the lowest possible) for several hours until the healing properties are extracted and the oil is slightly coloured and fragranced.

Mix with the beeswax as described in *Calendula,* pot and label.

*Cowslip* has to be grown in your garden as cowslips in the wild are protected plants. If you can grow your own, this ointment will be a treat for your hands or face. It has an old reputation as a superior beauty treatment for ageing skin and is very soothing. It is further improved with the addition of essential oil of frankincense.

Make the ointment as above, steeping the cowslips, (yellow part of flowers only) in sweet almond oil over a very low heat for several hours. There should be as many flowers as you can push beneath the surface of the oil. Thicken with liquified beeswax as with other ointments and as you pour the ointment into the pots add 2 drops of essential oil of frankincense to each pot. Give them a quick stir and seal immediately.

## ALTERNATIVE herbal ointment
To each jar of cold cream (which should be pure and unscented) pick sufficient herb to fill the liquified cream. Spoon the cold cream into a small heat-proof bowl and set this over a pan of gently boiling water. While the cold cream is melting, wash the herb in cold water to remove any insects and pat dry on kitchen paper-towels. Place the herb in a small nylon straining bag or a square of muslin.

Set the bag into the liquid cold cream, pushing the petals beneath the surface with a wooden spoon. There should be sufficient to completely "fill" the liquid. Leave for 45-60 minutes, checking now and then that the pan beneath is not boiling dry, and adding water as necessary. The colour of the cold cream should now be that of the herb.

When you are satisfied with the colour, remove the herb, and squeeze as much of the cold cream from the bag as you can between two wooden spoons. Pour into pots, label and store in a cool place for use. 2 drops of essential oil of lavender or 3 drops simple tincture of benzoin can be added to any of the creams or ointments at the end of the recipe.

If wished petroleum jelly may be used instead of cold cream.


## *Marigold footbath*
Put 3 tablespoons of pot marigold petals and 2 tablespoons each of chopped pot marigold leaf and comfrey leaf into a large bowl. Pour over 1.2 litres (2 pints) of boiling water and leave to stand for several minutes. After about ten minutes strain out the herb, being careful to squeeze leaves and flowers well. The comfortably hot, pulped herb can be applied as a poultice to any parts of your feet which are particularly painful. Dilute the infusion with a similar amount of water to bring it to a hot, but comfortable temperature. Add 2 drops essential oil of lavender. Soak your feet in this for ten to fifteen minutes and relax. Add extra hot water if the footbath cools too rapidly.

## *Yarrow, Sage and Peppermint footbath*
For feverish colds. Place 1½ tablespoons of each dried herb, (using the purple sage if you have it) in a large bowl. Pour over 1.2 litres (2 pints) of boiling water and breathe in the steam while waiting for it to cool. As soon as it is a comfortable temperature, sit with your feet soaking in the bowl for 10 minutes and then go straight to bed. Use once a day.

## Inhalant for catarrh

1½ tablespoons dried chamomile flowers
1 tablespoon dried purple sage leaves
1 tablespoon limeflowers and bracts
2 teaspoons dried peppermint
pinch of basil

Spoon the herbs into a mixing bowl and pour over 1.2 litres (2 pints) of boiling water. Lean over the bowl with your head covered by a towel, breathing in the fumes with your eyes shut. Take short breaks for "air" every few minutes and continue for about ten minutes, leaving the uncovered bowl close to you while the contents are cooling. Repeat if necessary once or twice a day. See page 142 for caution.

For any condition which does not respond within a few days, seek medical advice.

## Inhalant for young children

For toddlers still in a cot it may be found helpful to place a bowl of inhalant beneath the cot where the child cannot reach it, but receives the fumes. One tablespoon of chamomile to 1.2 litres (2 pints) of water will be sufficient for a child between 9 and 18 months. This can then be increased in effectiveness with the addition of ½-1 tablespoon of sage.

## Sage gargle

Make a pot of sage tea, preferably with purple sage leaves. Infuse 2 tops of sage with about 4 leaves each to 2½ cups of boiling water. The leaves should be washed briefly in cold water and then torn into a non-metal teapot or jug. Leave to stand for five minutes before pouring. Gargle with a wine glass of the tea as soon as it is cool enough to do so. Tea left in the pot can be used as a gargle a few hours later. The tea need not be swallowed, which means it can still be used in pregnancy. Gargle two or three times daily for a throat infection.

Sage tea can also be a soothing mouthwash for mouth ulcers, sore gums and a condition of the tongue which involves loss of the surface when eating certain foods, commonly known as map tongue.

## Garlic honey

Peel and slice 2 cloves of garlic, 3 if they are small. Pour over sufficient honey to cover them. Leave covered for 2 hours. Take one teaspoon as needed at the first sign of a cold.

## Horehound honey

Pour 0.45kg (1lb) of honey into a thick-bottomed pan and heat gently. Add 2 tablespoons of freshly gathered, washed and chopped white horehound leaves. Simmer the honey and horehound very slowly over a low heat for 25 minutes. Do not allow the honey to boil. Stir occasionally. Remove from the heat. When the honey is sufficiently cooled, pour both honey and herb back into the jar and set in a cool place for five days.

After five days, pour the honey back into a thick-bottomed pan and re-heat as before on a low setting. Simmer gently for a further 15 minutes and, when cooled enough, strain the honey back into the cleaned jar and seal. Label clearly. The honey will now be bitter to taste.

Take two teaspoons of the honey twice daily at the onset of a cold, repeating for two days even if all symptoms vanish. If taken later in the development of the infection, honey helps to ease catarrh.

Other herb honeys are made in the same way, see cookery 101.

### Marshmallow Syrup

If you wish to make this syrup from the freshly harvested root in spring or autumn, clean 120g (4oz) of root and chop into small cubes or slice. Place this, or 60g (2oz) of dried root into a large jug. Pour over 900ml (32 fl oz) of cold, boiled water. Leave to stand overnight. Next morning strain and measure the liquor. Add 2g of sugar to each ml of liquid, that is 800g (1lb 12oz) to 400ml (14 fl oz) of liquor. Heat in a thick bottomed pan to dissolve the sugar. Pour into sterilized bottles. Refrigerate after opening. This is a pleasant tasting, soothing remedy for a dry cough for children or adults. If there is no improvement after 3 days consult a medical practitioner.


## MEDICINAL TEAS

| | |
|---|---|
| Chamomile-German or Roman - | Soothing and calming for insomnia, as a mouthwash after dentistry and for toothache. |
| Elderflowers - | Colds, sinusitis, hayfever. |
| Fennel - | For flatulence and colic. Increases nursing mother's milk. Cold tea as eyewash for mild conjunctivitis. See recipes. AVOID early pregnancy. |
| White Horehound- | Bronchitis, whooping cough. Aids digestion. Externally for wounds. |
| Horsetail - | Mineral rich. Helpful for healthy growth of hair and nails. May aid joint problems. Must be *Equisetum arvense.* |
| Lemon Balm - | Stomach cramps, tension headaches, depression. Tonic for heart and circulatory system. |
| Motherwort - | Delayed menstruation, tonic in menopause, helpful For anxiety. AVOID early pregnancy. |
| Marshmallow - | From leaf for lung problems and inflamed urinary system. From root for digestive system. Please note. The absorption of other drugs taken with marshmallow tea may be delayed. |
| Meadowsweet - | Anti-rheumatic and anti-inflammatory. Best antacid herb, easing nausea and heartburn. Reduces fever. Do not take meadowsweet tea if you are allergic to aspirin. |
| Nettle - | Pleasant, mineral rich tea, helpful against chilblains and rheumatism. Tonic in spring, diuretic. |
| Peppermint - | Fevers, colds. Mild anaesthetic to the stomach wall, relieves nausea and vomiting. |
| Rosehip - | Winter tea against colds. Extra vitamin C. |
| Rosemary - | Stimulates circulation and nerves, good for mental exhaustion. Calms digestion. AVOID when pregnant. |
| Purple Sage - | Inflammations of mouth, tongue, gums or throat as mouthwash or gargle. Increases nursing mother's milk. AVOID during pregnancy. Reduces sweating and hot flushes. Antiseptic wash externally for minor injuries. |

Thyme -                           Colds, sore throat, irritable coughs, Childhood
                                  diarrhoea and nightmares. Antiseptic wash. AVOID in
                                  pregnancy. See recipes.

Most herb teas should be made with 1-2 teaspoons dried herb in a non-metal teapot.
Warm the pot first, pour boiling water over the herb and leave to stand brewing for 10
minutes for a medicinal effect. Serve strained with honey if needed to sweeten. Blends
of herbs are often more effective than a single herb. 2 or 3 cups of any tea will give you
the medicinal effect and a particular tea should not be taken over many days unless this
is required. A medical herbalist should be consulted for all but those conditions you
would normally treat yourself at home. Taking some herb teas in a medicinal dose
alongside certain drugs may alter their action, seek advice. Some herbs are appropriate
only at certain periods during pregnancy, again seek advice.

## *Thyme tea with honey*
Infuse 5 good sprigs of flowering thyme or 2 level teaspoons of thyme dried when
flowering in 2½ cups of boiling water for five minutes. Strain and sweeten with one
heaped teaspoon of honey per cup. Drink slowly while hot for coughs, colds and
bronchial problems.

## *Fennel tea*
Infuse 2 teaspoons chopped or torn fresh fennel in 2 cups of boiling water. Leave to
stand until the tea is cool. Soak pads of cotton wool in the tea and lay these over the eyes,
dripping a little into the eye itself, or use as an eyebath. The first method is often
preferable as this involves lying down for 10-15 minutes with your eyes closed,
relaxing, which is always a welcome rest to the whole body.
This will relieve sore eyes after swimming and mild conjunctivitis. If the symptoms of
inflammation persist after two treatments - that is, after 24 hours - consult your medical
practitioner.

# Herbs to grow for use at home
*Chamomile*

CHAMOMILE has a Victorian image in many people's minds. It is associated with granny's cures for headaches, stomach aches and cramps, colds and fevers. A soothing, calming agent, it reduces inflammation while fighting infections and therefore is useful as a compress for wounds and swellings. Of course, the Victorians didn't discover chamomile; they simply carried on the traditional remedies of previous generations. Chamomile lawns, popular before grass was cut and tended as it is today, yield a health-giving aroma which once eased the suffering of consumptives.

Long, long ago the ancient Egyptians dedicated chamomile to the sun because it was so effective against fevers. The tea was also used to soak compresses for sore eyes and skin infections. To treat toothache, linen bags were filled with the flowers and these held against a hot water bottle to warm them before placing them next to the cheek. At least this cure had no nasty taste! A mouthwash of the tea made it an even more effective painkiller. Today we can still hold warm chamomile tea in our mouths after dental treatment, or warmed chamomile teabags against the affected cheek to soothe pain. I have found this helpful. To calm babies and infants add chamomile tea to their bathwater. Test first for skin reaction by placing just their hand in a diluted infusion and wait 24 hours to be sure no skin reaction follows before placing them in the bath with added infusion.

The oil in the flowerheads consists mainly of esters of tiglic and angelic acids and chamazulene. The effect is analgesic, anti-inflammatory and antispasmodic, while reducing the temperature. Chamomile is also disinfectant and encourages bile and gastric secretions, discouraging vomiting. The lotion is applied to wounds, sore nipples and nappy rash.

Since steam distillation extracts the anti-inflammatory chamuzulene content of chamomile, its use in the steam inhalant in the recipes is particularly helpful if the bowl is kept covered, allowing recondensing steam to drain back into the inhalation. Chamomile tea for infections is made even more effective by the addition of a slice of lemon to the infusion. The double chamomile flower or wild *Matricaria recutita* is recommended for medicinal use. Flowers should retain their white colour when dried to be of the best quality. Neither double nor single flowers should be taken together with medicines containing quinine.

Chamomile flowers have been smoked as tobacco by asthma patients and chewed by those trying to give up smoking. Liquid extract and chamomile oil are available. In homoeopathy chamomilla is best known for calming distressed children who are teething, have sunburn or fevers. Both chamomile German and chamomile Roman oils are used in aromatherapy for quietening children, treating nausea, fevers, depression, eczema and so on.

## *Dill*

As already explained in earlier sections, dill has been appreciated as a digestive and tranquillizing herb for nearly 5,000 years and possibly much longer. Other medicinal uses of dill have now been discontinued, but it is always interesting to look back at these treatments, since occasionally some are revived in the light of modern knowledge.

Historically dill was made up into plasters with sheep's tallow to ease the pain of haemorrhoids. Pregnant women were advised to sit in baths containing decoctions of dill for the pains and "windiness" suffered in their condition. Dill flowers were steeped in oil to treat headaches and the seeds in oil applied to moist ulcers. The cooked seeds, either roasted or fried, were added to plasters to relieve itchings of the private parts.

Perhaps again we are talking about haemorrhoids with "imposthumes of the fundament".

In modern times dill has been regarded as antispasmodic for colic and gastric problems, and as a reliable stomachic in gripe water. It is useful for nursing mothers as well as babies.

Dill grown in East Anglia, England, has been used pharmaceutically, as the English oil contains phellandrine, also present in Spanish dill, but not necessarily in useful amounts in the herb grown elsewhere.

The fruits contain between three and five per cent of essential oil, about 50 per cent of this being carvone. The composition of the oil is similar to that of caraway, with less carvone. It also contains limonene, phellandrine, anethole and eugenol. Concentrated dill water is given for wind and colic.

Dill is not used in homoeopathy, but in aromatherapy the oil finds a similar place to that of the herb in herbal medicine. It is used to treat indigestion, wind, gastric problems, constipation and nervous headaches; the last returning our attention to earlier times when the flowers were steeped in oil. One, at least, of those discontinued applications has returned with a fresh therapy.

## *Fennel*

This herb is famous for treating sore eyes and conjunctivitis. Pliny wrote that serpents, after shedding their skins, sharpened their sight by rubbing against the plant. Whether this observation began the use of fennel as an eyewash, or simply reinforced it, is not clear. However, tea of the green leaf or the seed is certainly effective. Midwives once washed the eyes of newborn babies with fennel tea and a strong decoction was applied for cataracts in older patients.

The healing properties of fennel are not confined to eye treatments; the Greeks used fennel to treat 40 different diseases. Further back in history we find it mentioned in the medical papyri of Egypt. An ancient use of modern interest, is in slimming. The first Olympic Game's competitors were fed on Florence Fennel bulbs to give them strength without putting on weight. In Elizabethan times we find much emphasis on fennel for those who wished to grow lean. Recent research indicates, sadly, that sufficient fennel oil to actually make you lose weight would involve an almost lethal dose!

Syrup of fennel was once given as an expectorant for coughs and the grated root was eaten with bran as a laxative. Centuries ago, sufferers from measles and smallpox might have found themselves treated with fennel.

The seeds contain the highest amount of essential oil, 5 per cent or more, with anethole being the main constituent. Anethole and a tincture of fennel have been used in experiments to reduce the toxic effects of alcohol on the body with some success.

Fennel is antispasmodic and digestive, helping with colic, expectorant, as suggested by the earlier mention of cough mixture, and increases the milk of nursing mothers when taken as a tea. The diuretic effects make it a good herb to treat bloating, before or during menstruation. It is also helpful to the liver. Do not take in pregnancy.

Excessive doses cause spasms and delusions. Administered wisely, fennel has a reputation for giving longevity and strength - and even for improving your memory!

In aromatherapy fennel oil has similar uses to the plant. Though of course it would be dangerous to apply neat fennel oil to the eyes! It has been used as a digestive, to stimulate milk in nursing mothers, as an expectorant and antispasmodic. Fennel oil can help rehabilitate alcoholics when used by a trained aromatherapist. It is also the main oil for cellulitis. The oil should not be used by epileptics.

## *Feverfew*

Although its recent popularity in treating migraines and rheumatoid arthritis may classify this herb in some people's minds as a "modern discovery", feverfew has a long history of medicinal use. The Anglo-Saxon Leechbooks mentioned it, as the name suggests, in relation to treating fevers. There is a wonderful recipe for lent addle, or typhus, as it has been translated, where feverfew is given together with fennel and other herbs. Masses are first sung over the herbs after which they were soused with ale and boiled in holy water. More charms and prayers accompanied taking the medicine.

By the 16th century feverfew was taken by women during a difficult childbirth. The herb was also crushed to make an analgesic poultice; it was bound to the wrists or made into infusions for fevers and even pressed into suppositories to treat piles. Gerard recommended feverfew also for giddiness, vertigo and melancholy. Culpeper commented that the herb was not much used at that time, but deserved more notice. In 1772 John Hill directs us to its modern use by praising it as the best herb known for severe headaches. Over the following centuries feverfew was grown in many cottage gardens under the name of the "headache plant".

The leaves are most usually eaten in sandwiches, an exact dose being therefore difficult to determine. They are taken regularly to avoid migraine attacks, and the flowers are included in some medicinal preparations. The plant contains tannic acid and a bitter principle, anthemic acid. Other acids are present together with sesquiterpene lactones, the most important of these being parthenolide. The last is thought to inhibit prostaglandin production and the release of an acid in the body, which makes the herb effective against fevers. It also inhibits the secretion of certain substances in the blood which may explain feverfew's success in treating migraine and rheumatoid arthritis.

Side-effects are however experienced by some patients taking feverfew on a regular basis and these are being researched. Usually they consist of mouth ulcers or dermatitis but other symptoms can occur. Feverfew tablets and capsules are available, and safer to use than estimating the number of leaves to be eaten. It should be noted that neither these nor the leaf should be taken alongside arthritis drugs, warfarin or aspirin.

Feverfew is not used in homoeopathy or aromatherapy.

## *Garlic*

From the days of ancient Egypt through to modern times, garlic has had an important role as a preventative medicine. During epidemics and in countries where such diseases as cholera and typhus have been endemic, garlic has been eaten daily to maintain health.

During an epidemic of plague in the 18th century in France, four men were convicted of robbing plague victims. They were freed in return for the recipe of the vinegar which protected them from infection. Garlic was the main ingredient of this "Four Thieves Vinegar" which soon became famous.

Garlic is a powerful antiseptic which acts on the mucous membranes and fights bacteria in the digestive tract. It was given for gall bladder and liver diseases, fits, leprosy, skin problems, headaches, bronchitis, gout, sciatica, deafness, rheumatism, asthma and tuberculosis. Consumptives once wore masks soaked in diluted garlic juice over their mouths and noses in an attempt to kill the bacilli.

Although, in more recent times, it has generally been used to treat colds, bronchitis, asthma and influenza, use of garlic is increasing rapidly as its properties have been investigated. It is now known to have far more than an "antibiotic" action. Garlic oil reduces cholesterol in the blood and helps to avoid thrombosis by inhibiting the platelets in the blood from clumping together. It reduces high blood pressure and is antidiabetic: all important qualities in a herb which seems to have been created for the diseases of the 20th and perhaps 21st centuries. Taken regularly it may also be capable of preventing malignant tumours in the digestive tract. The oil neutralises the poison of insect bites and stings (apply the juice), and may help to lessen the effects of lead poisoning. The last is still being researched.

An old cure for whooping cough was to place a clove of garlic in the child's shoe. This was one of those remedies always good for a laugh, until it was realised that after an hour or so the amount of garlic in the breath was measurable, even when the clove has remained in the patients shoe!

Garlic juice, oil, syrup and tablets are available and, of course, garlic in food is healthy, even if it does make your breath smell. Nursing mothers, please note, it may give your baby colic if you eat it in any quantity.

## Lavender

Lavender is still used in modern herbal medicine, administered in a soothing role for symptoms arising from anxiety. It has treated a variety of diseases in the past. At one time the herb was so popular for treating illnesses involving the head, that caps were quilted with lavender inside, to keep the wearer in a constant atmosphere of the perfume. Historically lavender has been given to patients suffering from migraine, nausea, hysteria, sunstroke, paralysis and even convulsions. The extraordinary property of lavender was the way in which it was thought to have rendered snake and insect bites harmless. What is proven is that the essential oil of lavender can be of real help when applied to insect bites, and rather more surprisingly, it can combine with the venom of the black widow spider to form a compound which is harmless.

The antiseptic and analgesic properties of lavender are valuable in the treatment of burns, the neat essential oil being applied as soon as the area has been cooled. Decoctions of lavender have also been used to treat wounds and sores as well as burns. The powerful antiseptic qualities of the essential oil inhibit myobacterium, which has made it a helpful remedy for tuberculosis, diptheria, typhoid and pneumonia. Compresses steeped in lavender water have cooled many a feverish forehead.

Lavender oil itself has a low toxicity, even lower than chamomile. Compound Lavender Tincture and Lavender Spirit are also used medicinally. Tension headaches and hot flushes respond well to treatments with the herb. Whereas the oil is sedative, the herb can also be stimulating.

In aromatherapy, lavender oil is considered to be the safest to use, with the least likelihood of an allergic reaction. The oil is applied in a massage oil base wherever a patient needs to be relaxed and soothed. During labour it helps to strengthen the mothers contractions. In other situations it also relieves pains; a low-back and abdominal massage can be given to relieve period pains for instance.

Lavender oil is a popular remedy to balance heightened feelings after a shock, or the stress of injury. It relieves tension headaches and insomnia. One of only two herb essential oils safe to use directly on the skin, it relieves eczema and dermatitis, while stimulating new cell growth and the immune system to complete the recovery.

## Lemon balm

Lemon balm was once looked to as a magic herb which might prolong life indefinitely. It was the main ingredient in *Primum eus melissae* made by Paracelsus, a physician and alchemist of the early 16th century, who sold this "elixir of life" to royalty and the nobility.

Lemon balm can hardly be said to justify quite such a reputation, although it has been recommended by several men reputed to have lived to be well over 100 years old. It is certainly far more valuable than its present dismissal to quiet corners of the herb garden suggests. In fact many people are even more surprised to learn lemon balm is a herb at all.

The herb contains 5 per cent tannins and a small amount of essential oil which is unstable. Citral, citronellal, geraniol, linalool and limonene are some of the substances with a sedative and antiseptic action. Eugenol glycoside, caffeic acid derivatives, ursolic acid and flavonoids are also present.

In earlier centuries it was known both as a wound herb and for treating morning sickness in pregnancy and womb troubles, including a retained afterbirth; toothache, colds and headaches, cramps, nightmares, rheumatism, epilepsy, melancholia, vertigo, hysteria and insect bites. An impressive list! It is sedative, tranquillizing and anti-depressant, as well as promoting perspiration. The antispasmodic properties make it useful to relieve cramps with period pains or digestive problems. It is a safe herb which may well help us to live longer if our bodily and mental tensions are regularly soothed by its calming influence.

Lemon balm was infused in wine as a cordial for strengthening the heart, and both eaten and taken in teas to ward off early senility and impotency. The tea is best appreciated made from the fresh herb on hot summer days when it will refresh and soothe stress. As a nightcap it promotes calm sleep. A slice of lemon can be added and makes the iced tea particularly delicious.

The role of lemon balm as a wound herb is now largely forgotten. The balsamic oil does however appear to give off ozone which is antiputrescent, supplying a basis of reason for the once-common application of lemon balm leaves as dressings for sword wounds. It was considered a valuable styptic, although a few leaves to a deep wound might need considerable pressure to stop the flow of blood.

## *Marshmallow*

Once a "must" in every physic garden, marshmallow has been regarded as "medicinal" from the roots up. Pliny wrote that whoever took a spoonful of any of the mallows would be free of diseases on that day. A hopeful prediction, echoed centuries later by the apothecaries of the 16th century who sold marshmallow root as an infallible cure for injuries of all kinds. The name, Althea comes from the Greek, "altho" - meaning "to cure" - and marshmallow has lived up to its name.

In medieval times marshmallow sap was mixed with fleabane and white of egg, in a lotion the clergy smeared on the hands of those to endure trial by holding a red hot iron. Any protection must have been more than welcomed by the unfortunate accused and marshmallow was widely used in burn ointments, suggesting it was at least helpful.

The root contains between 18 and 35 per cent mucilage which has proved valuable in soothing inflamed wounds, and, in the digestive tract, both reducing stomach acidity and inflammation from ulcers, dysentery and colic. By reflex action it also soothes bronchial coughs and urinary problems. In poultices, ointments, infusions and decoctions, it has been applied both internally and externally. The peeled root enjoyed a gentler reputation than most, being given to babies to chew when they were teething. Adults also chewed marshmallow to clean their teeth and to maintain healthy gums.

The original marshmallow sweets made from the roots of the herb in paste form, were soothing for coughs and chest problems. The root was ground to a powder and boiled in milk to treat dysentery. The syrup, too, has been a popular remedy for centuries, given to children suffering from coughs, colds, and whooping cough. See recipes. The crushed fresh roots were applied as a poultice to reduce inflammation, while bruised leaves were rubbed over bee and wasp stings to ease the pain.

The Liquid Extract and Marshmallow Syrup are available for herbal treatments. Marshmallow may slow down the absorption of drugs taken alongside it.

## Peppermint

Peppermint is a strong antiseptic which has been used to treat diseases for thousands of years. Familiar to the ancient Egyptians, Chinese and North American Indians, it has been grown in Japan for its menthol content for 2,000 years. The herb contains up to 2 per cent essential oil, half of this being menthol.

The antiseptic and anti-inflammatory properties have made it a treatment for diptheria, the early stages of influenza, bronchitis and consumption. Peppermint is also antispasmodic and acts as a light anaesthetic to the stomach wall, bringing it great popularity in treating stomach aches and gastric problems. As a digestive it helps to relieve wind and stomach cramps as well as nausea and vomiting. The essence has been used in lozenges for sea-sickness and colic. Its action in increasing bile secretion makes it a herb administered for gall bladder problems.

Hot peppermint tea is the most valuable home-remedy, as a digestive after a heavy meal, or taken for faintness, headaches and nausea. The tea can be a general tonic, refreshing when drunk iced on hot days, or taken for painful periods. Nursing mothers should note that it reduces their milk. This property is used to advantage when applied externally to relieve breasts congested with milk.

Peppermint is a very useful herb which, nevertheless, should be treated with respect. I would not recommend it for very young children and have therefore included an inhalant with a gentler action in the recipes, which does not contain peppermint.

In homoeopathy *Mentha* is given for dry coughs. In aromatherapy the oil is widely used, taking full advantage of its properties as an antiseptic, digestive, anti-inflammatory herb which helps the respiratory system and the circulation. It is to be found in conjunction with other herbs in blends for varicose veins, rheumatism, influenza, indigestion, skin irritation, headaches, catarrh and bad breath.

The oil is not to be used when pregnant. It should also be noted that use of peppermint oil over long periods may cause disturbances in your sleep pattern. Even used occasionally in the evening it can cause wakefulness.

## Pot marigold

Pot marigold, otherwise known as calendula, is generally a safe, effective herb which has long been the friend of the poor, especially mothers and children. When saffron was believed to be a powerful remedy against measles, shingles, chickenpox and smallpox, those who could not afford saffron used marigold petals instead.

It is essentially antiseptic, anti-inflammatory, and a styptic, helping to control bleeding, making it an excellent wound herb. It also eases varicose veins and varicose ulcers and, without being toxic, renders warts and corns easy to remove. Marigold contains calendulin, glycosides and chlorogenic acid with other substances. The infusion is especially good for easing tired feet and will reduce pain and swelling when poured into a footbath. (see recipe page 144) The ointment can be made (see recipe page 143) or bought, and applied to cuts, chapped hands, sore nipples, nappy rash, sunburn and to reduce scar tissue.

The leaves share in the anti-inflammatory properties and can be used instead of the flowers in footbaths or applied as a compress to sprains. The flowers have a long history in being laid pulped on bee and wasp stings. The Romans used the juice from the flowers to make warts and corns easier to remove. Leaves have also been helpful in this role.

In the Middle Ages marigold tea was given to those with intestinal troubles, a practice supported by modern herbalists who still use preparations of the herb for duodenal ulcers. It should not be taken medicinally in the first three months of pregnancy.

An infusion of marigold added to your bathwater is soothing and will help to reduce any scars on your body. It is a herb to enjoy in this role, helping you to feel better in health and appearance. The petals were once made into a soothing lotion for scars, by boiling them in milk. An application which will keep rather longer is marigold oil (see recipe page 142).

*Calendula* as a homoeopathic preparation is not antiseptic as such, but inhibits the growth of germs and can be used to clean infected wounds. *Calendula* lotion can also be diluted as an eyewash and the ointment is recommended for nappy rash.

## *Rosemary*

Rosemary has always been looked upon in every sphere of its use as a protector and rejuvenator. Medicinally, these properties again come to the fore. Being a powerful antiseptic, rosemary was one of the first herbs to go up in price as soon as plague threatened. The herb has been carried in posies, burnt in sickrooms as a fumigant and, when desperate measures appeared to be needed, it was also burned in the streets against the spread of infection.

Fresh rosemary pounded with salt, or made into a lotion, was applied to wounds to cleanse and heal them. It dilates the blood vessels, increasing the blood circulation and has an anti-inflammatory effect, possibly due to the content of rosmarinic and ursolic acids and apigenin. This anti-inflammatory action is used to advantage in liniments for rheumatic pain and neuritis. Steeping or simmering the herb in wine gives a potent drink guaranteed to restore the coldest of limbs in winter. A little rosemary can be added to baths to stimulate both body and mind in a similar way. Avoid using if pregnant or suffering from hot flushes or high blood pressure.

The old belief that wearing a wreath of rosemary on your head increases brain power and memory was to have been put to the test by my son in his school examinations (reduced to a large spray for scratching his head to produce positive results). However, by the time everyone else had received a piece from his in their eagerness to try it, no-one had sufficient to find out whether it worked!

Historically rosemary is associated with restoring speech after strokes and treating nervous disorders. The tea (see recipe page 146) will certainly rejuvenate those suffering from mental exhaustion. One cup taken now and again is helpful, but it has a powerful action and repeatedly drinking rosemary tea is not recommended. It is particularly to be avoided in pregnancy. The leaves have been chewed to relieve toothache and burnt rosemary wood rubbed on as a tooth powder to preserve the teeth.

Although not generally used in home-remedies, Rosemary Oil and Rosemary Spirit are available. In aromatherapy the oil retains its familiar role as a stimulant to mind and body. It is valued in treating muscular sprains, fatigue, memory loss, headaches, influenza and arthritis.

## *Sage*

Although purple, or "red" sage is looked upon as the medicinal sage, green sage is as effective to treat mouth and throat infections and to disinfect wounds. The latin Salvia is from *salvare* - to save - and is an indication of its former importance as a healing herb.

Once given to reduce night sweats in tuberculosis, it can still be taken to lower the secretion of the sweat glands and can be helpful when suffering from hot flushes. It was also a popular remedy for snake bites, lowering blood sugar in diabetes, to treat liver problems, epilepsy, cholera and fevers and, on a popular scale, to treat the infirmities of old age.

The saying, "Why should a man die when he grows sage in his garden?" reminds us of the faith in sage to increase lifespan, by sustaining the heart and rejuvenating the eyes, mucous membranes, brain and glands.

The role of sage as a digestive has already been explored. As a home-remedy its other greatest value is in the form of a tea (see recipes page 146). The thujones and camphor in the oil are largely responsible for its strongly antiseptic effect as a mouthwash and gargle, inhibiting the growth of bacteria and fungi. It should not be taken while pregnant. The gargle can be used however without swallowing the tea.

In food, sage also prevents putrefaction by combating the toxin, cadaverine. A restorative medicinal wine can be made by infusing sage leaves in red or white wine. Drink one glass twice daily before meals. Two tops of young growth will be found sufficient for one bottle of wine. Leave to steep for four or five days before removing the herb. (This should not be taken by nursing mothers as sage can reduce lactation.)

Sage is a powerful ingredient in the inhalations included in the recipes for use against colds and influenza. It has also been one of the herbs in anti-asthmatic cigarettes and the syrup is valued for treating coughs. One of the simplest applications of sage is to rub the leaves over your teeth to clean them. The herb was once a popular ingredient in home toothpastes.

The essential oil of sage is no longer recommended in aromatherapy since reports of abdominal pains and haemorrhaging in women. Essential oil of clary sage is now used in place of common sage. However, neither should be used in any way when pregnant. Finally, essential oil of clary sage is useful in raising the spirits of patients suffering from depression.

## St John's wort

The fame of this herb for healing wounds became so great in earlier centuries that its other common name was Grace of God. The name St John's wort refers both to its flowering time around St. John's Day (24 June) and to the once-popular belief that the red healing oil seen in the tiny red dots at the sites of oil glands on the leaves and flowers, commemorated the blood of St John the Baptist. Only the perforate *hypericum* has these.

This oil, which contains hypericin is anti-inflammatory and therefore helpful for wounds, burns and rheumatism. The herb is also given to reduce anxiety in menopausal problems. St John's wort needs to be taken on a long-term basis as an infusion for anxiety. Since this can give side- effects when taken together with other medications it is not recommended as a home-treatment. It should only be taken under medical supervision. The recent warnings about St. John's wort, which has been taken in capsule form or as a tea, highlight the problems which may occur when herbal treatments are taken alongside drugs. These combinations are new and untested and may lead to unforeseen complications. If you wish to take St. John's wort check with your doctor or a medical herbalist that it is safe for you to do this. If you are already taking St. John's wort and another drug, and wish to stop taking the herb, again consult your doctor first. The official advice from the Medicines Control Agency warns those taking treatments for heart conditions, blood clots, migraine, epilepsy, asthma and chronic bronchitis,

H.I.V.; medication following transplants, and women using the contraceptive pill to check with their doctors. If you are on other medication, and wish to take St. John's wort consult your doctor or pharmacist first.

This warning does not apply to the external application of St. John's wort oil below.

Our interest in the herb for home-remedies is centred upon the ease with which the healing properties can be extracted by steeping the newly opened flowers in olive oil. (See recipes page 142). This St John's wort oil is an excellent application for minor burns and scalds. The first recipe I found for the oil, had written beside it, "Once you have this oil in your cupboard, you will never want to be without it". Little did I know at the time how true that would prove to be. Having cooled the burn with ice or cold water and dabbed it with neat essential oil of lavender to remove the pain and act as a powerful antiseptic, St John's wort oil is then applied directly or on dressings. This should be repeated three times daily until all scarring is gone.

The oil is also helpful in bringing out deep bruising, to ease rheumatic pains and for skin problems. It may be helpful as an application when recovering from shingles.

A homoeopathic preparation of *hypericum* is of benefit to patients who have had limbs amputated and suffer from phantom pains. It is used for damage to nerve endings, particularly from falls where the injury comes from landing on the coccyx.

*Hypericum* Lotion is applied homoeopathically to promote healing of burns and for injuries to nails, fingers and toes, where the nerves are damaged. It is also useful for splinter injuries. The tincture is applied to bee, wasp and hornet stings. There is no aromatherapy use associated with this herb.

## Thyme

The common garden thyme and the wild *thymus* are the only two used medicinally. The property of greatest benefit shared by them is that thyme is strongly antiseptic. We can take advantage of this by drying thyme as it is coming into flower, in readiness for autumn and winter teas. One cup of thyme tea (see recipes page 147) taken daily is a pleasant breakfast drink which will help to protect you from catching infections during the day. It is particularly effective against coughs, colds and influenza. If you have already caught a cough or a cold, then thyme tea will fight the infection, reducing the symptoms. When sweetened with honey it will also be beneficial for anyone suffering from whooping cough. Thyme honey, incidentally, has the same properties as the herb itself.

The antiseptic and antiviral properties of thyme and thyme oil come mainly from the thymol content, which is a potent disinfectant. Thyme tea can therefore, also be used to bathe wounds. Over the centuries it has treated those with chest problems, weak digestion, long and heavy periods, coughs, catarrh, headaches and nervous diseases. More interestingly it has been part of a remedy for drunkenness and taken as a preventative medicine against nightmares. I have tried this second use with a child suffering from persistent nightmares and can only observe that the tea drunk just before going to bed, was successful over a months trial.

Thymol remains an ingredient in cough lozenges, although it is now synthetically replaced in some mouthwashes and toothpastes. Thyme Liquid Extract, Thyme Oil and Elixir of Thyme are available and thyme is included in some medicinal preparations. It should be noted that overdoses of thyme are toxic, and it should not be taken in quantity during pregnancy. In aromatherapy the oil has an important role as an antiseptic but unlike ti-tree and lavender, it is not safe to be applied directly to the skin. Its antiviral and antibiotic properties are best used under the direction of a trained aromatherapist. Only thyme oil of the linalol type, from thyme grown at high altitudes is safe for use with children. Thyme oil should not be used during pregnancy.

## White horehound

Horehound is a pleasure to grow, but a little care needs to be taken when harvesting if the seedheads are already on the plant. Their enthusiasm to take hold of your clothing, clinging in particular to woollen fibres, has to be experienced to be believed. For any family with a history of repeated colds or bronchial problems, I recommend a sizeable patch of horehound in their herb garden.

Marrubin, the bitter principle in the herb, stimulates the appetite when the herb is included in tonics and acts as an expectorant in bronchitis. I have heard of numerous sufferers from chronic bronchitis who make a flask of horehound tea at night in readiness for coughing fits. As well as being included in modern herbal cough remedies, horehound is used to treat asthma. The oil dilates the veins and has antimicrobial properties. It continues to be used externally for ulcers and wounds. This use was well known in Roman times when wounds were irrigated by injecting a horehound infusion. Extensive use has been made of horehound in cough candy and ale. Today it is available as a liquid extract, syrup, concentrated infusion and powder. Some medicinal tea bags contain horehound.

At home, unless you enjoy making candy, the easiest way to use horehound is in honey. (See Recipes page 145). At the very first sign of a cold coming, take a teaspoonful of the honey. If the cold has already become established then it will reduce the symptoms. In either case repeat the dose twice daily for three days. Horehound contains traces of certain alkaloids and should be taken with care. Do bear in mind that several cold remedies alongside each other can constitute an overdose.

# Medicinal herbs of interest

## Betony

ONCE the proverb, "Sell your coat and buy betony", expressed just how valuable the herb was considered to be in treating a host of diseases. In the time of Emperor Augustus it was said to cure no less than 47 different maladies. Apuleius wrote that it was good for a man's soul as well as his body, for it protected him against visions and fearful dreams; a role echoed hundreds of years later.

The Anglo-Saxons loved betony, often mixing it with several other herbs in a variety of preparations. Studying their Leechbooks cannot fail to bring a sense of the trust placed in betony as a healing wort. We find it given for loss of appetite, sore ears, sore loins, foot addle (gout), fevers, headaches, joint pains, nosebleeds, toothache, haemorrhages and dropsy. The greatest compliment one could give in those days was to say someone had as many virtues as betony.

As a nervine it was particularly important in remedies for the head and spine. Taken as a snuff, or the flowers made into a conserve with sugar, it relieved severe headaches; while for back pain a decocotion was prescribed. For ruptures, varicose veins, cramps, digestive problems, rheumatism, heartburn, bladder and kidney problems, sores, worms, cataracts and even serpent bites, betony was a well-known remedy. Juice pressed from the herb was applied to cuts and ulcers.

It seems amazing that such a familiar and valued herb over many centuries could slip almost from notice. It finds no inclusion in *Potter's New Cyclopaedia of Botanical Drugs and Preparations*. However it appears in the new *Physicians Desk Reference* in present use for bronchitis and asthma. The herb's ancient role as a sedative is here too, for neuralgia and anxiety. The herb is listed as containing betaine, caffeic acid derivatives, diterpene lactone and flavonoids.

## Elecampane

Elecampane was already appreciated as a medicinal herb in ancient times. Prepared in many ways by different generations it has been valued over the past 2,000 years. With wondrous soft, downy leaves it was a great favourite with the Anglo-Saxons, who called it Elf-Dock. The root was an important ingredient in a famous cordial made by monks in the Middle Ages. Later the roots were infused in white port with sugar and currants. In rather different preparations the Crusaders found elecampane a useful remedy for the ills of their horses.

Roots of the plants which were over three years old, have long been gathered to make an expectorant cough candy which was suitable for bronchial coughs, asthma, colds, hay fever and the more serious pulmonary diseases, such as tuberculosis. It was presumably a fairly effective remedy even for this, as we now know elecampane contains helenin, which can destroy tubercle bacillus. Elecampane irritates the mucous membrane removing mucous and adding the antiseptic at the same time. A number of recipes for elecampane candy exist, the most popular and recently commercial being one coloured with cochineal. Elizabethan herbalists were much in favour of the soothing qualities of the herb; again they are supported by modern evidence. Elecampane is the richest source of inulin, with up to 40 per cent in the root when it is gathered in spring or autumn.

While, in the east elecampane flowers were included in herbal tonics and laxatives, and the Arabs used sprays of the leaves in steam baths to cure rheumatism, the Germans made St. Paul's wine from the root as an antidote to the plague. In England too, the root was the part of the plant most used. We now understand that the root contains both the highest quantities of helenin and inulin. It also contains a volatile oil with sesquiterpene lactones, mainly alantolactone, which is anti-inflammatory. Helenin, mentioned with reference to tuberculosis, is the active, bitter principle, a powerful antiseptic and bactericide.

Today the herb is included with other herbs in herbal teas and mixtures for asthma and bronchitis. The liquid extract, tincture, syrup, powder, decoction and medicinal wine, all have their place in modern herbal medicine.

## Evening primrose

Brought to this country from North America in 1619, the evening primrose appears only in recent years to have been fully appreciated as a medicinal herb. Use has however been made of it over the past 350 years in treating skin diseases with a decoction of the herb, a poultice, or an ointment. It has also found a place amongst the many "chest herbs" taken for asthma and bronchial problems. Having a soothing effect on the mucous membrane, evening primrose, along with marshmallow has been given for gastro-intestinal diseases and disorders. The leaves were also applied as a poultice for female problems.

Since 1917, when the seeds were first analysed and their 15 per cent oil content discovered, interest has deepened. The potential uses of this oil became more apparent two years later when it was found to contain a comparatively rare polyunsaturated acid, gamma-linoleic acid. Evening primrose oil is the most polyunsaturated oil available and was researched with reference to treating heart disease almost 30 years ago.

It has been shown to lower cholesterol, reduce blood pressure, and helps to reduce clots in the blood by resembling and complementing naturally occurring substances in the body. Patients with muscular sclerosis usually suffer from a deficiency of linoleic acid in their blood which has led to their being given evening primrose oil. The widest use has been in treating premenstrual syndrome and potential treatments in controlling hyperactivity in children, schizophrenia and arthritis are still being researched. The value of evening primrose in treating atopic eczema and psoriasis has been accepted.

The oil is usually taken with vitamin E to prevent oxidation. Epileptics should only take it on medical advice. In aromatherapy evening primrose oil provides a base massage oil to carry other essential oils.

## *Motherwort*

This herb is one which always draws attention and provokes questions by its singular appearance. Respected and almost worshipped at times in very different parts of the world for its medicinal properties, it has long held an honoured place in physic gardens.

The saying, "Drink motherwort and live to be a source of constant astonishment and grief to waiting heirs" has led to many taking the infusion or syrup in the hope of a very long life. The Japanese dedicated a festival to the herb, perhaps because it was observed that many inhabitants of a village supplied with water from a hillside covered in motherwort, lived to be well over 100 years of age.

Since the age of ancient Greece it has been given as a safe remedy for anxiety in pregnant women, hence its name of motherwort. In the Middle Ages the herb was given to women enduring a difficult labour, or those with angina during or after pregnancy. A syrup of the leaves boiled with honey eased palpitations. It is only given in late pregnancy.

Modern research has endorsed the confidence in motherwort as a cardiac tonic, sedative, antispasmodic and nervine. It contains iridoids, glucosides, and caffeic acid, amongst other substances. Chinese studies have proved a direct action on the cells of the heart muscle and the property of preventing blood clots by altering the level of certain chemicals in the blood. Motherwort is an effective sedative for angina pain and calms nervous irritability. It has long been valued for those recovering from fevers and for menopausal disorders.

Some herbal tablets for heart and blood pressure problems contain motherwort.

## *Rue*

Rue was once looked upon as a saviour from the plague and all manner of fevers and contagious diseases. Carried in a posy to give protection, it was one of the best-known herbs for centuries. When Pliny wrote his masterful volumes which brought together much encyclopaedic knowledge, including medicinal remedies – it has to be said, some from unquestioned sources - rue was prescribed for no less than 84 complaints.

Next to protection from infection its most popular use seems to have been to strengthen the eyes and eyesight. Many artists and engravers depended upon eating rue to sharpen their vision. It was a small step from the reputation gained by rue in this area to believing it would also sharpen the second sight to give prophetic visions and dreams as well. It is not a good idea to try eating rue, as you may be sensitive to the caustic nature of the herb. The third famous role of rue in ancient medicine was as a poison antidote. The seed of rue was steeped in wine to make the required drink.

The Anglo-Saxon Leechbooks record the herb in recipes for sore eyes, nosebleeds, poor sight, headaches, unconsciousness, heart pains, snakebites, insect stings, sore breasts, womb sickness, liver complaints and worms. There followed centuries of prescriptions for lung inflammations, gout and sciatica, colic, hysteria, cramp, epilepsy and headaches.

Rue remains in use in modern herbalism only on prescription and should not be taken during pregnancy as the oil causes abortions. It is in fact poisonous in large doses. Many people are allergic to the herb itself which makes rubber gloves a wise precaution for those with sensitive skin when handling the plant in the garden.

The herb contains rutin which strengthens the capillary blood vessels and helps to lower blood pressure. Rue is generally used to stimulate the uterus and increase blood flow to the stomach and intestines. The furanocoumarins present in rue make it an effective treatment for psoriasis in ointment form. The powdered herb and a liquid extract remain in use. Rue retains its opthalmic applications and is considered anti-epileptic.

Homoeopathically *Ruta* is given to relieve pain from torn tissue soon after injury, for sprains, eyestrain, eye injuries, sciatica and "dry socket" after having a tooth out. The essential oil is dangerous and not used in aromatherapy.

## Greek Valerian

No physic garden could be complete without valerian. It was widely grown as early as the fifth century B.C. and has never been absent from herbal medicine since. Even during the Dark Ages it continued in regular use. The Anglo-Saxons believed it drove away the elves which caused diseases. In the Middle Ages valerian was used to treat tuberculosis, poisonous snakebites and gout and has long been one of the most powerful sedatives. The root was dried for nerve tonics and sleep inducing teas.

To my knowledge the first record of valerian being used to treat epilepsy was in 1592 and the herb was added to baths to relieve nervous exhaustion. It remains a nerve tonic when given in combination with other herbs. The cold tea is drunk about an hour before retiring to bed to bring sleep sooner and to give sleep of a better quality with no after effects in the morning. The tea needs to be taken for several days to begin having its full effect, but should not be continued without a break every now and again as the cumulative effect over time can produce a restlessness exactly opposite to the state intended.

Tincture of valerian was given for shellshock in the First World War and is used by homoeopaths for hysteria and over-sensitive nerve conditions. A lotion or ointment of valerian has also been applied to sores, skin rashes and swollen joints.

The sedative action is now thought to be due to the valepotriates and other substances present in the oil. These depress the central nervous system, while having a low toxicity. The herb remains in popular use in Europe for insomnia, exhaustion and excitability. It is anti-depressant, hypotensive and anti-epileptic. The oil is regarded as particularly effective in treating neuroses.

The liquid extract, ammoniated tincture, concentrated infusion and medicinal tea bags are produced. Valerian is also included in nervous headache mixtures and the tablets are on sale. For anyone thinking of gathering and drying the root for themselves, I would make the comment that it is not known as the "phew plant" for nothing. It is best and safest to buy preparations! In aromatherapy it is considered sedative and calming, treating neuralgia, nervous trembling, insomnia and palpitations.

## Yarrow

Although archaeological evidence suggests yarrow was used as a medicinal herb 60,000 years ago, tradition attributes the first use of the wound herb to Achilles. Greek legend tells us that he learnt of its wondrous healing properties from Chiron the centaur, and

*Peppermint*              (Top right) *Pot marigold*

                          (Right) *Rosemary*

*St. John's wort*         (Below right) *Purple sage*

# Medicinal

*Evening primrose*

(Top left) *Betony*

(Left) *Elecampane*

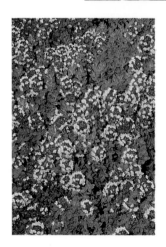

(Far left) *Thyme*

(Left) *Greek valerian*

(Top left) *Horehound*                    *Yarrow*

(Left) *Marshmallow*

(Below left) *Rue*          *Motherwort*

# Compassionate herbs for stress

*Cushion covers worked in needlepoint provide perfect 'slow release' fragrance for a room when filled with herb blends. Both fresh herb flowers and foliage and illustrations from old herbals inspire needlepoint and embroidery designs.*

# Poisons and Irritants

**(Top left)** *Aconite*

*Datura*

**(Top right)** *White Bryony*

*Black Bryony*

# Poisons and Irritants

(Top left) *Belladonna*

*Amaryllis*

(Left) *Tobacco*

(Below left) *Arum maculatum*

healed the wounds of his warriors with it in the Trojan War. It was certainly a herb famous for its application as a field dressing on many battlefields; so much so, it has been variously known as Knight's milfoil and Herbe militaris.

Even in the 20th century the herb was carried into battle in the First World War as a first-aid treatment to dress minor wounds. As might be expected from the exceptional reputation of yarrow, it is antiseptic, anti-inflammatory and effective at staunching bleeding. In addition it purifies the blood and increases sweating in fevers. Acting as a decongestant and diuretic, it is also used to treat colds and infections. Earache too has been treated by placing wads of the leaf soaked in an infusion of yarrow into the affected ear. Many herbs seem to have been chewed against toothache, yarrow being one of them. Sometimes the juice was mixed with vinegar and applied. Since yarrow is a bitter herb this has the ring of a desperate remedy!

Modern herbalists have used yarrow in fever management, where its anti-inflammatory properties from the content of chamazulene, apigenin and salicylic acid are useful. Also in colics, asthma and convulsions and, in treating some vascular difficulties. Eugenol in the herb gives the local analgesic effect and the alkaloid betonicine (achilleine) is the agent which controls haemorrhages. It is a popular herb around the world for treating childrens convulsions, painful and heavy periods and hypertension; as well as the colds and fevers already mentioned. It has a low toxicity. It should not, however, be taken by pregnant women.

In homoeopathy yarrow is known as millefolium and a tincture of the whole plant is given for haemorrhages of varying degrees, from nosebleeds to "flooding" periods. In aromatherapy yarrow oil is included in treatments for burn blisters, skin rashes, inflamed joints, rheumatoid arthritis, constipation and menstrual problems.

# HERBS NOT TO BE TAKEN MEDICINALLY IN PREGNANCY

Qualified advice should always be sought on medication in pregnancy. Some herbs which are not to be taken in the first three months may be helpful later, these are marked with a star. Seasonings in food are unlikely to be a problem in low amounts. The list only covers herbs mentioned in this book.

| | | |
|---|---|---|
| angelica* | marigold* | rosemary |
| basil | marjoram | rue |
| coltsfoot* | motherwort* | sage |
| comfrey | mugwort | southernwood |
| fennel | parsley | tansy |
| hyssop | pennyroyal | thyme |
| juniper | peppermint (large doses) | wormwood |
| lovage | raspberry leaf* | yarrow |

**Essential oils not to be used in pregnancy**

| | | |
|---|---|---|
| Aniseed | marjoram | peppermint |
| Basil | mugwort | rose |
| Clary sage | origanum | rosemary |
| Fennel | parsley | sage |
| Hyssop | pennyroyal | thyme |

*Note:* These oils are a particular danger in the first three to four months of pregnancy. Chamomile and lavender may be used with care in small doses for healthy mothers. After six months lavender can be helpful, as can neroli, geranium and lemon.

Always check before using oils in pregnancy, ask your doctor, or an aromatherapist.

The following tables are a guide to those plants most likely to be irritant or produce symptoms of poisoning, mainly in a garden situation. Some irritants affect a relatively small number of people. This is not intended to be a complete listing, but reflects those plants mentioned in my books, or commonly grown. A few more have been added as I have been asked about them on a number of occasions. In the following tables either the common or latin name is set first according to common usage for faster recognition in an emergency.

The plant list below is simply a caution for gardeners to wear gloves when tending some plants. You might also consider siting them where a child or unsuspecting visitor is unlikely to brush against or pick them.

# IRRITANTS

*Angelica: A. archangelica* - The furanocoumarins in the plant juice, particularly that from the base of the stem can cause inflammation from contact followed by exposure to sunlight.

*Black mustard Sinapis:* Contact with this plant may produce a skin allergy.

*Bryony roots Bryonia alba and cretica*: The juice of the roots of both the red and *White bryony* plants contains cucurbitacins which can cause blisters.

*Black bryony Tammus communis:* Freshly cut root rubbed on the skin causes inflammation.

*Clematis C. recta:* Prolonged contact with the foliage which contains protoanemonin, followed by exposure to sunlight can cause blisters. Plants in shade are not as powerful.

*Traveller's Joy Clematis vitalba:* This wild plant in the hedges has the same properties.

*Daphne D. mezereum:* Swelling and blisters can be caused from skin contact with the juice of any part of this plant. Beggars once used it to cause ugly sores to gain sympathy. Severe conjunctivitis could result from eye contact. Toxic diterpenes are the cause.

*Euphorbias:* There are many species. Some euphorbias are found in the wild and many are grown in gardens. Skin contact with the fresh latex can produce inflammation. The diterpene esters which have the irritant properties vary in strength with the age of plants and the season. Summer is usually worst.

*Hogweed: Heracleum sphondylium* Inflammation and blisters can occur after contact with fruits, root, or stem, followed by exposure to the sun. This is caused by the furanocoumarins.

*Giant Hogweed: H. mantegazzianum* Again the furanocoumarins are responsible for blistering which may last for several days after contact with the stem, followed by exposure to the sun.

*Nettle Urtica urens:* The well known irritant effects are frequently encountered and believed to be caused by a histamine-like substance. For the Antidote crush a thick stem and rub on the stem juice.

*Orris root: Iris germanica & Iris pallida* The juice of the fresh root has irritant properties, take care when preparing for drying and use.

*Primrose* and other *Primulas* may cause irritation.

*Rue Ruta spp:* Highly irritant from the presence of furanocoumarins with long-lasting effects on those sensitive. The effects can take weeks to subside completely. The historical antidote was oil of henbane, however, medical advice would need to be sought on this.

162

***Mexican marigold*** *Tagetes minuta:* If the stem of this plant pierces the skin it can cause severe irritation.

***Thuja*** *occidentalis:* Planted as hedges, this member of the *Cupressaceae,* also known as white cedar, is strongly irritant. Carrying hedge clippings with bare arms can result in an angry rash.

The plants listed each contain one of the following chemicals. Furanocoumarins found in some *Umbelliferae* and *Rutaceae,* produce sensitivity to sunlight in the skin. Hypericin in St. John's wort also produces this effect in white cattle. Protoanemonin which is present in many members of the *Ranunculaceae* family, making the latex of several species of buttercups caustic in varying degrees, is also present in Clematis – and the pasque flower. Terpenes are biosynthesisized by the plants and are divided into several groups, each with toxic effects, the cucurbitacins in bryony roots are triterpenes. Both borage and comfrey belong to the family *Boraginaceae* and have hirsute leaves. Those of borage can be quite bristly. Most people have no problem with them, but perhaps 10% may experience irritation from handling these plants, or applying comfrey directly to the skin. They do not however contain irritants as such.

A number of other herbs including yarrow, may cause allergic reactions in a few people. However, I have tried to list those which are the most likely to cause problems. These range from a slight redness usual with nettles which passes quickly, to blisters from hogweed or daphne which take several days to pass.

Bulbs are generally also looked upon as irritants. Daffodil bulbs in particular causing dermatitis in workers who handle them over long periods.

Aconite foliage and flowering aconite stems have caused reactions when handled as aconitine is easily absorbed through the skin.

## POISONS

In the table below I have chosen berries commonly found in hedges, parks and waste areas in towns as well as on country walks. This list includes those which produce the highest number of enquiries and some dyes recommended in my books. It also includes some which raise suspicions repeatedly but are not in fact likely to produce symptoms. Sometimes, having learned berries will make them sick, small children may announce they have eaten berries simply because they feel ill. If you have not seen them eating berries, calmly ask the child to show you the bush where they picked them.

It is much more valuable for a child to be taught the appearance of poisonous and irritant plants and to learn not to touch them, than not to know them. Then they, in turn can warn others. With a very small child the berries can be shown to them and the reason for their removal given. When they are older they will remember the poisonous plant. Irritants may still be seen and enjoyed in the garden if wished, but set in places where a small child or unwary visitor cannot accidentally brush against them. When weeding next to irritants, or removing them, it is an easy precaution to wear gloves.

Poisonings from plants make up a very small percentage of cases of poisoning needing medical treatment. There is a far greater hazard to children and domestic pets in the home from medicines and household cleansers. Thoughtful planting and clearing away of dangerous hedge clippings can make this hazard even less.

As recently as 40 years ago details of plant poisons and antidotes have been ready to hand in popular household encyclopaedias. Most people were more familiar with the plants below and their properties. However, the scarcity of information on plant poisons today has been highlighted by the number of enquiries I have received on which plants are to be regarded as dangerous. I hope these questions are answered here.

The term poisoning refers to symptoms produced either by powerful irritants, or those substances which suppress body functions, they do not always result in death; especially if prompt action is taken. I have not given individual symptoms with each plant. In many cases eating the plant gives a burning sensation in the mouth and throat, either immediately or usually within 30 minutes. This may be followed by nausea, vomiting and diarrhoea. If you think a child has eaten one of the poisons below take a minute or two first to try to identify which plant it is, and then ring your local casualty department or doctor for immediate advice. What is appropriate for one plant may not be so for others. If the plant contains highly irritant material you may do more damage by making the child sick. Do not give milk, only water. If you are not sure of the identity of the plant **pick leaves with flowers or berries as appropriate and take this sample to the hospital with you.** They can then contact the Poisons Service for detailed advice.

It is a good idea to keep a wild flower guide with clear illustrations on hand. Being able to identify one of the plants below with certainty might save a life one day.

## QUICK REFERENCE - BERRIES.

**Always seek help immediately if a child eats even a few of these berries –**

***Belladonna*-** *Atropa belladonna:* Numerous children have been attracted by the black berries. Unusual in gardens, I have seen this herb grown in a public parks with no warning notice. If a child eats any berries seek help immediately. (see illustration).

***Black Bryony*** *- Tammus communis:* The red berries are attractive and contain a large amount of irritant calcium oxalate. The plant tends to grow in neglected areas in town as well as the country. It has spear shaped leaves. (see illustration).

***Red Bryony*** *– Bryonia cretica:* The red, shiny berries have a bitter taste. If despite this, a number were eaten a stomach wash might be necessary.

***White Bryony*** *– Bryonia alba:* Found in hedgerows and next to country paths. You may notice the curling tendrils which hang down like ringlets from the climbing plant.The white flowers, (see illustration), are followed by black berries.

***Daphne*** *D. Mezereum –* A common shrub in gardens, flowering in spring. This is an extremely irritant plant which causes caustic damage to the digestive tract if swallowed. **Do not** make the child sick. Ring the doctor or a casualty department for immediate advice.

***Dwarf Elder*** *– Sambucus ebulus:* In appearance similar to the common elder but only 90cm (3 ft) tall. Eating raw berries leads to violent sickness.

***Fly Honeysuckle*** *– Lonicera xylosteum:* Reports about this honeysuckle are old and may be unreliable. However it is better to be safe. Other honeysuckle berries are only known to cause sickness.

***Holly*** *– Ilex aquatica:* A few holly berries may simply produce vomiting, but more than ten, or less with a small child, may need hospital treatment.

***Pokeberry*** *– Phytolacca americana:* The berries on this majestic dyeplant are particularly attractive, looking like blackcurrant sweets. More than 2 or 3 can make a small child seriously ill.

***Yew*** *–* If the child has swallowed only the fleshy part of the fruit, spitting out the seeds, they may be fine. If they have chewed on the seeds, or you are not sure whether they have swallowed any, seek medical help.

**MAY PRODUCE SYMPTOMS – Seek medical help if these are violent or persist.**
The plants listed below may produce violent symptoms in some children, or only at certain stages of the plants maturity. It is a question of finding out how many berries have been eaten and acting accordingly.

If the child is violently sick, seek medical help. If the symptoms appear mild they may pass quickly without further problem.

Especial care should be taken if arum maculactum or nightshades are involved. Act promptly with these. If you do not know what kind of berberis it is seek medical help immediately.

**Lords and Ladies** – *Arum maculatum:*  Commonly thought to be very poisonous, the power of these sweet, red berries – (see illustration) is dependent on how ripe they are. Only mild symptoms are recorded in children eating a few of these bright red berries. They contain soluble and insoluble salts of oxalic acid. Inflammation in the mouth and nausea are likely. If the child has eaten many then seek advice immediately as more serious symptoms may then follow.

**Elder** – *Sambucus nigra:*  I have talked to numerous people who recounted eating raw elderberries as children, sometimes in quite large amounts with no more than a "tummy ache". Some children are more susceptible than others. Cooked berries are perfectly safe.

**Guelder Berry** – *Viburnum opulus:*  The same applies as for elder. Eaten raw they are likely to make the child sick and may also give diarrhoea. They are perfectly good when cooked.

**Honeysuckles** – *Lonicera:*  Most honeysuckle berries are not believed to be poisonous as such but they may well give rise to gastric symptoms if eaten in large amounts. See also fly honeysuckle.

**Ivy** –  These are so bitter children are unlikely to eat many. Sickness if any, it is believed will be caused by the saponins.

**Pyracantha** – *Pyracantha coccinea:*  These attractive red berries have only been known to give mild symptoms.

**Nightshades:** These plants come into this category as both with Bittersweet and Black Nightshade the greatest concentration of steroid alkaloid glycosides is in the unripe berries. Children are highly unlikely to eat these, certainly not in quantity. With unripe berries of Bittersweet the lethal dose is given in the Atlas of Poisonous Plants as 200 berries, although as few as 10 may cause nausea and vomiting.

**Rowan** -  *Sorbus aucuparia:*  Cultivated varieties contain less cyanogenic glycosides than wild. Large amounts of raw berries will cause sickness. They are harmless when cooked.

**Snowberry** – *Symphoricarpos albus:* A few berries are likely only to cause sickness. If more than 8 have been eaten seek advice.

**Spindle** – *Euonymous europaeus:*  This plant has been classified formerly as poisonous when eaten raw. There is no available evidence.

**Berberis** *B. vulgaris* – This is the only berberis which appears to be safe. Berries of others may well produce symptoms and need advice.

**Mistletoe** -  These familiar white berries, long thought poisonous are not. The toxins are concentrated in the leaves and stems only.

# QUICK REFERENCE - FLOWERS
## Seek help immediately if any flowers below are eaten

**Daphne** – *D. mezereum:* - Eating daphne flowers has produced severe symptoms lasting for several days. All parts of the bush are toxic.

**Datura** - *D. stramonium* – Also known as thornapple. The trumpet shaped flowers are very attractive and the plant is commonly available. The seeds are better known as poisonous, but the flowers can also produce severe symptoms in children which are long-lasting.

*Laburnum* - *L. anagyroides*- Sucking the flowers has led to children needing hospital treatment. The toxic cytisine usually produces vomiting in time to avoid serious damage.
*Rhododendron spp.* —With many hybrids available it is difficult to know which contain toxins and which do not. It is safest to regard all rhododendron flowers as poisonous.

## QUICK REFERENCE – SEEDS
**Seek help immediately if any seeds below are eaten or chewed**
*Castor Oil Plant* - *Ricinus communis* – There have been numerous cases of poisoning relatively recently. If treatment is started straight away lives can be saved. Whether or not the seed is chewed makes a big difference. Treatment may need to be intensive for weeks rather than days, note the symptoms can take from 2-24 hours, or even up to 3 days to appear. If you think a child has eaten these seeds seek medical help immediately. The seeds are sufficiently attractive to have been made into necklaces and produced severe anaphylactic shock in a wearer with cracked skin.
*Colchicum* – *C. autumnale* – The seeds rattle delightfully in the pods, attracting interest. The alkaloid, colchicine is concentrated in the seeds. Symptoms do not appear for 2-6 hours. Medical help should be sought if you suspect a child has eaten the seeds. Do not wait for the symptoms which are similar to those of arsenic poisoning. The glory lily, *Gloriosa superba* contains the same alkaloid in the tubers.
*Datura* - *D. stramonium* – The thorny seedcases are very attractive. The seeds have been abused and used for murder and suicide.
*Laburnum* - *L. anagyroides* – One of the commonest poisons to affect children. Symptoms following chewing the seed will appear 30 - 60 minutes later. Salivation, sweating and vomiting. Seek help immediately. Symptoms can last for several days. A new variety of laburnum is now available which is non-toxic.
*Lupin* – *spp.* All lupin seeds except those of the *alba,* which is rarely grown, should be considered poisonous. Lupins contain sparteine, the same alkaloid found in laburnum. Seek help immediately.
*Wisteria* - *W. sinensis & floribunda* – This is rarely a problem as flowering sprays often do not set seeds. However, just 2 seeds can cause serious symptoms in children.

## QUICK REFERENCE —- ROOTS
**Seek help immediately if any roots below are eaten**
*Aconite* - *Aconitum napellus*—-This root is extremely poisonous but is unlikely to be a hazard to humans unless it is mistaken for horseradish in winter and used to make a sauce. This has been known to happen with fatal results. Roots of aconites should not be left on a compost heap as these are then a hazard to animals.
*Cyclamen* – *C. purpurascens:*—-Poisoning can result from eating very small amounts of the tuber. This is more likely to affect animals.
*Daphne D. mezereum:*—-The roots are as irritant and dangerous as other parts of this bush.
*Hellebores:* —-All hellebores should be regarded as poisonous. Roots should be disposed of by burning.
*Lily Of The Valley:* – Convallaria majus—-Chewing on this root will cause violent sickness, but it is unlikely to be tried by children.

*Poisoning from LEAVES.*
The most likely circumstances of poisoning from leaves is when one plant is mistaken for another and used in a salad; or a herb tea is taken as a medicine without proper regard to dosage. Foxglove has been mistaken for comfrey in the past and cooked and eaten. In

fact comfrey is no longer recommended as an edible plant since the alkaloids which with regular intake can cause liver damage were identified in it. Coltsfoot contains the same pyrrolizidine alkaloids. Yellow dock, *Rumex crispus* has been served in salads, presumably as a substitute for sorrel. Both this plant and sorrel in overdose can produce oxalic acid poisoning. Wood sorrel also contains oxalic acid, as do rhubarb leaves.

The young leaves of pokeberry have been served in salad with seriously unfortunate results in America. Anyone gathering sweet cicely wild in northern England or Scotland should be aware that the leaves can be mistaken for hemlock. Both plants grow in similar shady situations and can occur side by side. Sweet cicely however, has a sweet aniseed smell when the foliage is crushed. Hemlock smells foul.

In recent years a henbane plant was brought to me for identification, having grown on nearby allotments, presumably from seed sown by birds. It would be unusual for this plant to cause poisoning other than through medicinal misuse. The same applies to opium poppies. Nicotine is readily absorbed by skin and mucous membranes. Prolonged skin contact or drinking tea from the tobacco leaves, once used as a pesticide, has caused poisoning.

Overdoses of medicinal teas have happened with tansy, *(Tanacetum vulgare)*, broom *(Cytisus scoparius)*, pennyroyal, *(Mentha pulegium)*, and foxglove *(Digitalis purpurea)*.

Others to treat with respect are rosemary and sage. Always remember if you are repeatedly taking three cups of the same herbal tea per day, then you are taking a medicinal dose. Always check herbs used are pesticide free.

# MOST DANGEROUS TO ANIMALS.
### Seek help immediately if plants below are eaten
*Aconitum napellus & vulgaris root:* It is unlikely a puppy will dig this up, but if it should chew on it, then the prognosis is poor. Take extra care not to leave these roots where an animal may find them.

*Amaryllis* and *Amaryllidaceae* family members - this includes snowdrops, daffodils and the kaffir lily. Do not leave these bulbs where animals can eat them.

*Lords and Ladies* - *Arum maculatum:* - Otherwise known as cuckoo pint. There have been fatal cases amongst livestock grazing in spring, when little else to eat. Contains oxalic acid.

*Box* - *Buxus sempervirens:* Hedge cuttings should not be left where they may contaminate the animals food and where puppies might chew them. They have proved fatal to dogs, pigs and horses. Cyclobuxine, a steroidal alkaloid makes all parts toxic.

*Meadow Saffron* - *Colchicum autumnale:* -Danger to grazing livestock from all parts of the plant.

*Cyclamen* -*purpurascens:*- Curious puppies are probably most likely to sample the tubers. The triterpenoid saponins produce poisoning if only a little is eaten. Keep potted plants out of reach.

*Daphne* - *D. mezereum:* - Small amounts of any part of this plant could prove fatal to dogs, horses or pigs.

*Delphinium D. consolida & staphysagria:* - There have been numerous poisonings of animals from this plant and seeds.

*Delphinium elatum, Consolida regalis & ambigua* also contain diterpene and nor-diterpene alkaloids found in other members of *Ranunculaceae.*

*Viper's bugloss* - *Echium lycopsis:* -A pretty wild flower beginning to be grown more in gardens. This plant has proved fatal to horses, pigs, chickens and ducks.

*Equisetum* - *E. palustre:* - Field horsetail (arvense) is safe for horses to eat but this horsetail is not. It is a marsh horsetail found in boggy ground.

*Euphorbia:* - Wild spurges are generally avoided by animals, but may accidentally be included in fodder. The diterpene esters remain active in the dried plant.

*Foxglove:* - *Digitalis purpurea & Lanata* - Pigs have been affected by leaves accidentally included in their food. Chickens would seem to be vulnerable, as I have heard of a cock which ate foxglove and died as a result.

*Goat's rue:* - *Galega officinalis.*-May poison sheep when eaten in large quantity.

*Ground Ivy:* - *Glechoma hederacea* - Once known as alehoof. Fatal poisonings in horses after eating large amounts.

*Hellebore:* - All hellebores should be considered as poisonous. The *viridis* has been involved in poisoning of animals. Both *niger* and *viridis* contain alkaloids in addition to saponins.

*Laburnum* - *L. anagyroides:* - Dogs have been poisoned by eating laburnum seeds. Puppies in particular should be kept away from them. There is a new variety available which is not poisonous.

*Lily of the valley* - *Convallaria majalis:* - My own dog was desperately sick as a puppy after digging this root up and chewing it. The saponins were probably the cause.

*Nightshades* - Unusual in cases of poisoning, but known.

*Poinsettia* - *Euphorbia pulcherrima* - Popular as an indoor plant. It is hoped most dogs are unlikely to eat the leaves, but it has been known.

*Ragwort* - *Senecio jacobaea:* - The poisonous nature of this plant is well known to those who keep cattle and horses. It produces slow poisoning from pyrrolizidine alkaloids.

*Rhododendrons:* - Many species contain diterpene acetylandromedol in most parts of the plant, including the nectar. The main danger is to goats which seem to find the leaves attractive. It could affect other grazing animals.

*St. John's wort* - *Hypericum perforatum:* - Eating this plant can produce serious skin blistering in white cattle in response to exposure to sunlight.

*Yew* – *Taxus baccata:* - Carelessness with hedge cuttings is particularly dangerous to horses.

This list covers those plants most often involved in animal poisonings by plants, it is not complete and there are many more poisonous houseplants which do not fall in the scope of this book. Dieffenbachia is the most famous perhaps, I mention the two above, poinsettia and cyclamen as they are far less widely known. *Solanum pseudocapsicum,* or Christmas cherry ia another. In addition many flower bulbs should be looked upon as potentially irritant and poisonous. There is no space to give details here.

Where symptoms may take a considerable time to appear, action should still be taken, seeking advice before they do.

The content of poisonous or irritant substances, alkaloids, protoanemonins, furocoumarins, thujones etc in plants varies according to numerous factors. Where they are grown, the season and how mature the plant is, recent climate - (for instance persistent heavy rain, or drought;) and with some, the phase of the moon.

For instance, foxglove leaves have a higher concentration of glycosides after a hot, dry period in summer, while aconite root is most dangerous in winter.

In animals, profuse salivation, diarrhoea, and vomiting, particularly with collapse or convulsions should lead to a strong suspicion of poisoning and requires immediate medical attention, whether you have seen them eat the plant or not. If you find them with a plant you suspect it is far better to take a few moments to gather any tell tale fragments from close to the animal to take with you, than waste much more time later. Even vomit can be valuable for analysis if it is all the evidence you have.

Take the animal to the vet immediately or call the surgery for advice. Do not make the animal sick. Do not give them milk.

Sources for the information on herbs to avoid in pregnancy and poisons and symptoms above, were:- *A Colour Atlas of Poisonous Plants; Physician's Desk Reference for Herbal Medicines; The Macdonald Encyclopedia of Medicinal Plants; Out of the Earth; Black's Veterinary Dictionary.* See Bibliography for further details and reading.

# *List of Suppliers*

Dried Herbs, Gum resins and spices – mail order.

**The Organic Herb Trading Company**
Milverton
SOMERSET
TA4 1NF
(formerly Hambleden Herbs)

**Back Flower Remedies**

The Dr. Edward Bach Centre
Mount Vernon
Sotwell
Wallingford
OXON
OX10 0PZ

**Herb Seeds (Organic)**

Suffolk Herbs
Monk's Farm
Coggeshall Road
Kelvedon
ESSEX
CO5 9PG

# *Index*

171

# *Bibliography*

## Herb Cultivation

*The Greek Herbal of Dioscorides*. English translation by John Goodyer. 1655, Edited & printed 1933 Robert T. Gunther. Pub. Hafner Pub. Co. New York 1959.

*Medieval English Gardens*. Teresa McLean. Pub. Barrie & Jenkins 1981.

*The Gardener's Labyrinth*. Thomas Hill, Ist published 1577. *Edited by Richard Mabey* Oxford University Press 1987.

*The Country House-wife's Garden*. William Lawson, 1st pub. 1617. Breslich & Foss, Country Classics. 1983.

*Five Hundred Points of Good Husbandry*. Thomas Tusser. Text from 1580 edition. Oxford University Press. 1984.

*Plants From The Past*. David Stuart & James Sutherland, pub. Viking. 1987.

*The Encyclopedia of Herbs and Herbalism*. Edited by Malcolm Stuart. Pub. Macdonald & Co. 1979.

*The Illustrated Flora of Britain and Northern Europe*. Marjorie Blamey, Christopher Grey-Wilson, pub. Hodder & Stoughton. 1989.

*Comfrey Past, Present & Future*. Lawrence D. Hills. Pub. Faber & Faber. 1976.

*Carnations & Pinks*. The Complete Guide. Sophie Hughes. The Crowood Press, 1991.

*Companion Planting*. Gertrud Franck, pub. Thorsons, 1983. (in Great Britain). 1980 in Germany.

*How to Enjoy Your Weeds*, Audrey Wynne Hatfield. Pub. Frederick Muller. 1969.

*Companion Plants*. Helen Philbrick & Richard B. Gregg. Pub. London Stuart & Watkins. Rev. ed. 1967.

*Herbs, Their Culture and Uses*. Rosetta E. Clarkson. Pub. Macmillan. 1942.

*The Sunflower*. Charles B. Heiser Jr., pub.University of Oklahoma Press. Norman. 1976.

*First Records of British Flowering Plants*. William A. Clarke. F.L.S., pub. London 1900.

*The Garden Book of Sir Thomas Hanmer. 1670*. Introduced by Eleanor Sinclair Rohde. Pub. Gerald Howe. 1933.

*A Modern Herbal*. Mrs. M. Grieve. Edited and introduced by Mrs. C.F. Leyel, pub. Saavas Publishing. 1984 in assoc. with Jonathan Cape.

*A New Herball*. William Turner. Edited by George Chapman Northumberland. Marilyn & Tweddle. Pub. The Mid Northumberland Arts Group & Carcanet Press. 1989.

*The Complete Herbal of Mons. Tournefort* 1730.

# Cookery

*Herbs for Health and Cookery*. Claire Loewenfeld & Phillippa Back. pub. Pan. 1965.

*Hedgerow Cookery*. Rosamund Richardson. Penguin. 1980.

*Cooking With Flowers*. Zack Hanle. 1st pub. U.S.A. by Price /Stern /Sloan. 1971.

*Cooking With Flowers*. Jenny Leggatt. Pub. Century. 1987.

*Elinor Fettiplace's Receipt Book*. Hilary Spurling. Pub. Viking Salamander. 1986.

*Under The Influence of Bright Sunbeams*. The Countess China de Burnay. pub. Thorsons. 1987.

*Food In England*. Dorothy Hartley. pub. Futura. 1985 edition.

*The Health Food Guide*, Edited by Michael Balfour. pub. Pan Books 1981.

*The Real Food Guide*. Cass McCallum. pub. Cass McCallum & Richard Drew Publishing Ltd., 1981.

*Fine Preserving*. Catherine Plagemann. pub. Simon & Schuster, New York. 1967.

# Flowers and Fragrance

*The Scented Garden*. Rosemary Verey, pub. Michael Joseph. 1981.

*The Story of Lavender*. Sally Festing. pub. Heritage in Sutton Leisure. 1982.

*Perfumery With Herbs*. Ivan Day. pub. Darton, Longman & Todd. 1979.

*Flowercraft*. Violet Stevenson. Hamlyn Publishing Group. 1977.

*Natural Perfume Materials*. Dr. Y.R. Naves & G. Mazuyer. Reinhold Pub. Corp. New York. 1959.

*Notes on Essential Oils*. T.H.W. Idris. F.C.S. London. 1898.

*Pot-Pourri. A Practical Guide.* Mary Lane. Pub. Bishopsgate Press. 1986.

*The Scented Garden.* Eleanour Sinclair Rohde, rev. ed. 1948.

*Potpourris and Other Fragrant Delights.* Jacqueline Heriteau. 1st pub. U.S.A. Simon & Schuster. 1973. Britain. Lutterworth Press. 1975. Penguin Books reprint 1979.

# Medicinal

*Green Pharmacy.* Barbara Griggs. pub. Jill Norman & Hobhouse Ltd. 1981.

*Out of the Earth.* Simon Y. Mills. pub. Viking Arcana. 1991.

*The Macdonald Encyclopedia of Medicinal Plants.* Roberto Chiej. Pub. Macdonald Orbis 1982. (in Milan). 1984 (Britain).

*Potter's New Cyclopedia of Botanical Drugs and Preparations*, R.C. Wren. F.L.S. C.W. Daniel Co. Ltd. rev.ed. 1988.

*The Illustrated Herbal Handbook for Everyone.* Juliette de Bairacli Levy. Pub. Faber & Faber, rev.ed. 1991.

*Feverfew.* Dr. Stewart Johnson. pub. Sheldon Press. 1984.

*Evening Primrose Oil.* Judy Graham. pub. Thorsons 2nd ed. 1988.

*The Complete Homoeopathy Handbook.* Miranda Castro. R.S.Hom. Macmillan. 1990.

*The Fragrant Pharmacy.* Valerie Ann Worwood. pub. Macmillan. 1990.

*The Art of Aromatherapy.* Robert Tisserand. pub. C.W. Daniel. 1977.

*Herbs and Aromatherapy.* Joannah Metcalfe. pub. Webb & Bower. 1989.

*Health From God's Garden.* Maria Treben. pub. Thorsons. Britain 1987.

*Grandmother's Secrets.* Jean Palaiseul. Translation 1st pub. Barrie & Jenkins. 1973.

*A Concise Guide in Colour, Herbs.* Dr. Frantisek Stary & Dr. Vaclav Jirasek. pub. Hamlyn. 1973.

*Gerard's Herbal.* Edited by Marcus Woodward from the 1636 edition. Pub. 1927.

*Culpeper's Complete Herbal.* 1815 edition. London.

*Leechdoms, Wortcunning & Starcraft of Early England.* 3 vols. Cockayne 1864.

*The Medical Background of Anglo Saxon England.* Wilfrid Bonser. London. pub. The Wellcombe Historical Medical Library 1963.

*P.D.R. for Herbal Medicines.* Medical Economics Co. Montvale New Jersey. 1999.

*A Colour Atlas of Poisonous Plants.* Frohne Pfander. A Wolfe Science Book. 1983.

# *NOTES*